Ken & Rhoda Miller
April 1972

LIFE HISTORIES
OF NORTH AMERICAN
JAYS, CROWS, AND TITMICE

by

Arthur Cleveland Bent

in two parts

PART I

Dover Publications, Inc.

New York

This Dover edition, first published in 1964, is an unabridged and unaltered republication of the work first published in 1946 by the United States Government Printing Office, as Smithsonian Institution United States National Museum *Bulletin 191*.

This work, which was originally published in one volume, is now published in two separate volumes.

International Standard Book Number: 0-486-21222-X

Library of Congress Catalog Card Number: 64-14302

Manufactured in the United States of America

Dover Publications, Inc.
180 Varick Street
New York 14, N. Y.

CONTENTS

INTRODUCTION

This is the fifteenth in a series of bulletins of the United States National Museum on the life histories of North American birds. Previous numbers have been issued as follows:

107. Life Histories of North American Diving Birds, August 1, 1919.
113. Life Histories of North American Gulls and Terns, August 27, 1921.
121. Life Histories of North American Petrels and Pelicans and Their Allies, October 19, 1922.
126. Life Histories of North American Wild Fowl (part), May 25, 1923.
130. Life Histories of North American Wild Fowl (part), June 27, 1925.
135. Life Histories of North American Marsh Birds, March 11, 1927.
142. Life Histories of North American Shore Birds (pt. 1), December 31, 1927.
146. Life Histories of North American Shore Birds (pt. 2), March 24, 1929.
162. Life Histories of North American Gallinaceous Birds, May 25, 1932.
167. Life Histories of North American Birds of Prey (pt. 1), May 3, 1937.
170. Life Histories of North American Birds of Prey (pt. 2), August 8, 1938.
174. Life Histories of North American Woodpeckers, May 23, 1939.
176. Life Histories of North American Cuckoos, Goatsuckers, Hummingbirds, and Their Allies, July 20, 1940.
179. Life Histories of North American Flycatchers, Larks, Swallows and Their Allies, May 8, 1942.

The same general plan has been followed, as explained in previous bulletins, and the same sources of information have been utilized. The nomenclature of the 1931 check-list of the American Ornithologists' Union and supplements has been followed.

An attempt has been made to give as full a life history as possible of the best-known subspecies of each species and to avoid duplication by writing briefly of the others and giving only the characters of the subspecies, its range, and any habits peculiar to it. In many cases certain habits, probably common to the species as a whole, have been recorded for only one subspecies. Such habits are mentioned under the subspecies on which the observations were made. The distribution gives the range of the species as a whole, with only rough outlines of the ranges of the subspecies, which in many cases cannot be accurately defined.

The egg dates are the condensed results of a mass of records taken from the data in a large number of the best egg collections in the country, as well as from contributed field notes and from a few published sources. They indicate the dates on which eggs have been actually found in various parts of the country, showing the earliest and latest dates and the limits between which half the dates fall, indicating the height of the season.

The plumages are described in only enough detail to enable the reader to trace the sequence of molts and plumages from birth to maturity and to recognize the birds in the different stages and at the different seasons. No attempt has been made to describe fully the adult plumages; this has been well done already in the many manuals and State bird books. Partial or complete albinism is liable to occur in almost any species; for this reason, and because it is practically impossible to locate all such cases, it has seemed best not to attempt to treat this subject at all. The names of colors, when in quotation marks, are taken from Ridgway's Color Standards and Color Nomenclature (1912). In the measurements of eggs, the four extremes are printed in boldface type.

Many who have contributed material for previous volumes have continued to cooperate. Receipt of material from nearly 500 contributors has been acknowledged previously. In addition to these, our thanks are due to the following new contributors: J. R. Arnold, B. W. Baker, E. R. Blake, R. M. Bond, W. P. Bonney, F. W. Braund, N. R. Casillo, A. D. Cruickshank, D. E. Davis, O. E. Devitt, P. F. Eckstorm, J. H. Ennis, H. S. Gilbert, W. E. Griffee, J. G. Griggs, B. E. Harrell, C. F. Holmes, J. S. Y. Hoyt, W. A. Kent, A. J. Kirn, J. M. Linsdale, W. H. Longley, D. D. MacDavid, E. A. Mason, M. L. Miles, A. B. Miller, D. L. Newman, E. P. Odum, F. M. Packard, E. J. Reimann, A. C. Reneau, Jr., H. G. Rodeck, W. F. Smith, M. Sullivan, W. P. Taylor, J. K. Terres, Jr., H. O. Todd, Jr., B. W. Tucker, H. E. Tuttle, H. D. and Ruth Wheeler, and J. B. Young. If any contributor fails to find his or her name in this or in some previous Bulletin, the author would be glad to be advised. As the demand for these volumes is much greater than the supply, the names of those who have not contributed to the work during the previous ten years will be dropped from the author's mailing list.

Dr. Winsor M. Tyler rendered valuable assistance by reading and indexing, for these groups, a large part of the literature on North American birds, and contributed two complete life histories. Dr. Jean M. Linsdale and B. W. Tucker, of the Department of Zoology, Oxford University, contributed two each; and Edward von S. Dingle, Dr. Alfred O. Gross, and Alexander Sprunt, Jr., contributed one each.

Egg measurements were furnished, especially for this volume, by the American Museum of Natural History, Griffing Bancroft, Herbert W. Brandt, Frank W. Braund, California Academy of Sciences, Colorado Museum of Natural History, Charles E. Doe, Field Museum of Natural History, James R. Gillin, Wilson C. Hanna, Ed. N. Harrison, Turner E. McMullen, Museum of Comparative Zoology, Museum of Vertebrate Zoology, Laurence Stevens, George H. Stuart, 3d, and United States National Museum.

Our thanks are also due to William George F. Harris for many hours of careful work in collecting and figuring the egg measurements and for handling and arranging the vast amount of data used in making up the paragraphs on egg dates. Dr. Eugene E. Murphey did considerable work on one species, and Stephen Waldron helped with typewriting. Through the courtesy of the Fish and Wildlife Service the services of Frederick C. Lincoln were again obtained to compile the distribution and migration paragraphs. The author claims no credit and assumes no responsibility for this part of the work.

The manuscript for this Bulletin was completed in August 1941. Contributions received since then will be acknowledged later. Because of the war, publication was delayed, and in September 1945 the author recalled the manuscript to bring it up to date although only information of great importance could be added. The reader is reminded again that this is a cooperative work; if he fails to find in these volumes anything that he knows about the birds, he can blame himself for not having sent the information to—

THE AUTHOR.

ADVERTISEMENT

The scientific publications of the National Museum include two series, known, respectively, as *Proceedings* and *Bulletin.*

The *Proceedings* series, begun in 1878, is intended primarily as a medium for the publication of original papers, based on the collections of the National Museum, that set forth newly acquired facts in biology, anthropology, and geology, with descriptions of new forms and revisions of limited groups. Copies of each paper, in pamphlet form, are distributed as published to libraries and scientific organizations and to specialists and others interested in the different subjects. The dates at which these separate papers are published are recorded in the table of contents of each of the volumes.

The series of *Bulletins,* the first of which was issued in 1875, contains separate publications comprising monographs of large zoological groups and other general systematic treatises (occasionally in several volumes), faunal works, reports of expeditions, catalogs of type specimens, special collections, and other material of similar nature. The majority of the volumes are octavo in size, but a quarto size has been adopted in a few instances in which large plates were regarded as indispensable. In the *Bulletin* series appear volumes under the heading *Contributions from the United States National Herbarium,* in octavo form, published by the National Museum since 1902, which contain papers relating to the botanical collections of the Museum.

The present work forms No. 191 of the *Bulletin* series.

Alexander Wetmore,
Secretary, Smithsonian Institution.

LIFE HISTORIES OF NORTH AMERICAN JAYS, CROWS, AND TITMICE

ORDER PASSERIFORMES (FAMILIES CORVIDAE AND PARIDAE)

By Arthur Cleveland Bent

Taunton, Mass.

Order PASSERIFORMES

Family CORVIDAE: Jays, Magpies, and Crows

PERISOREUS CANADENSIS CANADENSIS (Linnaeus)

CANADA JAY

PLATES 1-3

HABITS

The name Canada jay, accepted by ornithologists, is seldom used by the backwoodsman, the hunter, the trapper, and the wanderer in the north woods, who know this familiar bird by a variety of other common names. The name most commonly applied to the bird is "whisky jack," with no reference, however, to any fondness for hard liquor; the old Indian name, "wiss-ka-chon," or "wis-ka-tjon," has been corrupted to "whisky john," and then to "whisky jack." It is also often called "camp robber," "meat bird," "grease bird," "meat hawk," "moose bird," "lumber jack," "venison hawk," and "Hudson Bay bird," all of which are quite appropriate and expressive of the bird's character and behavior.

Although cordially disliked by the trapper and the hunter, because it interferes with their interests, this much-maligned bird has its redeeming traits; it greets the camper, when he first pitches camp, with demonstrations of welcome, and shares his meals with him; it follows the trapper on his long trails through the dark and lonesome woods, where any companionship must be welcome; it may be a thief, and at times a nuisance, but its jovial company is worth more than the price of its board.

Throughout the breeding season at least the home of the Canada jay is in the coniferous forests, among the firs and spruces, or not far from them. Dr. Thomas S. Roberts (1936) says of its haunts in northern Minnesota:

During the late winter and the early spring, which is the nesting-season, it is confined closely to dense spruce, arbor vitae, and tamarack swamps and is rarely

1

seen unless such places are explored. After about the first of July, family parties, consisting of the two parents and four or five sooty-headed young, may be encountered roving through the open uplands and forests, keeping near together in their search for food. With the approach of winter, when the young resemble the adults, it seeks the vicinity of lumber camps, hunters' and squatters' cabins, and settlements, where it becomes very tame and fearless.

The above is mainly true of its haunts elsewhere, though it is not always closely confined to coniferous swamps, even in the nesting season. In the more northern portions of its range it is often found in the opener upland forests, nesting sometimes in solitary trees or in clumps of willows. In Labrador and in Newfoundland I found it common wherever there was any kind of coniferous growth, even where it was scattered or stunted.

Dr. Samuel S. Dickey tells me that in northern Alberta, where this species is common, it is often found in the higher, drier stands of aspen, balsam poplar, canoe birch, mountain-ash, spruce and fir trees, and in pure stands of jack pine *(Pinus banksiana)*.

Nesting.—The Canada jay nests so early in the season, while the snow is still deep in the northern woods, that few of us have been able to observe its nesting habits, in spite of the fact that it is an abundant bird over a wide range. Its nesting site is usually remote from civilization, the nest is usually well hidden in dense coniferous forests, and extensive traveling on snowshoes is very difficult at that season. Moreover, the birds, though exceedingly tame and sociable at other seasons, are quiet, retiring, and secretive during the nesting season.

One of the earliest and most interesting accounts of the home life of the Canada jay is that given by Oscar Bird Warren (1899), who, on February 22, 1898, found a pair of these birds building their nest near Mahoning, Minn. (see Barrows, 1912, p. 416). The birds were discovered while Warren was walking down a railroad track through a spruce swamp:

Looking up, what should I see but a pair of Canada Jays pulling beard moss and spider nests from some dead trees and making short trips to neighboring live spruce about 150 feet from the railroad track, where they were evidently building a nest.

Taking a short circuit I reached a position where I could watch their movements better without attracting attention. They brought small sticks, beard moss, spider nests and strips of bark from the trees and sphagnum moss from about the base of the trees where not covered with snow, and deposited all of this in a bunch of branches at the end of a limb,—a peculiar reversed umbrella-shaped formation commonly seen in the small spruce trees, probably caused by some diseased condition of growth. The female arranged the material, pressing it into the proper shape and weaving it about the small twigs to form a safe support. Though the birds obtained the material so near, where it was abundant, yet they carefully picked up any which accidentally fell from the nest, and there were no signs of sticks or any fragments of nesting material at any time during the construction of the nest. * * *

By the 3rd of March the nest was well formed and smoothly lined with fine grass and thin strips of bark. On the 12th it was completed, being beautifully and warmly lined with feathers picked up in the forest and representing several species of birds. Those of the Ruffed and Canada Grouse were in greatest evidence, a feather of the latter being stuck in the edge of the nest where it showed quite conspicuously. These birds had spent nearly a month building their nest, and as a result the finished abode was perfectly constructed. It was large and substantial and yet not bulky, being a model of neatness and symmetry. The bulk of the nest was composed of strips of bark, small sticks, an abundance of dry sphagnum moss, some beard moss and grass, the whole being fastened securely together by small bunches of spider nests and cocoons. The first lining was made of thin strips of bark and fine grass, and this received a heavy coating of feathers, making a nest so warm that a temperature far below the zero mark would have no effect on the eggs it was to receive, as long as the mother brooded over them. The small twigs growing from the cluster of branches in which the nest was built gave it a rough appearance from below, but they served the purpose of secure supports and as a screen for concealment. As there were dozens of similar masses of limbs in the trees all about, a good observer might pass underneath this tree a score of times, and never see the nest, though but a few feet above his head.

The nest described above is unusual in its location, out at the end of a branch; most nests have been found on horizontal branches against the trunk, or in an upright crotch; but otherwise the nest construction is fairly typical of the species. Bendire (1895) says of a nest taken by MacFarlane at Pelican Narrows:

It was placed in a small spruce tree, near the trunk, about 9 feet from the ground. It is composed of small twigs, plant fibers, willow bark, and quite a mass of the down and catkins of the cottonwood or aspen, this material constituting fully one-half of the nest. The inner cup is lined with finer material of the same kind and Jays' feathers, which are easily recognized by their fluffy appearance. * * * A nest taken near Ashland, Aroostook County, Maine, is composed externally of bits of rotten wood, mixed with tree moss, plant fibers, and catkins, and is lined with similar but finer materials.

Oliver L. Austin, Jr. (1932), records several Labrador nests; one was lined with "down, feathers, hair, fur and strips of the inner bark of willow felted together." Of another, he says: "Nest of juniper twigs, wood moss, rotten wood, grass, and lined with partridge feathers [doubtless spruce grouse]; 4 feet from the ground in a white spruce, no other tree within ten yards."

The above descriptions would apply very well to half a dozen or so nests that I have examined in museums and in my own collection. There is a nest in the Thayer collection in Cambridge, taken near Innisfail, Alberta, on March 1, 1903, when the thermometer was 32° below zero; it was 6 feet from the ground in a willow and was made largely of *Usnea barbata,* reinforced at the base and on the sides with twigs; it was profusely lined with feathers, mostly those of the sharp-tailed grouse, with a few of the pinnated and ruffed grouse. Macoun (1909) mentions three other Alberta nests, all of which were in willows; perhaps it is customary for the jays of this region, where there is comparatively little coniferous forest, to nest in willows. But I have also four records of Alberta nests in spruces. Elsewhere, nearly all the nests reported have been in spruces, with an occasional nest in a larch, firm, or hemlock.

Nests have been reported at various heights above the ground, from 4 feet to 30 feet, but the majority of the nests are placed 6 to 8 feet above ground, and very few have been found above 12 feet up. All the nests that I have seen have been well made, the materials being compactly felted; they are neatly finished around the rim and more or less decorated on the exterior with plant down and with cocoons and nests of spiders, wasps, and other insects; the walls are thick, and the inner cavity is warmly lined with feathers, fur, and plant down, furnishing a warm and cozy cradle for the young, to protect them from the low temperatures of late winter in northern latitudes. I have seen one nest, taken in Nova Scotia late in April, that was profusely lined with pine needles; perhaps the warmer lining was not needed at that season. The outer diameter of the nest varies from 6 to 10 inches, but most nests measure 7 or 8 inches; the outer height varies from 3 to 5 inches; the inner cavity measures 3 to 3½ inches in diameter and is 2 to 2½ inches deep.

There are four sets of eggs of this jay in my collection, now in the United States National Museum, two from Labrador and two from Newfoundland. The latter two were collected by J. R. Whitaker, about one of which he wrote to me as follows:

The nest was firmly built on some small twigs of a spruce and placed close to the trunk of the tree at about 18 feet from the snow level. There was no noticeable litter on the snow under the nest. The nest was partly constructed on February 26, 1920, it held one egg on April 10, and was collected, with its complement of three eggs, on April 15. The nest is a very compact structure composed largely of larch twigs, for which the bird would have to go some distance, as the clump of trees in which the nest was placed is composed of nothing but fir and spruce. Mixed with the larch twigs is a good deal of Spanish moss and a large number of spider nests; there are also quite a few feathers in the structure; the lining is composed of moss, rabbit fur, caribou hair, etc., and next to the eggs quite a few jay feathers.

Robie W. Tufts has sent me the following notes on a nest of this jay that he discovered on April 4, 1919, in Annapolis County, Nova Scotia:

The bird was seen to fly to the nest and settle down as if incubating. At my close approach it left the nest, hopping about the twigs at close range and showing no sign of fear or excitement. Its mate was with it. On examination, the nest was found to be empty. Immediately upon my leaving, the bird was observed to fly back and nestle down again. The nest was not visited again until April 20, when the bird was sitting (on two half-incubated eggs) and the mate perched nearby. The sitting bird was loath to leave the nest, and not until the slender spruce was shaken did it hop off, sailing on outspread wings to a dead stub a few inches from the ground. During the two hours spent about the nest, one of the pair never left us, while the other had an uncanny way of vanishing and reappearing unannounced at intervals of about 20 minutes. The behavior of the birds was characterized by a furtive silence. The nest was placed about 12 feet up in a slender spruce in woods of open growth in a wilderness district some miles from human habitation. Little, if any, attempt was made at concealment.

Eggs.—The Canada jay lays ordinarily three or four eggs, but five have been reported, as well as full sets of two. They are normally ovate in shape, rarely short-ovate, and they are usually somewhat glossy, occasionally quite so. The ground color is grayish or greenish white, sometimes very pale gray or pearl gray, and rarely nearly pure white. They are usually quite evenly covered with small spots or fine dots of "deep olive-buff," "dark olive-buff," "olive-buff," or "buffy olive"; Bendire (1895) calls the colors "different shades of brown, slate gray, and lavender." The largest spots that I have seen on any of the eggs that I have examined are not over one-sixteenth of an inch in diameter, and these were grouped chiefly about the small end of the egg. Some eggs are very finely peppered. The measurements of 40 eggs average 29.4 by 21.3 millimeters; the eggs showing the four extremes measure **33.0** by 20.3, 29.0 by **22.8, 26.4** by 20.4, and 28.2 by **20.1** millimeters.

Young.—Mr. Warren (1899) found the period of incubation to be between 16 and 18 days; it was performed by the female alone. Both parents assisted in the care and feeding of the young, which remained in the nest for about 15 days. He writes:

The food given to the young was always in a soft, partially digested state, and was placed deep in the mouths of the young by the old birds. I often watched them feeding the young when my eyes were not three feet from the birds, thus giving a chance for the closest possible observation. I have held my hand on the side of the nest while the mother unconcernedly fed her babies, but I was never able to take as great liberties with the male.

During the first few days after the nestlings were born, the male brought most of the food, the female remaining at the nest and, when the male returned, assisting in giving the food to the young by putting her bill into their mouths and forcing down any troublesome morsels. As the birds grew older the female took a more active part in carrying the food. I have timed them during the feeding hours and found that they came and went about every fifteen minutes with great regularity until the young were satisfied. When the male had discharged his burden he left immediately without waiting for the return of the female, but the mother always stayed until the male had returned or was in sight. The male was never seen on the nest during the period of incubation, nor afterwards, and as his color is much darker than the female's there was never any trouble in distinguishing between them, even at a distance.

The female cleaned the nest often and very carefully, keeping it perfectly free from any filth. It seems this was done both for cleanliness and for the purpose of keeping the nest dry and warm. * * * The male always picked up any droppings which were cast over the nest and had clung to the branches, carrying all away almost every time he left the nest. By this constant care no trace of the presence of the nest was allowed at any time. It should also be added here that the young never made any noise excepting a weak chirp while with open mouths they waited their turn to be fed.

Ben East sent me an article he wrote for the Grand Rapids Press telling of his experience with brood of young Canada jays, near Isle Royale, Mich., on April 30, 1935. The nest was about 10 feet from the ground in a small balsam. He climbed a nearby birch to examine the nest, and the disturbance caused one of the young birds to flutter out and down to the ground. "I gave up my climbing attempt," he says, "and slid back to the ground. Instantly I was the center of a spirited attack by two distraught, angry gray jays. They did not actually strike me, but they flew back and forth over me, darting at me from behind with angry excited cries, fluttering less than a foot above my head and doing all they could to drive me away."

The youngster fluttered and ran along the ground, but it was captured and finally became quite tame and contented, perching on the fingers and heads of Mr. East and his two companions. They placed the young jay on a low branch of the balsam and took several photographs (pl. 3) of it while it was being fed by its parents. It was finally returned to the nest, where it seemed glad to nestle down among its nest mates.

In Newfoundland, in June, and in Labrador from Hopedale to Okak, in July, we found jays of this species common wherever there was coniferous timber. They were traveling about in family parties, and, although the young were fully grown and fully feathered in their dark juvenal plumage, they were still being guarded and probably partially fed by their parents. Both old and young birds were stupidly tame, often coming too close to shoot, but after one of the family had been shot the others immediately vanished. Young birds collected around the first of August were beginning to molt into their first winter plumage.

Mr. Tufts tells me that Ronald W. Smith records having seen a flock numbering from 25 to 30 birds in Kings County, Nova Scotia, on June 19, 1932, and another flock of about 25 birds on July 20, 1937. "This latter flock was seen several times during the same afternoon and evening."

Plumages.—I have seen no very young Canada jays; all that I have seen in life, or in collections, have been fully grown and in full juvenal plumage. This has been very well described by Dr. Dwight (1900) as follows:

Everywhere brownish slate-gray, darker on the crown, paler on the abdomen and crissum. The feathers are lighter basally and faintly tipped with brown producing an obscurely mottled effect. Lores, region of eye and forehead dull black. Malar region whitish with a dull white spot anteriorly. Wings dull clove-brown with plumbeous edgings on secondaries and inner primaries, all the remiges tipped with grayish white, the greater coverts with smoke-gray. Tail slate-gray tipped with brownish white.

Young birds in this plumage are so unlike adults, that Swainson and Richardson (1831) considered them to be another species. As the Canada jay breeds very early in the season, it also begins to molt early in the summer. Young birds begin their postjuvenal molt in July, and some have nearly finished molting their contour plumage before the end of that month, though this molt often continues up to the middle or end of August, or even later. I have collected young birds in Labrador in full juvenal plumage as late as August 9. This molt includes all the body plumage, but not the wings and tail, which are retained until the next postnuptial molt. At this molt old and young become practically indistinguishable in first winter plumage, though the forehead in the young bird is usually somewhat tinged with brownish and the back is darker and more brownish than in the adult. Adults have a complete postnuptial molt beginning early in July, which is generally completed in August.

Food.—The Canada jay is almost omnivorous; it has been said that the "camp robber" will eat anything from soap to plug tobacco, for it will, at least, steal and carry off such unsavory morsels; some Indians have said: "Him eat moccasins, fur cap, matches, anytink" (Bendire, 1895). About camps the "whisky jack" is an errant thief; it will eat any kind of meat, fish, or food left unprotected, will carry off what it cannot eat, and will damage or utterly ruin what is left. It will even enter the tent or cabin in search of food, prying into every open utensil, box, or can. It comes to the camper's table at mealtime and will grab what food it can with the utmost boldness, even seizing morsels from the plates or the frying pan. It shares the hunter's or the fisherman's lunch at noontime, confidently alighting on his knee or hand. It steals the bait from the trapper's traps, sometimes before his back is turned; and it often damages the trapped animal.

William Brewster (1937) wrote in his journal:

After the leaves fell, they were met with chiefly about openings, pastures, etc., hunting apparently for grasshoppers, often going out into the fields several hundred yards. * * * For about two weeks we fed them generously with all sorts of refuse from our table, placing this in one spot. After they had become accustomed to our presence, they spent the greater part of each day in carrying food back into the woods, coming sometimes together, but usually alternately every two or three minutes, filling their throats and bills to the utmost capacity, then by short flights, passing out of sight. They seemed to prefer baked beans to any other food which we had to offer them, and next to beans, oatmeal. They would take bread or cracker when nothing else offered, carrying pieces of large size in their bills, after having stuffed their throats with smaller fragments. They did not seem to care for meat when the things just mentioned could be had. Of baked beans they regularly took four at one load, three in the throat and one held in the bill. * * *

We spent the greater part of one day in following them in order to ascertain what they did with the great quantity of food which they carried off. * * * They took it various distances and to various places, rarely or never, so far as we could ascertain, depositing two loads in the same place. They would place a mouthful of oatmeal perhaps on the horizontal branch of a large hemlock, three or four crumbs of bread on the crotch of a dead stub, a large piece of bread on the imbricated twigs of a living fir. On one occasion we saw one deposit four beans carefully on the top of an old squirrel's nest.

On another occasion they found two of their storehouses: "One in the top of a pine stub where a piece of wood was started off at angle contained about a pint of bisquit and brownbread. The other in a larch stub in three peck holes of either *Colaptes* or *Hylotomus,* the three holes all crammed full of bread packed tightly, in all nearly a quart." As soon as these latter birds learned that their storehouse had been discovered, they immediately removed every vestige of the food.

During spring, summer, and fall, this jay is largely insectivorous, feeding on grasshoppers, wasps, bees, and various other insects and their larvae. Mr. Warren (1899) saw them gathering "grubs from floating logs" and says he has "often seen them chasing a Woodpecker away from the trees just when he had uncovered the worm he had worked so hard to dig out."

W. H. Moore (1904) dissected a Canada jay "and was much surprised to find that nearly one thousand eggs of the Lorset tent-caterpillar had been taken for breakfast. The chrysalids of this caterpillar are also fed upon, and in the autumn while the birds are migrating south they feed largely upon locusts, beetles, etc. The young taken in June feed upon beetles and caterpillars."

Nuttall (1832) says that it "lays up stores of berries in hollow trees for winter; and at times, with the Rein-deer, is driven to the necessity of feeding on Lichens." Audubon (1842) reports that "the contents of the stomach of both young and old birds were insects, *leaves of fir trees,* and eggs of ants."

Behavior.—The most striking and characteristic traits of the Canada jay are its tameness or boldness, one could almost call it stupidity, and its thieving propensities. Its tameness often makes it an interesting and a welcome companion in the lonesome woods, but its boldness, coupled with its thieving habits, has caused many travelers to regard it as a nuisance. Manly Hardy expressed it very well when he wrote to Major Bendire (1895):

They are the boldest of all our birds, except the Chickadee *(Parus atricapillus)*, and in cool impudence far surpass all others. They will enter tents, and often alight on the bow of a canoe where the paddle at every stroke comes within 18 inches of them. I know of nothing which can be eaten that they will not take, and I had one steal all my candles, pulling them out endwise one by one from a piece of birch bark they were rolled in, and another pecked a large hole in a cake of castile soap. A duck which I had picked and laid down for a few minutes had the entire breast eaten out by one or more of these birds. I have seen one alight in the middle of my canoe and peck away at the carcass of a beaver I had skinned. They often spoil deer saddles by pecking into them near the kidneys. They do great damage to the trappers by stealing the bait from traps set for martens and minks and by eating trapped game; they will spoil a marten in a short time. They will sit quietly and see you build a log trap and bait it, and then, almost before your back is turned, you hear their hateful "ca-ca-ca" as they glide down and peer into it.

Curiosity is another characteristic trait of this jay. One can hardly ever enter the woods where these birds are living without seeing one or more of them; the slightest noise arouses their curiosity, and they fly up to scrutinize the stranger at short range, often within a few feet, and they will then follow him to see what he will do. The sound of an ax always attracts them, for it suggests making camp, which means food for them; and the smoke of a campfire is sure to bring them.

William Palmer (1890) relates the following case of unusual curiosity, or stupidity: "After spending the day on one of the Mingan Islands, which is very densely wooded, we started to drag our dory down to the water, necessarily making considerable noise. While doing so, and glancing towards the woods, I observed a jay perched upon the top of the nearest tree, evidently interested in our proceedings. I immediately shot him, and the report had hardly died away when another jay took his place. He, too, followed the first, when instantly another flew to the very same tree, only, however, to meet the same fate." This is in marked contrast to the behavior of these birds when they have young with them; for whenever I shot one of a family party the others immediately vanished.

The flight of the Canada jay is easy and graceful but not vigorous or prolonged. It seldom indulges in long flights in the open. It floats lightly from tree to tree on its broad wings, making very little noise and seldom flapping its wings except when rising from the ground into a tree. Its ordinary method of traveling through the woods is to sail down from the top of one tree to the lower part of another, and then to hop upward from one branch to another, often in a spiral fashion, until it attains sufficient height to make another scaling flight. Its broad wings and fluffy plumage seem to make it very buoyant and enable it to float upward at the end of a sailing flight.

Dr. Dickey says (MS.) that Canada jays seem to like to associate with such small birds as myrtle warblers, winter wrens, chickadees, purple finches, and some of the northern flycatchers. Lucien M. Turner (MS.) tells of feeding one on meat until it became so tame as to perch on one hand and eat out of the other.

Voice.—William Brewster (1937) writes:

It has a variety of notes, most of them shrill and penetrating, the commonest a loud, hawk-like whistle, very like that of the Red-shouldered Hawk, but clearly not, as in the case of one of the Blue Jay's calls, an imitation of it. Another common cry is a succession of short, rather mellow whistles, eight or ten in number all given in the same key. It frequently utters a loud *"Cla, cla cla, cla, cla, cla, cla,"* not unlike the cry of the Sparrow Hawk. It also scolds very much like a Baltimore Oriole. Twice I heard one scream so nearly like a Blue Jay that I should probably have been deceived had not the bird been very near and in full sight of me. In addition to these notes, it also has a low, tender, cooing noise which I have never heard except when two birds are near together, evidently talking to one another.

The Canada jay is credited with being something of a mimic, imitating more or less successfully the notes of the red-tailed, red-shouldered, and broad-winged hawks, as well as the songs of the small birds that it hears. Several writers have referred to its rather pleasing, twittering song, of which Mr. Warren (1899) writes: "On pleasant days the male trilled from a spruce top a song of sweetly modulated notes wholly new to my ears. He always sang in *sotto voce,* and it required an acquaintance with the songster to realize that he, though so near, was the origin of those notes which seemed to come from somewhere up in the towering pines which surrounded this strip of swamp, so lost was the melody in the whispering, murmuring voices of the pines."

Ernest Thompson Seton (1890) has heard it give a *chuck, chuck* note, like that of a robin; Knight (1908) says that "their cry is a querulous 'quee-ah' 'kuoo' or 'wah,' uttered as they perch on top of some tree or take flight." Langille (1884) adds to the list a note "sounding like *choo-choo-choo-choo."*

Field marks.—The Canada jay is not likely to be mistaken for anything else in the region where it lives. It is a little larger than a robin and much plumper. Its general color is gray, with a blackish hood and a white forehead. It looks much larger than it really is on account of its fluffy plumage; in cold weather, especially, its soft plumage is so much expanded as to exaggerate its size. Its small bill, fluffy plumage, and confiding manners suggest an overgrown chickadee. The only gray bird of similar size in the north woods is the northern shrike, whose black wings and tail and larger bill are distinctive.

Fall.—A. Dawes DuBois writes to me: "During my 11 years of residence in the Lake Minnetonka region, in Hennepin County, Minn., I have seen Canada jays in the fall of one year only. They visited us in October and November 1929. On November 24 two of them were attracted to a chunk of suet fastened to the trunk of a tree close to our house. Their method was to cling either on top of the suet or to the bark of the tree, at one side of it. They took turns at this repast. One waited in the tree while the other was eating; then it flew down to take its share. In this manner they alternated, with some regularity; but one of them seemed dominant over the other."

The Canada jay is supposed to be permanently resident in the north woods, where it breeds; and it probably does usually remain there during ordinary winters, provided there is no failure in its food supply. It undoubtedly wanders about more or less in search of food and at times has made quite extensive migrations to points south of its breeding range. The two following quotations illustrate this point. On September 5, 1884, Napoleon A. Comeau wrote from Godbout, Quebec, to Dr. C. Hart Merriam (1885) as follows: "We have lately had a most extraordinary migration of the Canada jay *(Perisoreus)*. One afternoon I counted over a hundred in the open space near the old Hudson's Bay Company's house here; and almost every day since the first of this month it has been the same. I believe this unprecedented flight must be owing to scarcity of berries in the interior, and, since they happen to be plentiful along the coast this fall, the birds follow the shore to feed on them."

M. Abbott Frazar (1887) writes from Quebec Labrador:

On my return to Esquimaux Point, the first week in September, * * * I was soon made aware of an immense migration of these jays which was taking place. Right directly back from the house the low hills terminated in a straight line at right angles with the coast, and in a path which ran along the foot of these hills I took my stand and waited for the jays as they came straggling down the hillside. The flocks varied in size from a dozen to fifty or so individuals and kept following each other so closely that an interval of ten minutes was a rarity and they never varied their line of migration but kept right on, taking short listless flights from tree to tree. I devoted but two forenoons to them and although I had nothing but squib charges of dust to kill them with, being out of medium sized shot, I killed ninety and could easily have trebled that number had I wished. How long the force of the migration kept up I cannot say but I know there were still a few passing by when I left the country ten days later.

Winter.—There are numerous winter records for various points in New England and New York, but Pennsylvania seems to be about the southern limit of its wanderings in the eastern part of the country. Todd's "Birds of Western Pennsylvania" gives but one record for that region, in February 1923. But N. R. Casillo writes to me that the Canada jay comes down into that part of the State "more or less regularly," as borne out by his observation of two individuals in Lawrence County over a period of 4 years. The locality where these birds were seen, New Castle, Pa., is about 70 miles southwest of Forest County, where the previous record was made. It is flat or rolling country and sparsely wooded, with conifers conspicuously absent. The first bird was seen from a distance of 12 feet, on November 26, 1936, while it was feeding on the berries of a Virginia creeper that grew over a porch trellis near Mr. Casillo's kitchen window. He observed the second bird, apparently a younger bird, in the same vine on December 8. One or both of these birds were seen there on January 12 and February 4, 1937, three times in November and on December 14, 1939, and on January 1 and 13, 1940.

DISTRIBUTION

Range.—Northern North America south to New York, Minnesota, New Mexico, Arizona, and Oregon; not regularly migratory.

The range of the Canada jay extends **north** to northern Alaska (Kobuk River, Chandlar River, and Demarcation Point); Mackenzie (Horton River, Dease River, Fort Enterprise, and Fort Reliance); northern Manitoba (Du Brochet Lake, Fort Churchill, and York Factory); northern Quebec (Great Whale River and Chimo); and Labrador (Nain). **East** to Labrador (Nain and Rigolet); Newfoundland (Fogo Island and Salmonier); and Nova Scotia (Baddeck, Kentville, and Barrington). **South** to southern Nova Scotia (Barrington and Grand Manan); Maine (Milltown, Foxcroft, and Norway); northern New Hampshire (Mount Washington); northern Vermont (St. Johnsbury and Mount Mansfield); northern New York (Long Lake, Fulton Chain, and Watertown); southern Ontario (Latchford, North End, and Sudbury); northern Michigan (Pickford and McMillan); northern Wisconsin (Spring Creek); Minnesota (Mille Lacs Lake and White Earth); southwestern South Dakota (Elk Mountain); northern New Mexico (Cowles and Baldy Peak); and east-central Arizona (White Mountains). **West** to eastern Arizona (White Mountains); northeastern Oregon (Blue Mountains); southeastern Washington (Blue Springs); northern

Idaho (Coeur d'Alene and Clark Fork); British Columbia (Midway, Horse Lake, Hazelton, Flood Glacier, and Atlin); and Alaska (Iliamna Pass, Nushagak, St. Michael, Nulato, and Kobuk River).

The range as outlined is for the entire species. Three races are currently recognized and others have been proposed. The typical subspecies, known as the Canada jay *(Perisoreus c. canadensis)*, occupies the major portion of the range from northern Mackenzie and central British Columbia east to Labrador, Newfoundland, and Nova Scotia; the Rocky Mountain jay *(P. c. capitalis)* is found in the Rocky Mountain region from southern British Columbia and Alberta south to Arizona and New Mexico; while the Alaska jay *(P. c. fumifrons)* occurs throughout Alaska except the coastal region east and south of the Alaska Peninsula.

Casual records.—In fall or winter the Canada jay will sometimes The ranges of other subspecies are given under their respective names. wander south of its usual range. There are several records for Massachusetts (Amesbury, Quincy, Mount Greylock, Arlington Heights, Bernardston, Cambridge, and Newton). It was recorded from Utica, N. Y., in the winter of 1868-69 and was seen repeatedly at Cortland, in that State, during January 1928. Audubon reported one from Philadelphia, Pa., in October 1836. In Minnesota it has been noted in winter irregularly in the southern part of the State (Hennepin, Ramsey, Washington, and Anoka Counties); and there are several records for Nebraska (West Point in the late winter of 1886, near Fort Robinson in April 1891, head of Monroe Canyon in February 1896, near Belmont in the spring of 1889, and Antioch on February 2 and 26, 1930).

Egg dates.—Alaska: 2 records, April 10 and May 13.

Alberta: 56 records, March 11 to April 21; 28 records, March 18 to April 8, indicating the height of the season.

Colorado: 6 records, March 17 to April 30.

Labrador: 5 records, March 20 to April 23.

Newfoundland: 17 records, April 4 to 30; 9 records, April 10 to 16.

Nova Scotia: 9 records, April 2 to May 7.

PERISOREUS CANADENSIS ALBESCENS Peters

ALBERTA JAY

Based on the study of five specimens from Red Deer, Alberta, James Lee Peters (1920) describes this race as "similar to *P. c. capitalis*, but smaller; paler above, much paler below; lower breast, flanks, and abdomen, pale smoky gray, with only a faint drab wash. Similar also to *P. c. canadensis* in size and in the extent of white on the crown, but much paler throughout. * * * This form is strikingly paler than any of the known races of *Perisoreus canadensis*. The contrast between the white throat and the fore neck and the drab lower parts, so noticeable in the other subspecies, is quite lacking."

The above common name appears in the nineteenth supplement to our Check-list (1944), where the present known range of the race is said to be "central and southern Alberta." Its habits, so far as known, are included in those of the type race.

PERISOREUS CANADENSIS NIGRICAPILLUS Ridgway
LABRADOR JAY

At long last the A. O. U. (1944) committee on nomenclature has decided to admit to the new Check-list this fairly well marked subspecies, which Robert Ridgway (1882) described many years ago as "similar to *P. canadensis fumifrons* in darkness of coloration, but forehead, lores, chin, throat, and sides of neck distinctly white, in marked and abrupt contrast with the dark color of adjacent parts; crown, occiput, and upper part of auricular region decidedly black, with little or no admixture of slaty anteriorly. Differing from true *canadensis* in much darker coloration throughout, much blacker crown, black auriculars, less extensive white area on forehead, and more marked contrast of the white portions of head and neck, with adjacent darker colors."

Dr. H. C. Oberholser (1914) proposed the name *P. c. sanfordi* for the birds of this species found in Newfoundland, but this name has never been recognized by the A. O. U. committee. I have collected birds of this species in both Newfoundland and Labrador and have examined large series of both in the museum at Cambridge, where we all agreed that the Newfoundland bird is not sufficiently different from that of the Labrador Peninsula to warrant its recognition in nomenclature.

What we know about the habits of this race in Newfoundland and Labrador is included in our life history of typical *canadensis,* which was written before *nigricapillus* was formally recognized.

PERISOREUS CANADENSIS BARBOURI Brooks
ANTICOSTI JAY

The Anticosti jay was described by Winthrop Sprague Brooks (1920) as a distinct species, but is now to be admitted to our Check-list as a subspecies. Mr. Brooks gives its characters as follows: "Size about as in *P. canadensis nigricapillus* Ridg. of Labrador. In color this jay differs at a glance from *P. canadensis nigricapillus* in that the upper parts, including lesser wing-coverts and upper tail-coverts, are plain slate-color (instead of mouse gray), the black of crown and occiput slate-black (instead of brownish black), and the under parts deep gray, less brownish or smoky."

Its habits probably do not differ materially from those of the species in Newfoundland and Labrador, as described under the type race.

Braund and McCullagh (1940) make the following interesting comment on the Anticosti jay: "Contrary to the usual antagonistic feeling of Canadian trappers and woodsmen in general, the native Anticosti Islanders have a friendly attitude toward the bird. It seems that during the cold winter months when supplies are low on the mainland the 'poachers' visit the island to obtain deer and trap mammals. The Canada Jay's characteristic habit of being a camp follower has often led the island game protectors to these 'poacher' camps."

PERISOREUS CANADENSIS PACIFICUS A. H. Miller
PACIFIC CANADA JAY

This dark race of the Canada jay has been named and described by Dr. Alden H. Miller (1943a), based on a series of 11 birds collected in "the Rainbow Mountain area at the headwaters of the Dean and Bella Coola rivers, in the central coast range of British Columbia," which constitutes its present known range. He describes it as "similar to *Perisoreus canadensis canadensis,* but dorsal coloration darker and sootier (near Dark Mouse Gray of Ridgway, Color Standards and Color Nomenclature, 1912), hence less brown; in fresh plumage, dorsal gray collar of neck inconspicuous and in some individuals obsolete; white of forehead of same extent and comparably suffused with gray in fresh plumage, but not noticeably buffy as in *P. c. fumifrons;* size as in *P. c. canadensis.* * * * The race *P. c. pacificus* shows no approach in characters to *Perisoreus obscurus* of southwestern British Columbia. The coloration dorsally is blue or neutral gray, rather than brown as in *obscurus,* the shaft streaks of the back feathers are no more apparent than in any race of *P. canadensis,* and the underparts are deep gray posterior to the throat, not whitish and uniform as in *obscurus.* * * * Compared with *P. c. fumifrons, pacificus* is not only distinctly darker but less brown." Nothing seems to have been published about its habits.

PERISOREUS CANADENSIS CAPITALIS Ridgway
ROCKY MOUNTAIN JAY
PLATE 4

HABITS

This western race of our familiar "whisky jack" is described by Ridgway (1904) as similar to our eastern bird, but it is larger and lighter colored; the whole head is white, except immediately around and behind the eyes, which, together with the hind neck, are slate-gray; the upper and under parts are paler gray. Young birds, in juvenal plumage, are paler than the young of *canadensis* or *fumifrons,* the pileum being much paler gray or grayish white and the feathers of the under parts more or less tipped with white or pale grayish. Ridgway gave it the appropriate name of "white-headed jay," and, on account of this prominent character, it is locally called "baldhead," "tallowhead," or "whitehead"; it is also commonly known as the "camp robber," and many of the popular names applied to our eastern bird are also used to designate it. The name "jay" is usually used by the westerner for one of the races of the Steller's jay.

The Rocky Mountain jay is appropriately named, for it is confined mainly to the boreal zones in the Rocky Mountain region from southern Canada to Arizona and New Mexico. Its breeding range seems to be limited to the heavily forested regions in the mountains, from the lower limit of coniferous forests up to timberline, the altitude varying with the latitude. Referring to its haunts in the Yellowstone National Park, Wyo., M. P. Skinner (1921) says: "While I have frequently found Rocky Mountain Jays in the smaller meadows and openings, still it is apparent they like the forests best. Forests of lodgepole pine, limber pine, fir, spruce, cedar, and even aspen groves and willow thickets constitute their chosen haunts. Their nests are in the lodgepole pine belt between the 7500 and 8000 foot levels."

Aretas A. Saunders writes to me: "This bird is a common species all through the mountainous parts of Montana. Though a resident, and present throughout the year, it is much more in evidence from early in August to late in February than from March to July. From about August 5 on, these birds are likely to be encountered daily until late in February. But through the spring and early summer a sight of one of these birds is a rare thing. I find that I have records of their occurrence in every month of the year, but the records are very few, as compared to late summer and fall."

Fred Mallery Packard writes to me of the status of this jay in Estes Park, Colo.: "One of the commonest birds of the Canadian and Hudsonian forests in summer; usually found between 8,500 feet and timberline at 11,000 feet, but occasionally as high as 13,000 feet. In winter most of these jays descend to the lower edge of the Canadian and Upper Transition Zones (8,000 to 9,000 feet), some to Estes Park village at 7,500 feet, while a few winter as high as timberline."

Referring to Colorado, Dr. Coues (1874) quotes Mr. Trippe as saying: "I have never seen the Canada Jay below 9,000 feet, even in midwinter; and but rarely below 9,500 or 10,000. During the warmer months it keeps within a few hundred feet of timber-line, frequenting the darkest forests of spruce, and occasionally flying a little way above the trees."

In New Mexico its range seems to be mostly above 11,000 feet, where Mrs. Bailey (1928) says that "it belongs among the hemlocks and spruces of the Hudsonian Zone." She gives a number of records for north-central New Mexico, ranging from 7,800 up to 12,000 feet, but says that 9,500 feet is about the usual lower limit of its range in fall and winter.

Nesting.—W. C. Bradbury (1918), after several unsuccessful attempts and much heavy traveling in deep snow, finally succeeded in 1918 in securing three nests of the Rocky Mountain jay in Colorado. One nest was taken in Grand County on May 2 at an altitude of 8,600 feet; the nest, which contained only two heavily incubated eggs, was in a lodgepole pine "about twenty-five feet from the ground, in a rather bushy top, located close to the trunk on a small limb. Some of the strings used in the nest were neatly bound around the limb upon which it rested. The outside framework is "composed chiefly of pine and other twigs." The "nest proper" is "composed of fine grasses, cotton strings of several sizes, and large amounts of unravelled rags and white rabbit hairs; lined with same material and feathers. There are several pieces of cotton cloth spread between the twig foundation and the nest proper."

Another nest was at "about 8,700 feet altitude in Saguache County, Colo., in open stand of lodge-pole pine. The nest was on the south side of a tree fifteen feet high, located on two limbs two and one-half feet from the trunk and five feet from the ground. * * * Nest proper composed of fine grasses and bark fiber neatly and closely woven together, and warmly lined with chicken and occasional grouse and jay feathers." This nest contained three slightly incubated eggs on April 26.

The third nest was taken in Gunnison County, at an elevation of 10,600 feet, on April 21, containing two eggs with well-developed embryos. "The nest was in the top of a white spruce, fifty-five feet above the surface of the snow, which was fourteen feet deep on the level. * * * The entire structure is composed of spruce twigs and tree moss, with a small amount of coarse wood fiber and an occasional feather, all very closely and firmly intermixed and woven together. The cup is lined with tree moss, grouse and a few other feathers."

These nests are evidently quite similar to those of the Canada jay, and the size is about the same, though the inner cup seems to be shallower, 1¾ inches. The over-all outside diameter varies from 6½ by 7 to 7 by 9 inches; the outside height is 3 to 4 inches; and the inner diameter of the cup varies from 3 to 3½ inches.

Mr. Skinner (1921) says that in Yellowstone National Park "nests are built in tall lodgepole pines during early April at from 7500 to 8000 feet elevation. They are about thirty feet up, or two-thirds of the distance from ground to tree top, and made of straw placed in the angles between the trunk and a limb about two inches in diameter. The inner nest is mostly of pine needles."

Alfred M. Bailey tells me that he and R. J. Niedrach found two nests in the mountains of Colorado; one was 20 feet from the ground in a small Douglas fir, at 9,000 feet; and the other was 25 feet above ground in an Engelmann spruce, at an elevation of 11,000 feet (pl. 4).

Eggs.—The Rocky Mountain jay seems to lay usually two or three eggs, perhaps sometimes four. These are practically indistinguishable from those of the Canada jay, though some are more heavily marked. The measurements of 20 eggs average 29.9 by 21.7 millimeters; the eggs showing the four extremes measure **33.0** by 24.0, 32.0 by **24.5**, and **26.6** by **20.0** millimeters.

Food.—This "camp robber" has practically the same feeding habits as others of the species, frequenting the camps to steal, eat, or carry off almost anything edible. It often does considerable damage to food left in camp or to baited traps. Wilbur C. Knight (1902) writes: "Some years ago while deer hunting we had several carcasses hanging in the trees near by and some quarters that had been skinned. I noticed the birds flying away from the meat whenever I came into camp and upon examining the quarters that were skinned, I found that they had made several holes through the dried surface, large enough to admit their heads, and that they had eaten from each opening from one to two pounds of meat and had entirely destroyed the quarters."

Mr. Skinner (1921) says: "Truly omnivorous eaters, the Rocky Mountain Jays pick up oats dropped about stables or along the roads; catch caterpillars, black worms, and grasshoppers; and once I saw a Jay try for a locust, although he missed and did not try again that I could see." Mrs. Bailey (1928) adds "wild fruits, including elderberry, bearberry, sumac, and viburnum; also scattered grain in corrals; insects, especially grasshoppers and caterpillars; small mammals, meat, and camp food." On the Upper Pecos River she (1904) saw them eating toadstool.

Mr. Munro has sent me some notes on the stomach contents of Rocky Mountain jays taken in British Columbia. In four stomachs collected on September 20, 1939, one contained seeds of Rosaceae to the extent of 70 percent; two others contained 70 percent insects, including a large dipterous pupa, parts of two large Diptera, and other insect remains;

fragments of a beetle and seeds of the serviceberry were found in some of the stomachs. In the three stomachs taken December 3, 1926, seeds of Rosaceae figured largely, from 95 to 98 percent; mixed with them were a few seeds of serviceberry and a few insect fragments. Mr. Packard writes to me:

"Every camp and cabin in the higher parts of the park has its coterie of jays that depends to some extent upon food discarded by campers to supplement their own forage. A site may be used but once or twice a year, yet within 5 minutes of a person's arrival there the camp robbers are hopping on nearby trees in anticipation of a handout.

"On July 5, 1939, shrill cries coming from the top of a small Engelmann spruce near timberline at Milner Pass disclosed two ruby-crowned kinglets darting at a pair of camp robbers, each of which had a nearly grown kinglet in its claws. The jays paid little attention to the agitated parents, but calmly devoured the nestlings while we watched. In each case, the jay opened the stomach of its prey, ate the viscera, and then pecked at the head. I have also observed camp robbers carrying nestling Audubon's warblers in midsummer."

Behavior.—In general habits and behavior the Rocky Mountain jay is much like its better-known northern relative; it has the same thieving habits, is equally bold and inquisitive, and is quite as sociable and friendly, the camper's companion and a nuisance to the trapper or the hunter. Mr. Skinner (1921) calls attention to two points, not mentioned under the preceding race; he says:

The flight of a Rocky Mountain Jay seems weak. A few wing strokes carries the bird along slowly and upward slightly, then a sail carries him down at about the same angle, and this sequence is repeated over and over again, resulting in a slow flight of long, shallow undulations. * * * Birds of the air and of the tree tops as they are, when they are on the ground they move somewhat awkwardly in a series of long hops, a little sideways perhaps, a good deal like crows and ravens.

Its migrations, if they may be called such, are more altitudinal than latitudinal. It wanders to lower elevations in winter and often seeks the vicinity of permanent camps and settlements in search of food, retiring to the higher altitudes at the approach of the breeding season. During the nesting season it is very retiring and secretive but is much more in evidence during fall and early in winter.

Mr. Saunders writes to me: "They stay around lumber camps or other places, feeding on garbage, particularly scraps of meat or fat, but also bread. At such seasons, if one stops to eat lunch anywhere in the evergreen forests, the birds will appear shortly, and are very tame, and ready to share all the lunch one is willing to give them."

Mr. Munro says in his notes: "In the heavy still forest on a snowy day, they came fluttering silently from the heavy timber in response to an imitation of the pigmy owl call—soft, fluffy birds like overgrown chickadees."

Voice.—Mr. Saunders (MS.) says that this bird is an exceedingly quiet one, in contrast to other jays; only once or twice has he heard one make a sound.

Mr. Munro writes in his notes sent to me: "These birds were heard imitating the call of pine grosbeaks, which were nesting in the vicinity. They also imitated the calls of pigmy owl and red-tailed hawk. I was impressed by the exact imitation of the pigmy owl made by two pairs which were called up at different places by an imitation of the owl call. I was sure that a pigmy owl was answering me until the jays appeared. Both the single *hook* note and the quavering tremolo were given. In one instance, both were given after I had whistled only the single note."

PERISOREUS CANADENSIS BICOLOR A. H. Miller
IDAHO JAY

In naming this subspecies, Dr. Miller (1933) gives the following comparison with the type race: "Size, and tone and hue of coloration as in *P. c. canadensis* of central British Columbia, but dark color of occiput not surrounding or even extending to orbit; entire pileum, anterior breast and throat white, the white of head above and below standing in sharper contrast to dark grays and black of occiput and body; collar purer white and broader."

He designates its principal range as "in the relatively humid forest regions of northern Idaho, the principal trees of this forest being Engelmann spruce, western white pine, western larch and Douglas fir."

The A. O. U. committee (1944) applied the above common name to this race and gave its range as "southern British Columbia to central Oregon and central Idaho." A little farther south this race evidently intergrades with *capitalis,* and its habits are probably similar to those of this Rocky Mountain form.

PERISOREUS CANADENSIS FUMIFRONS Ridgway
ALASKA JAY
HABITS

Ridgway (1904) characterizes this northwestern race as "similar to *P. c. canadensis,* but dusky hood extending over the crown, leaving only the forehead white; the latter often more or less tinged with smoky gray; the general color of upper and lower parts browner, and size less. Agreeing with *P. c. nigricapillus* in greater extent of the dusky hood, but this browner, with the anterior portion more distinctly ashy, the forehead less purely white, and the general color, both above and below, decidedly paler, the under tail-coverts dirty whitish or very pale brownish gray."

The Alaska jay is known to inhabit the wooded portions of Alaska, except the coast region east and south of the Alaska Peninsula, but just where it intergrades with typical *canadensis* in eastern Alaska or western Mackenzie does not seem to be definitely known.

In the interior of Alaska, Lee Raymond Dice (1920) found this jay "common in white spruce-paper birch forest, in black spruce forest, in burned timber, and in lowland willows along the streams. In the winter they also frequent the neighborhood of cabins and camps." Dr. Joseph Grinnell (1900a), referring to the Kotzebue Sound region, writes: "During September and October, in my tramps across the tundras lying along the base of the Jade Mountains, I frequently met with two or three jays far out on the plains a mile or more from timber, feeding on blueberries. * * * Later, in the coldest days of mid-winter, I found them in the dense willow thickets."

Herbert Brandt (MS.) writes: "Throughout the great wooded interior of Alaska, where for eight months the snow and cold reign, the only conspicuous living thing that gladdens the camp and trail of the dog-musher is the Alaska jay. Wheresoever he may go and make his camp in the snow, it is sure to find him; and by his friendly manner this jocund jay gives to the cheerless by-places a touch of life that the naturalist always remembers. At every habitation that we visited and at every camp we made from Nenana to the tundra rim, where we left the trees behind, the Alaska jay was always present. Those hardy pioneers that live in this vast wooded area are outdoor people, with all the keenness and skill in woodcraft that such a life produces, yet in spite of the fact that this neighborly bird is very plentiful, and that the timbered cover in which it lives is mostly open, we did not meet a single person who had seen its egg. Often along our trail the actions of this species made obvious the fact that it was nesting, but I could find no clue that would direct me to its abode. It is evident that during nesting time the bird forsakes the immediate vicinity of habitations, where it is wont to congregate, and retires to a secluded area, which it enters and whence it departs with great caution."

Nesting.—The natives in Alaska, and in other parts of the range of this species, are unwilling to collect the nests and eggs of this jay, as they are suspicious that some evil will befall them if the nest is disturbed or even if the eggs are counted. François Mercier (Nelson, 1887) offered a tempting reward which resulted in persuading a native to bring him two nests. The older natives in the vicinity "prophesied that the weather would turn cold, and that a very late spring would ensue as a result of this robbery. As chance would have it the prophesies of the old sooth-sayers came true in a remarkable degree, and the spring was the coldest and most backward by nearly a month of any year since the Americans have had possession of the country." After that, he was never able to persuade the natives to hunt for nests. This may be one reason why so few nests of this species have found their way into collections.

Dr. Grinnell (1900a) found a pair of Alaska jays building a nest on March 20.

It was ten feet above the snow in a dense young spruce growing among a clump of taller ones on a knoll. * * * Although I did not disturb the nest in the least, a visit two weeks later found it covered with snow and apparently deserted. * * * Not until May 13, however, did I finally find an occupied jay's nest, and its discovery then was by mere accident. It was twelve feet up in a small spruce amongst a clump of larger ones on a low ridge. There were no "tell-tale sticks and twigs on the snow beneath"; as Nelson notes, and in fact nothing to indicate its location. The nest rested on several horizontal or slightly drooping branches against the south side of the main trunk. The foliage around it was moderately dense, so that it could be seen from the ground, though only as an indistinct dark spot. The bird was sitting on the nest when I discovered it. Her head and tail appeared conspicu-ously over the edge of the nest, and she remained on until I had climbed up within an arm's length of her. She then left the nest and silently flew to a nearby tree where she was joined by her mate. They both remained in the vicinity, but ostensibly paid little attention to me. * * * The nest proper was built on a loose foundation of slender spruce twigs. The walls and bottom consist of a closely felted mass of a black hair-like lichen, many short bits of spruce twigs, feathers of ptarmigan and hawk owls, strips of fibrous bark and a few grasses. The interior is lined with the softest and finest-grained material. The whole fabric is of such a quality as to accomplish the greatest conservation of warmth. Which certainly must be necessary where incubation is carried on in below-zero weather!

Mr. Brandt found his first nest near Flat, Alaska, on April 9, 1924; it contained four eggs ranging evenly in incubation, showing that incubation had begun after the laying of the first egg, which is probably necessary to prevent freezing. For the first 6 days of April the temperature had ranged from 16° below to 35° below zero, though on the 8th it had risen to 30° above. He says in his notes: "The nest of the Alaska jay is placed usually in a spruce tree in a river or creek bottom, and, in the two in-stances of which I have information, they were poorly concealed; yet the forest at that time was so snow-laden that an object as small as a jay's nest is not at all conspicuous near a tree trunk. The incubating bird sits very close, is quiet about the nest, and its mate stays away from the vicinity during the entire time that an intruder is about. The incu-bating bird did not leave its charge until the climber was but a foot distant.

"The nest found at Flat was 9 feet above the ground and was placed against the trunk of a small scrubby tree 3 inches in diameter, which it partly encircled. It was built on a whorl of very thin branches but was supported largely by a pendant spruce limb, the branchlets of which were woven into the outer rim of the nest and which served also as a snow shelter for the brooding bird. The structure of this abode is just what one would expect of a bird that chooses the severest time of the year to breed. The nest is very bulky, of a silver-gray color, and like most nests of jays is of two distinct parts, a loosely made platform, in this case of tamarack twigs, and a very well-made, compact inner nest. It has very closely built walls varying in thickness from 1 inch, where it rested against the tree trunk, to 3 inches on the opposite side. It is composed largely of cotton from an old quilt and is lined with feathers of the Alaska spruce grouse and willow ptarmigan, some thread, string and fine strips of bark, with an inner lining of dog hair and feathers in liberal quantities. All this is matted and felted together in such a manner as to make the interior well insulated against the cold, and when the incubating bird is snuggled down into the close-fitting rim, but little warmth is radiated, even in the most rigorous weather. The dimensions of the nest are as follows: Height, 7 inches; total outside diameter, 12; outside diameter of primary nest, 8; inside diameter, 3.5; depth of cup, 3; thickness of wall, 1 to 3 inches."

Eggs.—The Alaska jay apparently lays three or four eggs, probably most commonly three. Dr. Grinnell's set consisted of three eggs, and Mr. Brandt collected one set of three and one of four. The latter describes his seven eggs as follows (MS): "The egg in outline is ovate to short-ovate, and exhibits considerable luster. The egg of this species is very distinctive, and resembles that of the shrikes, but has the typical shape and texture of the egg of a jay. The ground color is conspicuous because half of it is exposed, and the markings are of a neutral color. These markings appear like freckles on the egg and are most heavily concentrated about the larger end, sometimes taking the form of a wreath. The spots are small, angular in shape and irregular in size. Those of the underlying series are of a lavender hue, ranging from grayish lavender to pale violet gray and to pale purplish gray; while the overlying spots are reddish and richer, ranging from Saccardo's olive to burnt umber and Rood's brown."

The measurements of 20 eggs average 29.5 by 20.8 millimeters; the eggs showing the four extremes measure **31.2** by 21.0, **28.4** by **21.5**, and 30.8 by **20.1** millimeters.

Behavior.—In a general way the behavior of Alaska jays does not differ materially from that of the species elsewhere. But the following incidents are worth mentioning. Mr. Dice (1920) states that "in several instances these jays were seen to attack hawks and hawk owls." Joseph S. Dixon (1938) relates the following:

On June 1, at Savage River, Wright and I watched a pair of Alaska jays being chased away from camp by a red squirrel. Every time a jay would alight in the top of a spruce tree near camp the squirrel would look up at the bird, select the proper tree, and would run up the tree and jump at the jay, driving him away. This was repeated many times. If the spruce trees were close together the squirrel would jump from one tree to the next. If this was not possible he would go down and run across on the ground climbing the tree the jay was in. After the squirrel had driven the jays away, we saw the former take a bit of food— old discarded cheese—that he had kept hidden in the crotch of a tree. Then he carried it down the tree and hid it under an old rotten log.

There is considerable competition about the camps among the Alaska jays and red squirrels to see which will get the choicest bits of discarded table scraps.

On May 26, 1926, a robin was found trying to drive a jay away from its nest. Investigation showed that the jay was doing his best to steal the robin's eggs.

Early in May 1924 Otto W. Geist (1936) witnessed a fight between a pair of Alaska jays and a full-grown weasel. Thawing during the day and freezing at night had formed a crust on the snow, but there were some bare spaces and small holes in the crust. He says, in part:

The snow under the crust was to a great extent "honey-combed," leaving spaces through which small animals such as mice and weasels could find easy passage.

From not far away I heard the shrieks of birds which seemed to be coming closer. I decided to wait. Soon I saw two Alaska Jays flying from tree to tree, diving frequently at something on the ground. I kept still in order to see what was the matter. Soon a weasel, evidently full grown and still in his white winter coat which, however, was soiled with blood, ran toward a patch of snow directly in front of me and disappeared under it. Both birds were close behind and they rested on a limb of a small tree under which I was standing. * * *

Both flew excitedly over the patch of snow. They soon returned to the tree and to my astonishment ceased shrieking. All was quiet for possibly a minute or more when through one of the smaller holes in the snow there appeared the head and forepart of the weasel. The two birds became highly excited and again flew out over the patch. They would sweep down over the weasel, first one, then the other, striking with its beak. The weasel seemed cowed and ducked low after each strike. There were blood spots on the snow and it seemed to me the birds were doing very effective work.

I now moved a little closer, but neither the birds nor the weasel seemed to notice me. I talked aloud and whistled but they paid no attention. At times one of the birds would fly out, almost stop over the weasel, using the wings to brake with, and try to see how close he could get to the weasel with his feet. Each time this was done the weasel would stretch out, sticking his head and front of the body into the air. However, he did not seem to snap at the birds. On the contrary, frequently the weasel's mouth was open and it seemed to be panting and fairly well worn out. * * *

It seemed that not a single movement of the weasel was missed by the birds. At one place where the crust on the snow was thin, the weasel managed to work under and in doing so broke some of the crust. Both birds saw this and flew down to the place where the snow moved and crumbled. The fight was on again. The weasel rushed out and made a few jumps, one a very long one of about four feet, with the birds after him at once. However, by now the weasel had reached a pile of brush. The last glimpse I had of his coat it seemed bloodier than ever.

The weasel was now safe from further attack, and the jays had put up a brave fight to protect their young from one of the fiercest fighters in the woods.

PERISOREUS CANADENSIS OBSCURUS Ridgway

OREGON JAY

HABITS

The Oregon jay, according to Ridgway (1904), inhabits the "Pacific coast district, from Humboldt County, California, to southern British Columbia (Vancouver Island and coast of opposite mainland)." The 1931 Check-list gives its range as "Pacific coast from Western Washington to Mendocino County, California." Perhaps there is something yet to be learned as to where it intergrades with the other race, *griseus*.

It is a true "whisky jack," or "camp robber," replacing the Canada jay and its subspecies to the westward of the Rocky Mountains. It closely resembles the Canada jay in general appearance and habits, though it is smaller, browner on the back, where the feathers have distinct whitish shaft-streaks, and whiter on the underparts.

It seems to be confined mainly to the heavy coniferous forests at the higher altitudes in the mountains, at least during the breeding season.

G. Buchanan Simpson (1925), who gives an account of 8 years' friendship with Oregon jays, says: "In this district (Lake Cowichan, B. C.), these birds are usually to be found in the wilder mountainous regions. In winter, however, they often come down to within a few hundred feet of Lake level in the dense forest."

Courtship.—Mr. Simpson (1925) writes: "In February the male makes very pretty love to his spouse. The latter sits on a nearby perch, ignoring any food that is thrown out. She flaps her wings in a coy way, after the manner of a nestling being fed by its mother, making plaintive little cries. The male bird scrambles for the most pleasing bit of food which is to be found, and gallantly carries it to his wife, who receives it in her beak and eats it with a great show of satisfaction."

Nesting.—A. W. Anthony was evidently the first to record the finding of the nest of this jay, near Beaverton, Oreg. He wrote to Major Bendire (1895) about it as follows:

The birds were discovered building on March 4, 1885; one of them was seen clinging to the side of a dead stub, about 75 feet from the ground. He was tearing out bits of moss, which did not seem to suit, for they were dropped again as fast as gathered; but at last, finding some to his fancy, he flew off and I saw him go into a thick fir and disappear. I could as yet see nothing of a nest, but as both birds were flying in with sticks, moss, etc., I was sure one was being built there. Both birds worked hard, were very silent, and did not come very near the ground, getting nearly all of their building material from the tree tops, I think. On the 16th I again visited the place, and with the aid of a field glass discovered the nest, which was to all appearances complete, but the birds were not seen. On the 21st I took a boy with me to climb the tree, and found the nest finished, but no eggs. On March 31 we visited it again and found the set complete and the female at home. She stayed on the eggs until the climber put his hand out for her, when she darted off with a low cry and was shot by me. The eggs, five in number, were but slightly incubated; the nest was placed about 85 feet from the ground and 10 feet from the top of the tree; it was built close to the trunk, and was very well hidden.

Mr. Anthony generously presented this set of eggs, with the nest, to the United States National Museum. Major Bendire (1895) describes the nest as follows: "This nest, now before me, is compactly built and rather symmetrical, measuring 7½ inches in outer diameter by 4½ inches deep; the inner diameter is 3 inches by 2½ inches deep. Externally it is composed of fine twigs, dry grass, tree moss, and plant fibers, all well interlaced, and the inner cup is composed exclusively of fine, darklooking tree moss."

The major goes on to say:

Mr. C. W. Swallow writes me that he took a set of four eggs of this species in Clatsop County, Oregon, on May 8. This nest was placed in a small hemlock, about 10 feet from the ground. I believe as a rule they nest in high, bushy firs. I saw a pair of these birds evidently feeding young, in a very large fir tree, near the summit of the Cascade Mountains, on June 9, 1883, while en route from Linkville to Jacksonville, Oregon, but could not see the nest, which must have been fully 60 feet from the ground. But one brood is reared in a season.

S. F. Rathbun (1911) writes:

On April 18, 1909, the writer while looking through a dense strip of second growth of young red firs (*Pseudotsuga mucronata*) in a heavy wooded tract a few miles east of the city Seattle, found a nest of this species. The young fir in which it was built was alongside an old and seldom used path through the second growth, on the edge of a small open space about ten feet in diameter, having a further undergrowth of salal (*Gaultheria shallon*) and red huckleberry (*Vaccinium parvifolium*) shrubs. The tree was five inches in diameter tapering to a height of thirty-five feet, and the nest was placed close against its trunk on four small branches, at a height of twelve feet. It was outwardly constructed of dead dry twigs, next a thick felting of green moss into which was interwoven some white cotton string, and was lined with dry moss, a little dead grass and a few feathers, among the latter some of the Steller's Jay, and is a handsome compact affair. Dimensions: average outside diameter 6½ inches, inside diameter 3½ inches; depth outside, 5 inches; inside 2 inches.

There is a nest of the Oregon jay, with a set of four eggs, in the

Charles E. Doe collection, taken by J. C. Braly near Sandy, Oreg., April 20, 1932. It was about 30 feet from the ground close to the trunk of a small fir in a fir grove.

Eggs.—Major Bendire (1895) describes the eggs as "pearl gray or light greenish gray in ground color, spotted and flecked with smoke and lavender gray, and these markings are pretty evenly distributed over the entire egg. In shape they are ovate; the shell is smooth, close grained, and only moderately glossy."

Mr. Doe (MS.) describes his eggs as "ground color dark gray, boldly marked with almost black and a few lavender marks—very striking eggs."

The measurements of 21 eggs average 27.0 by 20.6 millimeters; the eggs showing the four extremes measure **29.7** by 21.6, 27.6 by **21.8,** and **25.4** by **19.3** millimeters.

Plumages.—Ridgway (1904) describes the young bird in juvenal plumage as follows: "Entire pileum and hindneck dull sooty brown or grayish sepia, the feathers narrowly and indistinctly margined with paler; no whitish collar across lower hindneck; sides of head similar in color to pileum, the auricular region with indistinct dull whitish shaft-streaks; nasal tufts sepia brown; chin and anterior portion of malar region dirty brownish white; throat dull grayish brown, intermixed with dull grayish white; rest of under parts pale broccoli brown, some of the feathers with indistinct paler shaft-streaks; wings, tail, back, etc., essentially as in adults; bill partly light-colored."

I have noticed in young birds I have examined that the wing coverts are not tipped with white, as they are in adults. A partial postjuvenal molt, including the contour feathers and wing coverts, but not the rest of the wings and tail, begins early in July and may continue well into September in some individuals; I have seen one bird that had not quite completed the molt on September 10. The complete postnuptial molt of adults begins early in July and is probably completed in August in most cases.

Food.—Very little has been published on the food of the Oregon jay, but it is apparently just as omnivorous as other members of the genus *Perisoreus.* It is a frequent visitor at the camps and feeds freely on anything edible, scraps from the table or any other food that it can beg or steal. Mr. Simpson (1925) writes about the birds around his camp:

We have tried the birds with all kinds of food and their undoubted favourite is cheese, of which they are passionately fond. * * *

The birds each had their morning morsel of cheese today. They hold it in their mouths for a long time, turning it over and over with their tongues, as if the taste were most pleasing to them. The cheese is often shifted to the 'pouch' under the chin and held there for some time. Then it may be deposited carefully on some safe perch, licked and mouthed again with intense satisfaction, then finally eaten. They do this with no other food. * * *

The Whiskey Jacks eat bread, porridge, uncooked rolled oats, cake, farinaceous food in general, and, of course, meat, raw or cooked. They have taken an occasional bite of apple or pear. Sometimes one will catch and eat an insect, but they will not look at an earth-worm. Fish, either raw or cooked, they dislike.

Mr. Rathbun has sent me the following note, made at Lake Crescent on April 21, 1916: "Today, while slowly rowing along the shore of the lake, I came across eight Oregon jays feeding among the growth of willows and the debris strewn at the water's edge. The birds were engaged in capturing the newly hatched stoneflies, very many of which were fluttering about in the air or crawling on the rocks and broken branches on the shore. The jays took the flies in the air as easily as flycatchers capture insects. In early April, at the time the stoneflies appear, these birds resort each morning to the shore of the lake to take the insects named, and evidently capture a great number of them. We have watched them do this time and time again."

Behavior.—The Oregon jay seems to be fully as fearless, sociable, and mischievous as our more familiar "whisky jack." Major Bendire (1895) quotes from Mr. Anthony's notes as follows: " 'Fearless' is an appropriate term to use in relation to this bird; it seems utterly devoid of fear. While dressing deer in the thick timber I have been almost covered with Jays flying down from the neighboring trees. They would settle on my back, head, or shoulders, tugging and pulling at each loose shred of my coat until one would think that their only object was to help me in all ways possible. At such times their only note is a low, plaintive cry." Mr. Simpson (1925) writes:

On the approach of a Hawk, whose presence is usually detected by these birds from afar, they at once become perfectly motionless in the thickest part of a bush, uttering a low, plaintive, warning cry. When hard pressed, they will successfully fight off a Cooper's or a Sharp-shinned Hawk. After all these years on the Lake shore, they continue to take a Gull or a Heron for a Hawk, and display the same symptoms of fear.

Unlike some of our race, they have a passion for soap! We cannot leave a piece of soap outside the house for a short time without it being carried off by the Jays. The camp soap suffers the same fate at 5000 ft. level in summer. When carrying anything beyond the capacity of their beaks, they use both feet with which to hold the object, the legs hanging straight down beneath the body as they fly.

As far as we have observed, these birds are a gentle, most lovable company, minding their own business in bird-land, and never robbing a small bird's nest (of which there are always several nearby of Song Sparrow, Yellowthroat, etc.).

The Jays make free with our small garden, in which we find them admirable companions, respecting all our cherished alpine plants as well as salads, tomatoes, berries and the like.

Ralph Hoffmann (1927) thus describes the behavior of these jays about a camp: "A bird * * * flits noiselessly out of the forest and starts to investigate the camp. With a soft *whee-oo* another follows, flying to the ground, hopping about or carrying back a scrap of refuse to a limb. A flock keeps constantly drifting on through the trees, flying now to the ground, then to a branch or even clinging to the side of a tree trunk. The soft, fluffy plumage gives the bird a gentle look in keeping with its fearlessness and soft voice. Let a hawk appear, however, and the Oregon Jays will mob him with loud screaming cries, *ke-wéep, ke-wéep*."

Field marks.—The Oregon jay is not likely to be confused with any other bird within its habitat, as its range does not overlap that of the Rocky Mountain jay. It is about the size of a robin; it has a white forehead, a white collar around the hind neck, a whitish breast, and a brownish back; the crown and back of the head are blackish. Its soft, fluffy plumage and its confiding habits are also distinctive. At close range the whitish shaft streaks on the back may be seen.

Fall.—Mr. Rathbun tells me that "this jay is resident throughout the entire region but is found more commonly in the higher altitudes from early in spring until late in fall, after which period many individuals come to the lowlands, and here the species will be often met with during the winter months. This movement from the mountain regions begins about the middle of October, and from that time on Oregon jays will be met with from time to time in nearly any part of the region."

DISTRIBUTION

Range.—The Northwest, from southern British Columbia south to central California; nonmigratory.

The range of the Oregon jay extends **north** to southern British Columbia (Della Lake, Malaspina Inlet, Alta Lake, and Lillooet). **East** to south-central British Columbia (Lillooet, Hope, and Chilliwack); Washington (Mount Baker, Kacheos Lake, and Bumping Lake); Oregon (Mount Hood, Crater Lake, and Lakeview); eastern California (Fort Bidwell, Warner Mountains, and Summit); and west-central Nevada (Glenbrook). **South** to central Nevada (Glenbrook); and northern California (Summit and Mendocino). **West** to western California (Mendocino, Cape Mendocino, and Orick); western Oregon (Applegate River, Sweet Home, and Beaverton); western Washington (Camas, Grays Harbor, Quinault Lake, and Lake Crescent); and southwestern British Columbia (Victoria, Mount Douglas, and Della Lake).

The range as outlined is for the entire species, which has been separated into two subspecies. The typical Oregon jay (*Perisoreus obscurus*

obscurus) is found only in the coastal mountainous regions from probably northern Vancouver Island, British Columbia, south to northwestern California. The remainder of the range is occupied by the gray jay *(P. o. griseus).*

Since the above was written, the A. O. U. (1944) committee has ruled that the two recognized races of *obscurus* are considered as subspecies of *P. canadensis.* See Hellmayer, Cat. Birds Amer., vol. 7, p. 69.

Egg dates.—Oregon: 4 records, March 31 to April 20.

PERISOREUS CANADENSIS GRISEUS Ridgway

GRAY JAY

PLATE 5

HABITS

Ridgway (1904) describes this jay as "similar to *P. o. obscurus,* but decidedly larger (except feet), and coloration much grayer; back, etc., deep mouse gray, instead of brown, remiges and tail between gray (no. 6) and smoke gray, instead of drab-gray, and under parts grayish white instead of brownish white." He gives as its range "interior districts of northern California (northern Sierra Nevada, upper Sacramento Valley, Mount Shasta, etc.), north through central Oregon and Washington to interior of British Columbia."

The above range evidently includes the entire length of the Cascade Mountains in Oregon, Washington, and British Columbia and probably both sides of these mountains.

The gray jay had not been separated from the Oregon jay when Major Bendire (1895) wrote his account of the latter. Apparently all his personal observations refer to *griseus.* He first met with it on the summit of the Blue Mountains, between Canyon City and Camp Harney, Oreg., at an altitude of about 6,500 feet. This is well within the range of *griseus,* being far to the eastward of the Cascades. Here, he says, "they are found only on the highest portions of the mountains, which attain an altitude of about 7,000 feet. I did not see any in the neighborhood of Camp Harney."

Nesting.—I can find no information on the nesting habits of the gray jay except the following from Dawson and Bowles (1909):

The eggs of the Gray Jay have not yet been reported from this State [Washington], but it is known that the bird builds a very substantial nest of twigs, grasses, plant fibre, and mosses without mud, and that it provides a heavy lining of soft gray mosses for the eggs. The nest is usually well concealed in a fir tree, and may be placed at any height from ten or fifteen feet upward, altho usually at sixty or eighty feet. Only one brood is reared in a season, and family groups hunt together until late in the summer.

There are a nest and three eggs of the gray jay, formerly in the collection of J. H. Bowles, now in the Ferry Museum of the Washington State Historical Society in Tacoma. W. P. Bonney writes to me that it was collected in Deschutes County, Oreg., but no date is given. He says that the nest "is about 6 inches in diameter, well built from few small sticks, some fiber, grasses, soft moss, some feathers and scraps of wool. The eggs are dingy gray, with *small* brown spots scattered all over."

Food.—Dawson and Bowles (1909) say: "Hunger is the chief characteristic of these docile birds, and no potential food is refused, nuts, acorns, insects, berries, or even, as a last resort, the buds of trees. Meat of any sort has an especial attraction to them; and they are the despair of the trapper because of their propensity for stealing bait."

Food taken from campers is mentioned by Taylor and Shaw (1927) under behavior, but they also add:

When food is scarce the camp robbers sometimes visit the garbage pile. They are fond of dead mice, often stripping off the skin before eating them. Fresh meat of any kind is relished also. Ben Longmire found a nest of young juncos on a small tree that had been cut down to make way for a new trail. He removed the nest with the young birds to another tree in plain sight so that the parent birds could find the young. The camp robbers carried off the young birds and devoured them. In some localities they are said to be called butcher birds.

Behavior.—Taylor and Shaw (1927) write of the habits of this jay in Mount Rainier National Park:

The vocal versatility and freedom from shyness of the gray jay, together with his occurrence in the deep woods where other birds are scarce, help to sustain his reputation as one of the park's most interesting bird citizens. The bird is likely to be heard, first, in the upper branches of the firs or hemlocks at some little distance. In a moment, perchance, a wisp of gray smoke seems to float into camp and there is the saucy whiskey jack, very quiet now, perched on a branch of the tree to which the camp table is nailed, and not 6 feet from where you are sitting. Cocking his bright eye at you in a knowing manner, he scans you with much circumspection. Then down he drops, as likely as not, right onto the table, and before you know it has seized a piece of butter from a plate at arm's length and made off with it! * * * By this time three or four more of the birds are waiting for a turn. Scraps of meat, bacon rind, bread, potatoes, butter, oatmeal, or almost any other foods are prized. When one breaks camp a company of four or six gray jays is usually on hand, patiently waiting to pick up any scraps which may be left over. Sometimes, but not often, the birds are shy. * * *

They are very jealous and have many a severe family fight. As a rule no two camp robbers will eat out of the same dish, though at other times friendly enough. They do not like to have the chipmunks too close to their food supply, either, and often combine forces to drive them away. The Steller jay and varied thrush are admitted to their company on equal footing, but woe be to the owl or the hawk that invades their preserves.

J. A. Munro writes to me: "Family groups, consisting of adults and three or four dark young, visited our camp and became tame enough to take food from the hand."

Voice.—Bendire (1895) says that "while some of their notes are not as melodious as they might be, the majority are certainly quite pleasing to the ear, and I consider this species a very fair songster. I have listened to them frequently, and have been surprised to find so much musical ability."

Mrs. Bailey (1902) writes: "The voices of the jays were heard around the log house on Mount Hood from morning till night. Their notes were pleasantly varied. One call was remarkably like the chirp of a robin. Another of the commonest was a weak and rather complaining cry repeated several times. A sharply contrasting one was a pure, clear whistle of one note followed by a three-syllabled call something like *ka-wé-ah*. The regular rallying cry was still different, a loud and striking two-syllabled *ka-whee*."

Taylor and Shaw (1927) give the gray jay credit for "a truly impressive variety of calls and whistles." They refer to the robinlike call, and add: "A cackling note *whut whut kadakut* is sometimes given. Very unusual ejaculations are their *retezzt, ritizzt* or *reckekekekz.* Their whistled calls may be rendered *wheet wheet, tseeuk* or *wheeup,* and very commonly *wheeoo wheeoo.* The notes are clear and can be heard for some distance through the forest."

CYANOCITTA CRISTATA BROMIA Oberholser

NORTHERN BLUE JAY

CONTRIBUTED BY WINSOR MARRETT TYLER

PLATES 6-10

HABITS

The blue jay is a strong, healthy-looking bird, noisy and boisterous. He gives us the impression of being independent, lawless, haughty, even impudent, with a disregard for his neighbors' rights and wishes—like Hotspur, as we meet him in Henry IV, part 1.

To be sure, the jay has his quiet moments, as we shall see, but his mercurial temper, always just below the boiling point, is ever ready to flare up into rage and screaming attack, or, like many another diplomat, beat a crafty retreat. He is a strikingly beautiful bird—blue, black, and white, big and strong, his head carrying a high, pointed crest which in anger shoots upward like a flame. Walter Faxon long ago told me of a distinguished visiting English ornithologist who was eager to see a live blue jay because he considered it the finest bird in the world. He was surprised to find that this beauty, as he called it, is one of our common birds.

Originally a wild bird of the woods, the jay was canny enough to adapt itself to civilization, and nowadays it often builds its nest close to man, even in our gardens.

Spring.—Although the blue jay is considered a permanent resident over a large portion of its breeding range, and instances are known of a banded bird visiting a feeding station throughout the year, there is plenty of evidence that as a species the jay is highly migratory. In New England we detect little actual migration in spring, as a rule. Although jays become more numerous and noisier as summer approaches, they steal in without attracting much attention. E. A. Doolittle (1919) cites an observation in Ohio that may account for the inconspicuousness of the jay in its northward migration. He says: "By chance I looked up and saw five Blue Jays flying about fifty feet above the tree tops, and before my glance had ended others came into view and still others behind them. They were flying northeast and keeping very quiet. I began to count them, and in about fifteen minutes' time had seen ninety-five Jays. And this does not begin to number those that passed, for, on account of the trees, my view to each side was much restricted, and there is no telling how many had gone on before I casually looked up. They were in a long stream, with now and then a bunch of five to fifteen."

W. Bryant Tyrrell (1934) describes a striking assemblage of jays at Whitefish Point, Mich., which were preparing "to cross the eighteen miles of Lake Superior to the Canadian shore"—a favorable migration route. He says:

Extending south, back of the dunes—along the Lake Superior shore, is a wooded region composed mostly of Jack pine, broken by small swampy areas. In this wooded region the birds [of various species] congregate by the thousands before migrating north across Lake Superior. It was in these Jack pines that I saw hundreds—if not thousands—of Blue Jays *(Cyanocitta c. cristata)* on the morning of June 5, 1930. It was a dull cloudy morning with a chilly northwest wind blowing off Lake Superior. When we arrived at the Point, soon after daylight, the birds, mostly Blue Jays * * * were exceedingly restless, apparently waiting to go north but not caring to venture across in a northwest wind. The Blue Jays made very little noise but were constantly milling around, usually in flocks of varying size. A flock would form and fly off towards the lighthouse, circling and rising all the time until they were over the lighthouse several hundred feet high. They would continue to circle and then would come quietly but quickly back to the pines, only to repeat the same procedure in a short while. By the middle of the morning they had broken up into small flocks and gone off into the woods for the day to feed, congregating again in the evening. Each morning the same maneuvers took place until the morning of June 11 when the wind changed to the northeast and the weather became much warmer. On this date the birds were again circling though flying so high that at times they were almost out of sight. I did not see a single flock actually start and fly off across the lake, but on the morning of the 12th there was hardly a bird to be found in the Jack pines.

Courtship.—A survey of the literature brings little to light in regard to the courtship of the blue jay. We may infer therefore that courtship is not a conspicuous feature of the bird's behavior. Mr. Bent describes in his notes some actions having the appearance of mild courtship. He says under date of April 30, 1940:

This morning about 7:30 I saw a flock of 7 or 8 blue jays having a merry time in the top of a large oak in my yard. They were apparently courting. I could not distinguish the sexes, of course. Perhaps there was only one female, and the males were all following her, just as male dogs follow a female in heat. Several of them, presumably males, were bobbing up and down as they do when they make that musical note often heard at other times, but I heard no notes. They were constantly changing places in the tree and chasing each other about. At least one was evidently trying to escape, or perhaps starting a game of 'follow the leader.' Finally, one did fly away and all the others trooped after it. Perhaps they were only playing a game; if so, it was a lively one.

I saw (Tyler, 1920) a similar gathering of jays at about the same time of year (April 6, 1913) acting in much the same way. "Ten of the birds were sitting in a bare tree. A few were mounting toward the top of the tree by stiff upward leaps; the others, well scattered high in the tree, sat quiet; most of the company were screaming. Every few seconds came the growling note, a sound which suggested a 'snoring' frog, the quick tapping of a Woodpecker, or the exhaust from a distant motorcycle —*g-r-r-r.* During the growl, and immediately after it, one or two birds, and perhaps more, moved up and down as if the branch on which they sat were swaying. There was none of the teetering motion of a Spotted Sandpiper; the whole bird rose and sank as a man would move up and down on his tiptoes. Soon the birds flew off [as did Mr. Bent's] in a screaming company and were joined by other Jays."

Hervey Brackbill sent the following account of "Courtship Feeding" to Mr. Bent: "About sunset, 7.06 P. M., May 9, 1939, I noticed three jays in the top of a tall oak but paid no attention to them until I saw one feed another. Then I began to watch and shortly saw another feeding. For a long time at least one of the birds frequently uttered the little note that sounds like *quick,* and for a while one sang much like a catbird. This went on for some minutes, but as the birds kept moving about in the treetops and were often hidden in thick foliage, I could not tell how many feedings there were or whether there was copulation."

Nesting.—Bendire (1895), in his excellent account of the blue jay, says: "It prefers mixed woods to live in, especially oak and beech woods, but for nesting sites dense coniferous thickets are generally preferred; oaks, elms, hickories, and various fruit trees, thorn bushes, and shrubbery overrun with vines are also used, the nests being placed in various situations, sometimes in a crotch or close to the main trunk, or on the extremity of a horizontal limb, among the outer branches. They are placed at distances from the ground varying from 5 to 50 feet, but usually below 20 feet. * * * I believe but one brood is usually reared in a season, but in the South they may occasionally raise two."

Describing typical nests, he says: "The nests are generally well hidden, and are rather bulky but compactly built structures, averaging from 7 to 8 inches in outer diameter by 4 to 4½ inches in depth; the inner cup measures about 3½ to 4 inches in diameter by 2½ inches in depth. Outwardly they are composed of small twigs (thorny ones being preferred), bark, moss, lichens, paper, rags, strings, wool, leaves, and dry grasses, the various materials being well incorporated and sometimes cemented together with mud, but not always; the lining is usually composed exclusively of fine rootlets. Occasionally the Blue Jay will take the nest of another species by force."

John R. Cruttenden writes to Mr. Bent from Illinois: "A peculiar habit of this bird is to line its nest with a piece of cloth or waste paper. This is true in the majority of nests placed near dwellings or in the city, undoubtedly because of the more abundant supply of materials in the city, although the habit is not unusual in nests situated away from man." Henry Mousley (1916) reports: "Evidently the Blue Jay betakes itself to very secluded spots during the breeding season, as I have only succeeded so far in finding one nest, in May of the present year (1915), and had never seen the bird before during the months of June, July and August." Mr. Mousley is speaking here of his experience in Hatley, Quebec. Farther to the south, in New England and the Middle Atlantic States, however, the jay commonly breeds in thickly settled regions, often near houses, as the following observations show.

Frederic H. Kennard (1898) writes: "We have a pair of Blue Jays (*Cyanocitta cristata*) in Brookline, Mass., that have this year built their nest in a most conspicuous place, between the stems of a Wistaria vine and the capitol of a pillar, supporting a piazza roof. This piazza is in almost daily use, and the path leading immediately beside it is also used constantly." Charles R. Stockard (1905), writing of Mississippi, says: "With the exception of the English Sparrow the Blue Jay is probably the most abundant bird in the State. The shade trees bordering the streets of towns, the groves near dwelling houses, trees along road sides, orchards, pastures, and pine woods as well as thick woods, are nesting localities of this bird. One nest was placed in a tree crotch not more than six feet from a bed-room window, thus one might look out on the bird as she sat calmly upon her eggs, and later she was not noticeably nervous while feeding her nestlings before an audience of several persons who observed the performance from the window."

I remember some years ago seeing a nest containing eggs in a situation with no concealment whatever—on the cross-beam of an electric-light pole. The pole stood near a flight of steps used continually by pedestrians in crossing over the tracks at the main railroad station in Lexington, Mass. From the steps I might have touched the sitting bird with an umbrella. Needless to say, the nest was soon knocked down, presumably by boys.

On June 12, 1942, in Tiverton, R. I., Roland C. Clement showed us a most unusual blue jay's nest under the overhang of a cutbank beside a woodland road, which held at that time a brood of nearly fledged young. As he did not get a chance to photograph it, he has sent us the following description of it: "The recessed face of the cutbank in which the nest is placed lies only 10 feet from the farm road, the cut itself being about 6 feet high and its concavity amounting to about 10 inches two feet below the overhanging brink. In this sheltered recess two stout oak roots of 1 inch diameter reach out horizontally into space, intersecting past their exerted centers, and in this crotch our adaptable jays have firmly anchored an otherwise typical nest. The nest is thus about 4 feet from the ground below and, though not absolutely secure from molestation by terrestrial predators which could probably clamber up to it without undue difficulty because of the moderate incline of the bank, it is indeed inconspicuous among the pendant roots and rootlets of the vegetation above, which presently consists merely of shrubs such as *Corylus* and *Myrica*.

"The nest itself is well and firmly woven of long, pliant dead twigs of various species, including some spiny stems of *Smilax* and a few culms of coarse grass, as well as a long strip of paper; and it is lined with fine rootlets, probably those of the brake fern *(Pteris)*, which abounds nearby. The nest cavity is 4½ inches long, parallel to the bank, and 4 inches wide."

Mrs. Harriet Carpenter Thayer (1901) watched the family life of a pair of blue jays at a nest at close range and states that the male aided in making the nest and that both birds incubated, "each relieving the other at more or less regular intervals. And the bird at play did not forget its imprisoned mate, but returned now and then with a choice bit of food, which was delivered with various little demonstrations of sympathy and affection."

Jays are very quiet about their nest. I knew of a nest near the center of the city of Cambridge, Mass., and if I had not happened to see the nest, I should not have suspected that jays were breeding near.

Bendire (1895) quotes W. E. Loucks, of Peoria, Ill., as saying: "A nest of a pair of Robins, built in an elm tree, was stolen and appropriated by a pair of these birds. It was fitted up to suit their needs, and eggs were deposited in it before the eyes of the angry Robins."

A. D. Dubois sent the following note to Mr. Bent: "While listening to the Memorial Day exercises in the auditorium at Chautauqua Grounds (a large pavilion with open sides) I noticed a jay which flew in from the side and up to a nest in one of the roof trusses, where it fed its young and flew out again. This is the first jay's nest I have ever found in a building of any kind."

Dr. Samuel S. Dickey (MS.) reports that nests found by him have been in the following trees: 20 in white pines, 18 in hemlocks, 2 in red spruces, 2 in intermediate firs, 12 in white oaks, 5 in alders (*Alnus incana* and *rugosa),* and one each in a pitch pine, sour gum, Cassin's viburnum (only 3½ feet from the ground), and flowering dogwood.

Eggs.—[AUTHOR'S NOTE: The northern blue jay ordinarily lays four or five eggs, sometimes as few as three, frequently six, and very rarely as many as seven. These are quite uniformly ovate in shape, with occasionally a tendency toward short or elliptical ovate; they have very little or no gloss. The ground color is very variable, and shows two very distinct types, an olive type and a buff type, with a much rarer bluish type; the olive type is by far the commonest. In eggs that I have examined, I have noted the following colors: "Olive-buff," "deep olive-buff," "dark olive-buff," pale "ecru-olive," "pale fluorite green," pale "lichen green," "pale glaucous green," "sea-foam yellow," "light buff," "light ochraceous-buff," "pinkish buff," "pale pinkish buff," and pale "vinaceous-buff." There are also many intermediate shades of pale olives, buffs, greens, and very pale "wood brown," down to pale dull blue, bluish white, or greenish white.

The eggs with the pinkish-buff ground color are often very pretty, being sparingly marked with small spots of bright or purplish browns, and with underlying spots of pale quaker drab or lavender. The pale greenish and bluish types are also sparingly marked with pale, dull browns or olives and a few underlying spots. The olive types are usually, but not always, more heavily marked with spots and small blotches of darker browns and olives of various shades. Some eggs are evenly marked over the entire surface with spots or fine dots, and in others the markings are concentrated at one end; an occasional egg has a few black dots.

The measurements of 135 eggs in the United States National Museum average 28.02 by 20.44 millimeters; the eggs showing the four extremes measure 32.8 by 19.6, 25.9 by 22.4, 25.2 by 20.1, and 25.9 by 18.8 millimeters.]

Young.—From a comprehensive, carefully prepared study of the blue jay, a thesis for the degree of doctor of philosophy, sent to Mr. Bent in manuscript by John Ronald Arnold, the following observations are abstracted: The period of incubation was found to be 17 or 18 days in the vicinity of Ithaca, N. Y., and 17 days in New Jersey. The young at the time of hatching were limp, blind, and entirely naked. When 3 hours old they were able to raise their heads to the rim of the nest. By the fifth day the eyes were just beginning to open, and the birds grasped the lining of the nest with their claws. "During the eighth and ninth days the feathers in all the body tracts except the head and neck regions begin to break from their sheaths." By the seventeenth day the nestlings begin to resemble a blue jay and are almost ready to leave the nest. They leave 17 to 21 days after hatching.

In close agreement with these dates, Isabella McC. Lemmon (1904) gives the incubation period between May 2 and 19 and reports that the young flew on June 6.

Donald J. Nicholson (1936) writes, referring to the young Florida blue jay:

They leave the nest in from fifteen to eighteen days, at which time the tails are quite short, and the feathers not fully developed on any part of the body or wings. Their power of flight is not by any means strong when they first leave the nest, and only short spaces can be covered. Many a young bird at this time of the year falls an easy prey to cats and various snakes. * * *

In three weeks to a month, it is difficult to distinguish the young from the adults, but the face and throat is a smoky, dark color, instead of the rich black of the adult, and the bill is horn-colored, instead of black as in the parents; otherwise the plumage is apparently the same to all outward appearances. By the following spring no difference is seen. Even by fall I can not discern a particle of difference. A fledgling when caught, if caught by anything, emits terrified screeches as if in mortal agony, bringing the parents to its defense at once.

Apparently the voice develops early; I have heard a young bird on leaving the nest shout almost as loudly as its parents.

Francis Zirrer has sent us the following note: "Although considered more or less a raptor, the young blue jay must learn about the various small game before it will touch it. At our woodland cabin we were greatly annoyed by various species of wild mice, especially *Peromyscus*. Throughout the winter many were caught and deposited on the feeding table in the morning. We noticed, however, that the majority of the blue jays, apparently the young birds of the previous summer, were plainly afraid of the mice. Coming to the table they would, with all signs of fright, jerk back, flutter with the wings and fly away. It was up to the old birds to take the mouse, fly with it to a nearby branch, and begin to tear it to pieces. And then the young birds would come near and were fed by the adults."

Plumages.—[AUTHOR'S NOTE: The following abstracts are taken from the manuscript thesis of John R. Arnold, referred to above. He has made a thorough study of the plumages of the blue jay, and says that the young are hatched naked and have no natal down at all. On the eighth and ninth days the body plumage begins to break the feather sheaths, and when the young bird leaves the nest, at an age of about 20 days, the juvenal plumage is largely grown and the bird is able to fly. He describes this plumage as follows:

"Pileum between cadet gray and columbia blue. Feathers of forehead black at base with bluish-white tips. Superciliary line grayish white. Throat bluish white to white. Nuchal band black. Black of lores less pronounced than in adult. Back and lesser wing coverts light to deep mouse gray, tinged with blue. Wing and tail feathers as in first winter and similar to adult. Breast and flanks smoke gray, belly and under tail coverts white."

A partial postjuvenal molt takes place when the bird is between 50 and 90 days out of the nest; this produces a first winter plumage that is hardly distinguishable from that of the adult, though somewhat paler and less violet on the head and neck, and with the bars on the tail less pronounced. This molt involves the contour plumage and the lesser wing coverts only.

Adults have a complete postnuptial molt between June and September.]

Food.—The blue jay eats almost every kind of digestible food; like its relative, the crow, it may be considered omnivorous. F. E. L. Beal (1897), in an exhaustive study to determine the exact economic status of the jay, published the results of an examination "of 292 stomachs collected in every month of the year from 22 states, the District of Columbia, and Canada." He says:

One of the first points to attract attention in examining these stomachs was the large quantity of mineral matter, averaging over 14 per cent of the total contents. The real food is composed of 24.3 per cent of animal matter and 75.7 per cent of vegetable matter, or a trifle more than three times as much vegetable as animal. The animal food is chiefly made up of insects, with a few spiders, myriapods, snails, and small vertebrates, such as fish, salamanders, tree frogs, mice and birds. Everything was carefully examined which might by any possibility indicate that birds or eggs had been eaten, but remains of birds were found in only 2, and the shells of small birds' eggs in 3 of the 292 stomachs. * * *

Insects are eaten by blue jays in every month in the year, but naturally only in small quantities during the winter. The great bulk of the insect food consists of beetles, grasshoppers, and caterpillars. * * * The average for the whole year is nearly 23 per cent.

Under vegetable food Professor Beal lists corn, wheat, oats, buck-wheat, acorns, chestnuts, beechnuts, hazelnuts, sumac, knotweed, sorrel, apples, strawberries, currants, blackberries, mulberries, blueberries, huckleberries, wild cherries, chokecherries, wild grapes, serviceberries, elderberries, sour-gum berries, hawthorn, and pokeberries. He continues: "Grain is naturally one of the most important groups, and may be considered first. Wheat, oats, and buckwheat occur so seldom and in such small quantities (1.3 per cent of the whole food) that they may be dismissed with slight comment. Wheat was found in only eight stomachs, oats in two, and buckwheat in one. The wheat was eaten in July, August, and September; oats in March and July, and buckwheat in October. Corn was found in seventy-one stomachs, and aggregates 17.9 per cent of the food of the year. This is less than that eaten by the crow (21 per cent) or by the crow blackbird (35 per cent)." Professor Beal summarizes his findings thus:

The most striking point in the study of the food of the blue jay is the discrepancy between the testimony of field observers concerning the bird's nest-robbing proclivities and the results of stomach examinations. The accusations of eating eggs and young birds are certainly not sustained, and it is futile to attempt to reconcile the conflicting statements on this point, which must be left until more accurate observations have been made. In destroying insects the jay undoubtedly does much good. Most of the predaceous beetles which it eats do not feed on other insects to any great extent. On the other hand, it destroys some grasshoppers and caterpillars and many noxious beetles, such as Scarabaeids, click beetles (Elaterids), weevils (Curculionids), Buprestids, Chrysomelids, and Tenebrionids. The blue jay gathers its fruit from nature's orchard and vineyard, not from man's; corn is the only vegetable food for which the farmer suffers any loss, and here the damage is small. In fact, the examination of nearly 300 stomachs shows that the blue jay certainly does far more good than harm.

William Brewster (1937) describes jays collecting acorns thus: "1898, September 30.—Several Jays spent the entire day harvesting acorns in a Red Oak that shades a village street of Bethel, Maine, taking them thence across open fields to rather distant woods. They invariably plucked them from the twigs while hovering on fluttering wings and not when perched. The acorns were still green where the cups covered them. Each Jay apparently always carried two at once, one in the mouth or throat, the other held in the tip of the bill."

Mr. Brewster (1937) also speaks of the jay as a flycatcher: "1888, September 9.—At sunset this evening when the air was warm, damp and calm, I saw about a dozen Blue Jays scattered about in the tops of small aspens growing by the Lake-shore where they were catching flying insects. In pursuit of these they would mount straight upward from ten to twenty feet and then return to their perches by swooping downward on set wings. Their flights were altogether so very like those of King-birds similarly engaged that I mistook them for birds of the latter species at first glance."

G. Gill (1920) tells of a blue jay trying to catch a mouse. "On Feb. 2, 1918," he says, "the scream of a Blue Jay rang out through the air, and, looking toward the barn, I saw the bird swooping down to the ground after something. I was interested at once, and at first I could not see what was running across the snow; when it reached the barn, where it was clear, I saw that it was a mouse.

"The Blue Jay boldly followed it right into the barn, dodging in and out of the wagons and pecking at the mouse at every chance it got. About this time the Blue Jay's mate joined the chase, but she was just a little too late. The mouse, nearly beaten, hopped into a friendly hole and escaped. For a little while the pair watched the hole, and then gave it up."

This would appear strange prey for a jay, but F. E. L. Beal (1897) states that "the jay kept in captivity by Mr. Judd showed a marked fondness for mice, and would devour them apparently with great relish."

W. L. McAtee (1914) calls attention to a bizarre feeding habit of the jay apparently seldom resorted to. He quotes Grace Ellicott from the *Guide to Nature,* 1908, p. 168, as follows:

The occupants of a recently disturbed ant hill were excitedly crawling about the hill and the adjacent cement walk. They were large, and to a blue jay in a neighboring tree they must have looked luscious, for flying down, the jay began to pick them up with an eagerness that seemed to say that this was an opportunity that might come his way but once. As rapidly as he could do it he seized the ants, with each capture lifting a wing, sometimes one, sometimes the other, and seemed to deposit his prey amongst the feathers back of and under-neath it. So quickly he worked and with such evident eagerness to make the most of this rare occasion that, as he lifted the wing, putting his bill amongst the feathers, it often seemed that he must lose his balance and topple over backwards. But he kept his poise, worked on with all speed and had laid in quite a store when a passerby frightened him from his task. Whether this jay had only just discovered the most convenient of all storehouses for his use or whether this food was to be carried to the nest for the young, for it was nesting time, he was most interesting.

McAtee comments on the observation as follows:

This Blue Jay was therefore taking advantage of the instinct of ants when disturbed to fasten their jaws onto any object that presents itself. * * * These three most interesting observations suggest that numerous birds may have the same or other wonderful habits about which we are ignorant. They should stimulate minute and careful research and comfort those who fear that all the interesting things have already been discovered. [See Auk, vol. 57, pp. 520-522, 1940, and vol. 58, p. 102, 1941, for other similar performances.]

Behavior.—The jay commonly progresses through the air steadily and rather slowly, although with full and regular quick flips of the wings. He keeps on an even keel and maintains a characteristically level flight. The long axis of the body is parallel to the ground, although his beak appears to point slightly downward, perhaps only because his crest gives the impression of a downward-sloping profile.

A company of jays, like their small relatives the chickadees, almost always fly across a wide, open space one at a time, at some distance from each other. They generally fly directly to the place where they are about to alight, rarely deviating from their course by swerving from side to side, and, on arriving at their perch, often come to a stop deftly upon it in perfect balance, although they may sometimes alight, with head held proudly high, after a short upward-slanting sail. I have seen a jay come to rest on a slender vertical rod (a radio aerial) as neatly as any kingbird.

Sometimes, in making short flights, jays will undulate a little, sailing with wings held open longer than in the steady, level flight. Now, as they fly overhead, slowly and silently, they flap the wings back and without an instant's pause fan them out full again. Here there is a short pause with the wings expanded, during which the bird sinks a little in the air before the next stroke carries him on and upward again—very different from the undulating flight of a woodpecker, which closes its wings on the downward plunge.

William Brewster (1937) describes an unusual method of flight which he observed at Lake Umbagog. He writes: "1895, September 20.— About eight o'clock this morning I was standing on a wooded knoll near our camp at Pine Point, watching some small birds, when a sound resembling that of strong wind blowing through pine-tops came from directly overhead. It could not be ascribed to such an origin, however, for the air was then perfectly calm. The mystery remained unsolved until an hour or so later when I saw a dozen Blue Jays mount in a compact flock, by a spiral course, to a height of several hundred feet above the tallest trees and then dash almost straight down together, with half-closed wings, like so many stooping falcons, thereby producing a loud rushing sound exactly like that heard earlier in the morning."

The motions of a company of jays as they flit about among the branches of a tree are surprisingly easy, light, and graceful. The wings move slowly, like great moth's wings, yet the birds alight accurately on the branches, or float to the ground from which they often almost bounce up to a high perch again. With all their energy, alertness, and spirited behavior, jays seldom seem to be in a hurry; we never see them move with that intensely rapid, flashlike speed which is characteristic of many birds.

Nowadays we regard the blue jay as rather a tame bird—almost as tame as the robin—but Witmer Stone (1926) states that in Germantown, Pa., the bird's habits have changed in the last 3 or 4 decades. He says: "When studying birds in Wister's woods and vicinity from 1880 to 1897, the Blue Jay was a very wild species occurring only during autumn flights, but upon returning to reside in the old neighborhood after some thirty-five years absence I found the bird's habits totally changed. I was surprised to find a pair of Jays present about the end of May, 1922, acting as if they were located for the summer. Later, I detected them constructing a nest in a beech tree close to the railroad station about ten feet above a path along which hundreds of persons passed to and from the trains, and not over fifty feet from the tracks."

On the other hand, Nathan Clifford Brown (1879), writing of Coosada, Ala., says that the blue jay is a "very common resident, and, to one who has known the species only at the North, remarkably tame. I observed them feeding in the streets of Montgomery, and unsuspiciously flying about much after the manner of the domestic pigeons of Northern cities."

Individual jays react differently in the presence of man. Wilbur F. Smith (1905) gives an instance of remarkable tameness in a sitting bird. He says:

To those knowing the Blue Jay only as a wild, shy bird of the tree-tops, so hard to approach, or, by reputation, as a thief or a robber of other birds' nests, there remains a pleasure like unto finding some new and rare bird, to watch a pair of Jays through the nesting season and to find them so devoted to their nest and young that they lose much of their shyness and allow a familiarity which very few other birds will tolerate. One pair of Jays built for several years in a tangle of briers near my home, and the female became so tame, through constant visiting, that I could at last spread her wings and tail-feathers without her leaving the nest, and even stroke her back with no further sign of disapproval than a settling lower in the nest and a parting of the bill.

Mrs. Harriet Carpenter Thayer (1901) says of a pair which nested in her garden: "The Jays were not at all shy, but on the contrary were very valiant and determined in standing by their home. Soon after the eggs were laid, the house-painters began work opposite the nest, and many sharp pecks they received on their ears and backs."

In its relation to small birds, consensus classes the blue jay as an outlaw and robber. Bendire (1895) says:

Few of our native birds compare in beauty of plumage and general bearing with the Blue Jay, and while one can not help admiring him on account of his amusing and interesting traits, still even his best friends can not say much in his favor, and though I have never caught one actually in mischief, so many close observers have done so that one can not very well, even if so inclined, disprove the principal charge brought against this handsome freebooter. He is accused of destroying many of the eggs and young of our smaller birds, and this is so universally admitted that there can be no doubt of its truth. * * *

Mr. Manly Hardy, of Brewer, Maine, fully corroborates these statements, writing me as follows: "It is a great robber of birds' nests, taking both eggs and young. I also feel quite sure that in some cases it kills adult birds. * * * There is little doubt that they destroy many nests of eggs and young; all of the *small birds say so*."

Mrs. Marie Dales (1925) thus adds her testimony against the jay: "I saw a Blue Jay harassing a Mourning Dove, eighteen or twenty feet up in a tree. He would pluck out a mouthful of feathers and then retreat for a moment. When the dove had settled down, back would come the jay to torment her again. On closer observation I discovered the nest, wonderfully well hidden for a Mourning Dove's nest. The jay kept up his attacks for several minutes and finally the dove left the nest and went to her mate sitting on a limb farther out. This was just the opportunity the jay was waiting for. He hopped to the nest, pecked a hole in the egg and carried it off." William Brewster (1937) states that he "saw a Blue Jay take an egg from a Robin's nest and fly off with it, hotly pursued by the outraged Robin."

The following story, sent to Mr. Bent by Dr. Daniel S. Gage, gives an interesting sidelight on the blue jay's character: "I once saw a demonstration that animals note the warning cries of the blue jay. I was walking on a trail in the Flat Top Mountains of Colorado. A porcupine was waddling along ahead of me. The trail ran through an open space several hundred yards across, dense woods bordering it on all sides. The porcupine was going away from me and did not notice me, as he could not see behind him as he waddled along. He stopped repeatedly to nibble at some plants at the side of the trail. I halted each time he stopped to bite at a plant, and he did not note me at all, although I was only a few feet behind him. Suddenly, from the woods some hundred of yards away, a blue jay shrieked his *jay, jay, jay.* He had seen me. Instantly, the porcupine raised his quills, rose to his hind feet and sniffed in each direction. Then he noticed me, although I was standing perfectly still, eyed me carefully, his quills erect. Then finally, with angry mien and raised quills, he dropped down and ran as fast as he could into the forest."

Aretas A. Saunders (MS.) reports: "A family of jays came to my bird bath fairly regularly late in summer. Six birds would come together and stand about the edge of the bath while each one in turn bathed," and Mr. Bent (MS.) calls attention to the jay's habit of sunning itself. He says: "I have been amused lately in watching them sunning themselves on my lawn, even on the hottest days. Usually the bird turns over on one side, with its breast toward the sun and the upper wing partially raised, so as to let the sun in on its under plumage, remaining in this position for several minutes. At other times it lies prone on the ground, breast down, with both wings widely spread, so as to sun the wings."

Henry C. Denslow sent to Mr. Bent a record of a banded blue jay that lived for 15 years. Other banded individuals have been recorded as 9, 11, and 13 years old.

The jay's tendency to pester owls and hawks is one of its best-known habits. If a jay comes upon an owl hidden in the daytime, he sets up an outcry to which all the jays within hearing respond, and, collecting in a screaming mob, they drive the owl from tree to tree. It is sometimes to our advantage to follow up such a gathering when their voices rise to the high pitch of anger, for the jays may have found a rare bird.

In regard to the jay's habit of storing food for future use, Bendire (1895) says: "Where they are resident they lay up quite a store of acorns, corn, and nuts in various places for winter use, but where they are only summer visitors they do not resort to this practice."

Dwight W. Huntington (MS.) reports the following observation: "I had many small pheasants running at large in my gardens, and one day a blue jay lit on a small tree just above a bantam with a brood of golden pheasants. He evidently had his eye on the little birds, and the bantam led them away. The jay followed, lit in another tree, and this was repeated several times until, much to my surprise, he struck at the little birds just as a hawk does. The bantam flew up at him as he came down. The birds came together, and a fight was on. Blue feathers and black from the bantam soon covered the ground. The bantam won, and, seeing that the jay was dead, she proudly led her little brood away. I was dumbfounded and amazed at what I had seen and called a game-keeper to come and see the dead jay and the feathers scattered about."

Voice.—It is the blue jay's voice, more than his gay color, that makes him conspicuous. We cannot be long in the open air before we hear him—in woodland, in open country, in the suburbs of our large cities. At the least alarm he begins to shout, and often, with no apparent cause, even a lone bird will break out, like a schoolboy, it seems, out of pure joy in making a noise. Especially in autumn the jays shout so loudly that they fill all outdoors with sound.

The note we hear oftenest is a loud, clear cry often written *jay* or *jeer*, well within the range of human whistling and readily imitated by the human voice. *Peer* or *beer*, with no *r* sound, is perhaps a closer rendering, because the note lacks the hard *j* sound at the beginning. It is long drawn out, falling in pitch at the end and is generally repeated a number of times. This is the note we hear all through the autumn from screaming companies of jays traveling through the woods. It suggests to us various emotions or states of mind—remonstrance, taunting defiance, whining complaint, anger, but never, I think, fear. The tone of voice varies too. It may be harsh, hard and flat, or musical and delicate; sometimes it has a tin-whistle quality; and rarely it is pitched so high that it resembles a killdeer's piercing whistle.

The jay uses a great number of calls—too many for us to describe them all in detail—and the fact that they tend to run into each other makes enumeration difficult. Even dissimilar notes, by a slight alteration in inflection or tone, will often merge into one another. For example, when the *jay* call is produced in its purest musical form, and uttered as two notes, it becomes the well-known, bell-like *tull-ull* or *twirl-erl*. When a bird is near us we can sometimes detect the transition as one note is gradually converted into another.

Francis H. Allen (MS.) terms the *tull-ull* the anvil call, an apt comparison, and says that in making the note "the jay raises and lowers its head twice, once for each part of this dissyllabic note. This bobbing of the head is up and down, not down and up."

During the warmer months the jay often utters a pleasing whistled note that sounds like *teekle,* pronounced like our word tea-cup. Over and over he sings it as he flies about, sometimes giving it in pairs or series. It seems to reflect a quiet, happy mood in which the bird is free for the moment from antagonism. This note is allied to the creaking, wheel-barrow call, commonly written *whee-oodle.*

Frequently heard in the autumn gatherings is a chuckling, conversational *kuk.* This note differs widely in its mode of delivery. It may be extended into a bubbling chatter—a sort of tittering laugh—or, ranging up and down in pitch, it may run off into pretty, rambling phrases. The voice is not loud, and we have to be near the bird to appreciate the charm of the phrasing. Jays give a modification of the *kuk* when they are feeding in trees or when they visit feeding stations.

Quite different from the shouted or whistled notes is a dry, wooden rattle, almost a growl. A lone jay may give it, or one or more in a large company. The notes are often accompanied by an odd rising up and down on the perch. Francis H. Allen (MS.) speaks of it as "a grating, pebbly *r-r-rt,* generally given twice, but sometimes three times. The repetition is in the manner of most of the calls of the species. The grating quality I express by the *r,* but of course the *it* sound ran all through the note. 'Pebbly' seems to express it rather well."

Comparatively few observers are familiar with the song of the blue jay. When he sings, the jay throws off his boisterous demeanor. He retires to the recesses of a wood or seeks seclusion in a thick evergreen tree and there, all alone, sings his quiet solo. I have sometimes heard a song from a bird hidden in a tangle of second-growth, and have not at first recognized the author as a jay at all. The song is a potpourri of faint whistles and various low, sweet notes, some in phrasing and pitch, suggesting a robin's song—a mockingbird might be singing, *sotto voce*. But as the song goes on one realizes that most of the notes are clearly in the blue jay's repertoire but are disguised by being jumbled together and delivered gently and peacefully.

Francis H. Allen has noted the song several times in his journal. He heard it first on February 28, 1909, the notes "coming from a row of large hemlock trees. The bird was keeping in the very heart of the tree, near the trunk. The notes sounded not unlike the goldfinch's song, but very subdued in tone. The song consisted of sweet lisping notes and chippering, and was continuous and long." Again he says: "Sweet and rather loud song notes from a jay in one of our Norway spruces this morning (September 4, 1933). One was a sort of short descending trill, rather high pitched, that suggested a mockingbird." And on March 22, 1935: "Long subdued song from a jay in a hemlock. It lasted two or three minutes, I should say, and was absolutely continuous, with no pauses between phrases. Some notes were very suggestive of *Spinus tristis,* both the long upward-slurred note and a succession of short notes resembling *per-chic-o-pee.* The whole remarkably soft and sweet. The bird remained hidden among the foliage, as is the jay's custom in this sort of singing."

Isabel Goodhue (1919) speaks of the song as "sweet, tender and quite lovely; delivered * * * with a retiring modesty not perceptible in the Blue Jay's deportment on other occasions."

The jay's loud cry often sounds exactly like the *teearr* of the red-shouldered hawk. I have sometimes been misled and have mistaken one note for the other. On more than one occasion I have supposed I was listening to a hawk screaming in the distance but found that a jay near at hand was the author of the notes.

This similarity to the scream of the red-shouldered hawk and the resemblance of some of the jay's notes to those of other birds have given him a reputation as an imitator. It is difficult, perhaps impossible, to be sure that such cases are not coincidence, especially when we recall the multiplicity of the jay's vocabulary.

Enemies.—Jays are subject to attack from the smaller, quick-moving hawks but appear in the main to be able to protect themselves.

Taverner and Swales (1907), in their studies at Point Pelee, say: "During the hawk flights of 1905 and 1906 they were much harassed by the Sharp-shins but, as they are perfectly able to take care of themselves and kept pretty close in the grape vine tangles, it is not probable that they suffered much. * * * In fact once within the shrubbery, they seemed to rather enjoy the situation, and from their safe retreats hurled joyous epithets at their baffled enemies. * * * We have only once found the remains of a hawk-devoured bird of this species."

Frank Bolles (1896) speaks thus "of an encounter between a sharp-shinned hawk and a flock of blue jays":

The hawk arrived when several flickers were in the tree and hurled himself upon them. They fled, calling wildly, and brought to their aid, first a kingbird, which promptly attacked the hawk from above, and then a flock of blue jays, which abused him from cover below. When the kingbird flew away, as he did after driving the hawk into the bushes for a few moments, the jays grew more and more daring in approaching the hawk. In fact they set themselves to the task of tiring him out and making him ridiculous. They ran great risks in doing it, frequently flying almost into the hawk's face; but they persevered, in spite of his furious attempts to strike them. After nearly an hour the hawk grew weary and edged off to the woods. Then the jays went up the tree as though it were a circular staircase, and yelled the news of the victory to the swamp.

Henry C. Denslow sent the following note to Mr. Bent: "It is said that shrikes sometimes attack blue jays, but in one case the tables were turned. A shrike came to a feeding-table where eight blue jays were feeding and met a warm reception. The shrike alighted on a branch a little above the jays. They looked at him for an instant and then all started for him. He flew into a hedge for protection, but was driven out, then started for an evergreen tree, but the jays were so hot on his trail that he took flight—all the jays trailing after, each one screeching his loudest, until the sound of battle faded away in the distance."

Feathers and other remains of blue jays are often found in and about the nests of the duck hawk.

Dr. Herbert Friedmann (1929) mentions two records of the blue jay being imposed upon by the cowbird but suggests that "the eggs of the Blue Jay are so much larger than those of the Cowbird that there is little probability of the latter ever hatching if present."

Harold S. Peters (1936) lists as external parasites on the blue jay four lice *(Degeeriella eustigma, Menacanthus persignatus, Myrsidea funerea,* and *Philopterus cristata),* one fly *(Ornithoica confluenta),* one mite *(Liponyssus sylviarum),* and one tick *(Haemaphysalis leporis-palustris).*

Fall.—The migration of blue jays in autumn is much more conspicuous than the northward movement in spring. P. A. Taverner and B. H. Swales (1907) describe a flock leaving Point Pelee on their southward journey on October 14, 1906. They say:

We noticed a very interesting migration across the lake. All morning long we saw large flocks passing out the Point. In the afternoon we followed them to the end and, though most then had passed, we witnessed one small bunch of perhaps fifty birds essay the passage. The day was fine and clear and but very little wind blowing, but when they came out to the end of the trees they turned back and sought a large tree-top, where they settled to talk the matter over at the top of their voices. Then, reassured, they started out, rising above gun shot from the ground and making for the Ohio shore, not for Pelee Island as we supposed they would. When they got far enough out to see the blue water under them they slowed up, and when we waved our hats and shouted at them a few wavered, paused and then fled back to the shore to their tree again, followed a moment later by the whole flock. Another pow-pow was held and again they started, with great determination and seemingly filled with the motto, "Ohio or bust." This time they had hardly got well out over the lake when a Sharp-shin was discerned far in the distance, but it was enough to again send them shrieking back to their oak tree. This time the consultation lasted a little longer than before, but at last the coast seemed clear and they started once more. Again, as they drew over the water, they slightly paused as though doubtful, but no one shouted, there was not a hawk in sight and, as there was no possible excuse for backing out this time, they kept slowly and gingerly on until well started and away from land, when they settled into their pace and, when lost sight of in our glasses, were continuing on their way in a straight line that would carry them several miles to the east of Pelee Island.

William Brewster (1937), under date of September 21, 1895, gives this account of migrating jays at Lake Umbagog, Maine:

As I was bathing in the Lake at seven o'clock this morning a flock of seventeen Blue Jays started from the woods on Pine Point and rose above them to a height of fully *two thousand* feet, by a spiral course not less than a half mile across, making only one complete and another half, lateral turn during the entire ascent. They then started off towards the southwest and kept straight on, with ceaseless flapping; until lost to sight in the distance, thereby accomplishing what was obviously the initial stage of a diurnal migratory flight. * * * An hour later the members of another flock, seventeen in number, appeared over the Point at a height of about two hundred feet, probably arriving from somewhere further north. Setting their wings they came hurtling down altogether, precisely like those seen yesterday and making the same sound as of rushing wind. [Quoted under Behavior.] It was loud enough to bring Jim Bernier, my guide, running forth from his tent with the expectation, as he afterwards admitted, of seeing a big flock of Scoters pitching down into the Lake. That the first flock of Jays should have apparently started on a migratory journey, and the second have completed one at so nearly the same time of day seems very interesting, and also suggestive of the inference that these flights may often be of no great duration. While engaged in them the birds remain severely silent, in this respect differing from migrating Crows. Such, at least, has been the case with all that I have observed for not one has ever uttered a vocal cry of any kind within my hearing, when on wing.

I remember seeing, several years ago in mid-September, a migration of jays that covered a wide area. During a drive of 50 miles northwest out of Boston, Mass., jays continually crossed the road in front of my car. I soon noticed that all of them crossed from the right to the left side of the road and were therefore flying south. Most of them were single birds, but occasionally two or three flew near together. I noticed them for 20 miles or so. Again, also in September, I saw a flock of 15 or 20 jays fly southward across the parade ground on Boston Common, which is surrounded on all sides by miles of closely built-up city. These birds were so closely packed that I mistook them at first for a flock of grackles.

William Brewster (1937) speaks of a similar observation thus: "1888, September 13.—During the last three days I have seen many flocks of Blue Jays, containing anywhere from a dozen to twenty birds each, flying southward in the daytime over open country, not in scattered order, but as compactly 'bunched' as so many Blackbirds correspondingly employed. Without doubt they were migrating."

Rev. J. J. Murray writes to us: "In the Valley of Virginia, they are certainly migratory. Here they are much commoner in summer than in winter, being very scarce indeed during some winters. Migration is more noticeable in fall than in spring. Through October, and sometimes up to the middle of November, migrating flocks are seen moving south. I have seen as many as 25 or 30 blue jays pass a favorable location in an hour, usually in strung-out flight."

Maurice Broun (1941) reports heavy migrations of blue jays at Hawk Mountain, Pa., "from the third week in September until mid-October." He says:

The jays may be seen in loose flocks, or in orderly processions, on either side of the ridge, and at any elevation, in numbers varying from twelve to three hundred or more birds. I have noticed each season that jays are on the move by 7 a. m., but by mid-afternoon their flights terminate. As a rule, the birds keep just above the tree tops, and seldom is there much fuss or noise; indeed, observers at the lookout must be keenly alert to detect each passing group of jays. * * *

During a sixteen day period beginning September 24, 1939, I made an approximate count of 7,350 Blue Jays. Doubtless *many* jays slipped by uncounted. The majority of the birds passed through in a constant stream regardless of weather conditions, from September 30 to October 6. The peak of the migration came on October 1, a day of alternating rain and mist, with raw northerly winds; at least 1,535 birds passed the lookout, even during the rain, in groups of from 100 to 350. Again on October 3, despite obliterating mists during the forenoon, and fresh easterly winds all day, I counted several large flocks at various parts of the Sanctuary, and the far from complete count for the day was 1,250 birds.

Winter.—The blue jay is an attractive winter bird. He fits well into the wintry scenery—bright, clear sky, and the blue shadows on the snow. After his burst of noise in the autumn, he becomes comparatively quiet, and during the colder months uses mainly his *jeer* call, and this not overmuch. But on soft mornings in January and February, when the temperature is rising, we may hear his sweetly whistled *teekle* note. *Tea-cup, tea-cup,* he sings—a sure sign of a mild day.

DISTRIBUTION

Range.—The United States and southern Canada, chiefly east of the Great Plains; partially migratory.

The range of the blue jay extends **north** to central Alberta (Stony Plain, Lac la Biche, probably Poplar Point, and Battle River); southern Saskatchewan (probably Prince Albert, Regina, and McLean); southern Manitoba (Fort Ellice, probably Chemawawin, Gypsumville, and West Selkirk); Ontario (Indian Bay, Lac Seul, and Cobalt); New Brunswick (Restigouch Valley and Bathurst); and southeastern Quebec (Magdalen Islands). The **eastern** limit of the range extends southward along the Atlantic coast from southeastern Quebec (Magdalen Islands) to southern Florida (Miami). **South** to southern Florida (Miami and Fort Myers) and west along the Gulf coast to southern Texas (Houston and Atascosa County). **West** to central Texas (Atascosa County, Waco, and Decatur); Oklahoma (Norman); eastern Colorado (Lamar and Wray); eastern Wyoming (Torrington); western North Dakota (Killdeer Mountains and Charlson); and Alberta (Red Deer and Stony Plain).

While the blue jay is generally resident, it partly withdraws during some winters from the extreme northern parts of the summer range. It has been recorded in winter north to southern Alberta (Red Deer); southern Manitoba (Lake San Martin); northern Michigan (McMillan); southern Ontario (Plover Mills, Toronto, and Ottawa); southern Quebec (Montreal and Bary); and Maine (Foxcroft and Machias).

The range as outlined is for the entire species and is occupied largely by the northern blue jay *(C. c. bromia)*. The southern blue jay *(C. c. cristata)* is found in the Southeastern United States (except the southern half of the Florida Peninsula) north to North Carolina and west to Louisiana, while the lower part of Florida is occupied by Semple's blue jay *(C. c. semplei)*   *C. c. cyanotephra* is found from eastern Colorado and Nebraska to northern Oklahoma and the panhandle of Texas.

Migration.—Because of the fact that as a species the blue jay is found in winter throughout most of its breeding range, dates of arrival and departure of migrating individuals are difficult to obtain. A migratory movement is, however, evidenced in autumn, when troops of jays may be seen working southward through the trees, while a corresponding northward movement may be detected in spring. More positive evidence of the partially migratory habits of this species is found among the recovery records of banded individuals. In the files of the Fish and Wildlife Service there are many cases that show definite fall travel in the year of banding from Massachusetts to North Carolina; from New York to Virginia; from New Jersey to Virginia, North Carolina, and South Carolina; from Ohio to Alabama; from Wisconsin to Arkansas; from Minnesota to Missouri, Arkansas, Oklahoma, and Texas; and from South Dakota to Oklahoma, and Texas. Data illustrative of the spring movement are not so numerous, but records are available showing spring flights from North Carolina to New York; from the District of Columbia to Rhode Island; from New York to New Brunswick; from Massachusetts to Prince Edward Island; and from Iowa to northern Wisconsin.

Casual records.—The blue jay appears to be extending its range westward, as there are several records for the vicinity of Denver, Colo., that have accumulated during recent years. There are a few records for the southern part of Newfoundland made during the period from the last of June to the last of September. Apparently a specimen was taken at Moose Factory in northern Ontario, in 1862, while at Fruitland, N. Mex., one was seen on October 17, 1908, and three were noted the day following.

Egg dates.—Florida: 69 records, March 17 to August 29; 35 records, April 11 to May 11, indicating the height of the season.

Illinois: 62 records, April 18 to July 12; 32 records, May 5 to 26.

Kansas: 29 records, April 28 to July 29; 15 records, May 23 to June 12.

Massachusetts: 54 records, April 30 to June 17; 28 records, May 14 to 28.

Minnesota: 20 records, April 27 to June 11; 10 records, May 12 to 22.

Nova Scotia: 9 records, May 6 to June 16.

South Carolina: 14 records, April 5 to June 1; 8 records, April 20 to May 18.

Texas: 6 records, April 5 to June 18.

CYANOCITTA CRISTATA CRISTATA (Linnaeus)

SOUTHERN BLUE JAY

PLATE 11

HABITS

Dr. Oberholser (1921) has shown that the range of this race has been found to extend much farther north, including South Carolina, the type locality of *Cyanocitta cristata cristata* (Linnaeus), which, of course, necessitates the relegation of the subspecific name *florincola* and the common name Florida blue jay to synonymy. This would leave the northern blue jay without a name, for which Dr. Oberholser proposed the subspecific name *bromia*. The 1931 Check-list admits this extension of range as far north as North Carolina but entirely ignores the fact that the name *C. c. cristata* (Linnaeus) was based on Catesby's bird, which undoubtedly represents this southern race.

I prefer to use Arthur H. Howell's (1932) names, *Cyanocitta cristata cristata* (Linnaeus) and "southern blue jay," for this race. He says that its range covers approximately the northern half of the State, at least as far south as Volusia and Lake Counties, where it probably begins to intergrade with the extreme southern form, *semplei*. W. E. Clyde Todd (1928), who described *semplei,* seems to think that specimens taken north of the Everglades are not typical of either race, thus allowing a large area of intergradation.

This race is smaller than the northern race, with coloration paler and duller and with the white tips of the greater wing coverts, secondaries, and tail feathers smaller.

Nesting.—The nesting habits of the southern blue jay are not very different from those of the northern blue jay, with due allowance made for the difference in environment. Major Bendire (1895) writes:

Two nests found by Dr. Ralph were placed in low, flat pine woods, 25 and 30 feet, respectively, from the ground; these were composed of twigs, Spanish moss, pine needles, and pieces of cloth, and lined with fine roots. In some of the nests the material were cemented with mud. A third nest was placed in an orange tree standing within a few feet of a house, near the banks of the St. John's River, about 20 feet from the ground; it was composed of twigs, catkins, plant fibers, weeds, grasses, pieces of string, and a little Spanish moss, and these materials were cemented together with mud; the lining consisted entirely of wire grass *(Aristida).* Another nest was placed among some small branches at the end of a limb of an orange tree, about 11 feet from the ground, and was composed of similar materials outwardly, but no mud was used in its construction, and it was thickly lined with fine rootlets of the orange tree.

The average measurement of two nests is about 8 inches in outside diameter by 4 inches in depth, the inner cup measuring about 4 inches in diameter by 2¼ inches in depth.

Mr. Howell (1932) says that the "nests are placed in trees—commonly oak, orange, or pine—at a height of 8 to 35 feet above the ground"; and he quotes D. J. Nicholson as saying that two or three broods are raised in a season, beginning late in March and ending in August. There is a set of eggs in my collection, taken in Leon County, Fla., from a nest in a magnolia tree; it was made of materials similar to those mentioned above, including the mud.

In Texas, according to George F. Simmons (1925), the nests are placed in various oaks, hackberry, pecan, cedar elm, and cedar trees. Wayne (1910) says that in South Carolina it seems partial to live oaks.

Eggs.—The eggs of the southern blue jay are indistinguishable from those of its northern relative and probably would show in a large series all the wide range of variation in shape, color, and pattern exhibited in eggs of the northern blue jay. According to Mr. Nicholson (Howell, 1932), "the first sets nearly always comprised 4 eggs, the second sets either 3 or 4, the third sets nearly always 3." The measurements of 40 eggs average 27.1 by 20.4 millimeters; the eggs showing the four extremes measure 29.6 by 20.7, 27.4 by 21.3, and 23.2 by 18.4 millimeters.

Food.—The feeding habits of the southern blue jay are similar to those of the northern bird; it lives on such varieties of nuts, wild and cultivated fruits, grains, insects and their larvae, and other small forms of animal life as it can find within its range. It is said to do some damage to small cultivated fruits and to rob birds' nests of their eggs and young.

Dr. Walter P. Taylor tells me that in Walker County, Tex., these jays are useful in providing food for bobwhite quail, by dropping pieces of acorns that they have broken up.

Behavior.—Wherever I have been in Florida I have been impressed with the fact that the local blue jays are among the commonest and most familiar birds. They are not at all shy and seem to enjoy living in the towns and villages, in the gardens and trees close to houses, in the shade trees along the streets, and in the citrus groves, as well as in the open country. Mr. Howell (1932) says that they "are found less commonly in pine woods, hammocks of oak or mixed timber, turkey-oak scrub, and the borders of small cypress swamps. The birds are noisy and restless during the greater part of the year, moving about in small companies or loose flocks, calling vigorously as they go. While for the most part indifferent to the presence of man, they nevertheless retain a degree of caution and can scarcely be tamed enough to eat from one's hand, as can the Florida Jays. They take great delight in worrying owls whose retreats they may discover, and their reputation for robbing the nests of smaller birds is rather bad."

M. G. Vaiden writes to me from Rosedale, Miss.: "The blue jay is a very destructive bird to other small birds' nests in this area; many times have I seen the blue jay in the act of destroying cardinal, mourning dove, mockingbird, and Maryland yellowthroat nests. My notes give an instance of the determined and persevering way these birds have when bent upon the destruction of another species' nest. On May 5, 1928, a blue jay was caught in the act of robbing a cardinal's nest located in a crape-myrtle bush in my front yard. He was sitting on the nest with one egg in his bill when first noticed. I secured a 22 rifle and shot very close to the jay; he flew away with the egg, yet returned in a short while for another; and three shots were made as close as possible to the bird, with no intention of hitting it, before it would leave the nest locality. After a short interval it returned again and five shots were made, each shot hitting very close to the bird, yet it hopped to the cardinal's nest and secured another egg. The next shot made it leave, but it carried the second egg along, as with the first. I awaited his return, fired one shot which failed to make him fly away, so I proceeded to kill the bird with the next shot. The cardinals, both, produced only mild scolds toward the jay and failed at any time to put up a fight. The nest was left with the two eggs remaining, but the cardinals quit the nest after the following day."

CYANOCITTA CRISTATA SEMPLEI Todd

SEMPLE'S BLUE JAY

My friend John B. Semple collected some blue jays in southern Florida and sent them to the Carnegie Museum. Based on this material from extreme southern Florida, some 11 specimens, W. E. Clyde Todd (1928) described this bird as a new subspecies and named it in honor of Mr. Semple, who collected the type near Coconut Grove. He characterizes it as "similar to *Cyanocitta cristata cristata* (Linnaeus) of the South Atlantic and Gulf States, but general coloration paler, the under parts white, with less grayish suffusion, the lower throat with less bluish wash, and the upper parts paler and duller blue, with less purplish tone." He continues:

This new form is as much different from *C. c. cristata* as the latter is from the northern race *C. c. bromia*. Its pale coloration stands out well as the two series lie side by side. While occasional specimens from peninsular Florida (north of the Everglades) approximate in their pallor the characters above specified, it is only in the extreme southern part of the State that these characters become sufficiently constant and pronounced to justify giving a name to individuals showing them. * * *

In the average example of *cristata* the upper parts are "deep dull bluish violet No. 2" of Ridgway (as seen with the eye between the bird and the light), while the pileum is brighter, between "grayish blue violet No. 2" and "dull bluish violet No. 2." In the new race these parts are respectively "deep madder blue" and "deep plumbago blue."

Arthur H. Howell (1932) gives the range of this race as "southern and central Florida, from Osceola and Hillsborough Counties south to Key West."

Its habits seem to be similar in every way to those of the other Florida race.

CYANOCITTA CRISTATA CYANOTEPHRA Sutton

WESTERN BLUE JAY

Based on a study of some 49 specimens of blue jays from Colorado, extreme western Oklahoma, and Kansas, Dr. George M. Sutton (1935) named this pale western race and described it as "similar to all races of *Cyanocitta cristata* found to the eastward of the Mississippi, but coloration paler, especially on the crest and back; paler even than *C. c. semplei* Todd, from which it differs also in being decidedly larger and relatively smaller-billed; and much paler than birds from Michigan; Minnesota; Ontario and southeastern Canada; and the northeastern United States. White markings of wings and tail noticeably more extensive than in *semplei*, and somewhat more extensive than in breeding birds from Georgia, Louisiana, and northern Florida." He says further:

All available Minnesota specimens are far too dark for the present race; Manitoba specimens apparently tend to be a trifle paler than eastern Canadian birds; and a single mile from Alberta (Lac la Nonne, June 28, Canadian National Museum No. 21512) is decidedly paler than any other Canadian specimen at hand, especially on the crest.

It is my present belief that the most typical examples of *cyanotephra* are to be found in extreme western Oklahoma, where the Blue Jay is decidedly rare as a breeding species, in eastern Colorado; in western Kansas; and in the northwestern corner of the northern Panhandle of Texas; but that the race ranges throughout Kansas and northern Oklahoma (save in treeless regions); throughout Nebraska (save presumably in the northeastern part where the race found in Minnesota should occur); and along the eastern foothills of the Rocky Mountains to the northwestward of Nebraska.

CYANOCITTA STELLERI STELLERI (Gmelin)

STELLER'S JAY

HABITS

Jays of the *stelleri* group are widely distributed in western North America and Central America, from the Rocky Mountains to the Pacific coast and from the Alaska Peninsula southward to Nicaragua. They are the crested blue jays of this vast region, where they replace our familiar blue jay of the East and share many of its interesting habits and some of its bad manners. The subject of this sketch is the northern race, extending its range in the Pacific coast region only as far south as Washington. There are five other races that are found north of the Mexican boundary.

Steller's jay is the oldest known race of this species, named by Gmelin in 1788, yet after more than 150 years it is far from being the best-known subspecies. It was known by description to all the early writers on American ornithology and was figured by Swainson and Richardson (1831), Wilson and Bonaparte (1832), and Audubon (1842). Bonaparte says, in his continuation of Wilson's "American Ornithology," that "it is mentioned by Pallas as having been shot by Steller, when Behring's crew landed upon the coast of America. It was first described by Latham from a specimen in Sir Joseph Bank's collection, from Nootka Sound."

The haunts of Steller's jay are chiefly in the coniferous forests of southern Alaska, British Columbia, and Washington as far south as the Columbia River, where it begins to intergrade with the subspecies *carbonacea*. But it is not wholly confined to the forests, as it often ventures out into the clearings, orchards, and farms on its mischievous raids for food. Bendire (1895) says: "It is usually a constant resident and breeds wherever found. It is an inhabitant of the canyons and pine-clad slopes of the higher mountains, and is not as often seen in the deep forests as on their outskirts near water courses."

Nesting.—We waited nearly 3 weeks for our ship to sail from Seattle to the Aleutian Islands, but we made our headquarters in the meantime at the little town of Kirkland, across Lake Washington from the city, and spent our time profitably by collecting in the vicinity. At that time much of this region was heavily wooded with a primeval forest of lofty firs, but the greater part of it had been lumbered and had grown up to small or medium-sized second-growth firs. Much of it had been cleared and cultivated, with houses and little farms scattered through it. There were two or three species of firs forming the principal forest growth, with a considerable mixture of hemlock and a very handsome species of cedar; the deciduous growth consisted of large alders and some maples and flowering dogwoods. Here we found Steller's jays quite common and discovered several of their nests between April 30 and May 20. The first nest we found, on April 30, was new but still empty; it was placed about 10 feet from the ground against the trunk of a small fir in the coniferous woods. It had a bulky foundation of large sticks, on which was a layer of dead leaves and mud and then a firmly woven, deeply hollowed nest of coarse rootlets. Another nest was 14 feet up in a thick fir in an open situation in the coniferous woods; it held four young only a few days old; the old bird remained on the nest until I almost touched her, when she flew off and scolded me with a mewing squawk. We found one other new nest and several old ones, all similarly located and constructed.

There are three sets in my collection from the same general region. In one case the nest was 10 feet from the ground and 15 feet out on a limb of a small lone fir on the edge of a prairie pond, near some mixed fir and oak growth, and 100 yards from a house. One of the others was 12 feet up in a green spruce; and the nest from which the other was taken was said to have been on a shelf in a woodshed!

Published accounts of the nesting of Steller's jay are not numerous, but the following from D. E. Brown (1930) is worth quoting: "This species usually nests at a moderate height. The majority of nests will be found from eight to fifteen feet from the ground, but the writer has found them only two feet up, and has seen them well over one hundred feet from the ground on the horizontal branches of giant firs.

"In the early part of the season coniferous trees are used almost exclusively. * * * Later when the deciduous trees are in full leaf they are quite often used. This fact is brought out by the number of old nests that are found in the fall when the leaves have shed."

The location of one nest, well within the city limits of Seattle, puzzled him until it was found "only two feet from the ground in the center of a mass of salal bushes and blackberry vines. He continues:

The birds nest regularly in Seattle city parks often on trees or branches that lean over trails that are used by hundreds of people daily. I have seen at least three such nests that were so low that they could be touched with the hand from the trail. * * *

The nest is usually very large and sometimes composed of twigs so large it hardly seems possible that the birds could handle them. A very thick layer of mud weighs down and cements the nest together, and it is lined with rootlets that are worked in while wet. The very start of the nest is always some light colored material such as cedar bark, leaves of the maple tree, shreds of decayed wood or pieces of newspaper. Samuel F. Rathbun of Seattle once found a nest in one of the parks that had a handkerchief worked into its foundation, a variation somewhat unusual in nest material.

Mr. Rathbun has sent me his notes on several nests of Steller's jay, and says: "With one exception all the nests of this jay I have found were placed in coniferous trees, usually firs of not large size, and oftener the location of the tree would be in a rather dense part of the wood. Often the place selected for a nest is the fork formed by several small branches jutting from the trunk wherein are lodged a number of dry, dead leaves, and on these is placed a little platform of twigs that forms the base of the nest, as if the jay attempted to convey the idea that the structure is only some rubbish caught by the branches. In fact, more than once our attention has first been caught by noticing dead leaves in what might be considered an out-of-the-way place, and on a nearer approach the material was seen to be the commencement of a jay's nest.

"As to the height of the nests, the lowest was only 8 feet from the ground, the highest 40, and the average of all 20 to 25 feet. I have always found Steller's jay to be quiet and secretive in the general locality where it was breeding—one would not know that there was a jay anywhere around; but when its nest is disturbed the jay makes a great outcry, and then silently leaves the place."

He gives the dimensions of one nest as follows: Extreme outside diameter, 14 inches; outside height, 6 inches; inside diameter, 5 inches; and inside depth, 2¼ inches.

Eggs.—Steller's jay lays three to five eggs, usually four. These are ovate and only slightly glossy. The ground color is pale greenish blue, or pale bluish green, "pale turquoise green" to "pale Nile blue" or paler, or "pale sulphate green" to "microcline green" or paler, sometimes almost greenish white. Some eggs are more or less sparingly marked with fine dots; others are more or less irregularly spotted with small spots, fine dots and markings of indefinite shape. The markings are in different shades of dark browns or purplish brown, or shades of olive, more or less evenly distributed.

The measurements of 40 eggs average 31.4 by 22.5 millimeters; the eggs showing the four extremes measure **34.5** by 22.8, 33.5 by **24.0**, **27.8** by 22.3, and 30.4 by **20.6** millimeters.

Plumages.—Ridgway (1904) describes the juvenal plumage as follows: "Wings and tail as in adults, but the blue usually more greenish (china blue to cerulean blue) and usually (?) without distinct black bars on secondaries or rectrices; under parts, rump, and upper tail-coverts dull slate-grayish, the former becoming darker and more sooty anteriorly; head and neck plain sooty or dark sooty slate, the forehead without any blue streaks."

Young birds begin the postjuvenal molt late in July or early in August; this molt, which involves everything but the wings and tail, is usually completed during August, but it sometimes continues until after the middle of September. In this first winter plumage young birds are practically indistinguishable from the adult female, having the black barring on the secondaries and rectrices less distinct than in the adult male, or sometimes entirely wanting.

The complete postnuptial molt of adults begins in July and is often completed before the middle of August; I have records of adults in fresh winter plumage as early as August 10. The molts average somewhat later in the more southern subspecies. The sexes are alike in all plumages, except that the females are somewhat smaller and have less distinct bars on the secondaries and tail feathers.

Food.—As the food of the California subspecies has been much more thoroughly studied than that of this northern race, and as the feeding habits of the species probably vary but little in the different portions of its range, this subject has been more thoroughly discussed under the blue-fronted jay. Two reports, however, are worth quoting here. Referring to Vancouver Island, Harry S. Swarth (1912) writes: "At Errington, in September, the jays were exceedingly abundant, particularly about the edges of the pastures and grain fields. Harvesting operations were in progress at this time, and a wheat field near our camp had just been cut and the grain piled in shocks. On those nearest the edges of the field, close to the shelter of the woods, the jays were feeding by scores; when startled most of the birds departed, carrying one or more long straws with them, to be thrashed out at their leisure in the nearby woods. Certain favorite stumps and logs were well covered with straws from which the grain had been eaten."

Ford Dicks (1938) reports considerable damage done by these jays in filbert orchards near Puyallup, Wash., and says: "As a matter of fact, the writer has known of instances where the entire nut crop was lost due to the depredations of Steller's Jays in late summer and early fall, at which time the fruit is approaching maturity."

Behavior.—Although bold in the defense of their nests and rather tame about camps and houses, where their intelligence tells them that they are not in danger, they are very shy in the open woods, much shier than our eastern blue jay, and difficult to approach or shoot when pursued. They often escape by "climbing" some tall spruce or fir, starting on one of the lower branches and hopping or flitting upward from branch to branch around the trunk, as if climbing a spiral staircase, until the summit is reached, when off they go with a derisive scream. At such times their movements are so lively that it is not easy to shoot one. They sometimes travel through the forest in this way, descending from the top of one tree to the lower part of another and so on from tree to tree, until out of sight. The best way to outwit them is to remain well concealed and imitate their notes, to which their curiosity will generally lead one or more of them to respond. They are notorious as nest robbers and seem to be cordially hated and dreaded by the smaller birds, but they are not always guilty of this practice. William L. Finley (1907) says of a pair that he watched: "If this pair of jays carried on their nest robbing, they did it on the quiet away from home, for in the thicket and only a few yards away I found a robin's nest with eggs, and the nest of a thrush with young birds. Perhaps the jays wanted to stand well with their neighbors and live in peace. I am sure if the robins had thought the jays were up to mischief, they would have hustled them out of the thicket. I think we give both the crow and the jay more blame for nest robbing than they deserve."

Alfred M. Bailey (1927) writes:

They are robbers of the first order, and steal anything edible about camp. I do not know whether we are able to give birds credit for a sense of humor, but if we do, then the Jays surely must come in for first place. I have watched a pair of these fellows tease a spaniel. They would alight in a path, only to be chased away by the dog, and they kept returning so often as to completely exhaust him; then, when the dog refused to chase them longer, they would alight over his head and talk to him,—undoubtedly they were cursing him, until he finally got up and walked away. The same performance was carried on daily. This species is not particularly in favor among hunters, for when one is quietly crossing a muskeg in the hope of jumping a deer, it is the usual thing to have a couple of Jays open a serenade, and then keep just ahead of the hunter, talking all the time.

Voice.—Dawson and Bowles (1909) give the best description of the varied notes of this jay, as follows: "The notes of the Steller Jay are harsh and expletive to a degree. *Shaack, shaack, shaack* is a common (and most exasperating) form; or, by a little stretch of the imagination one may hear *jay, jay, jay*. A mellow *klook, klook, klook* sometimes varies the rasping imprecations and serves to remind one that the Jay is cousin to the Crow. Other and minor notes there are for the lesser and rarer emotions, and some of these are not unmusical."

Leslie L. Haskin writes to me that, like so many other jays, it has a scream like that of the red-tailed hawk, which may be a true jay note rather than an imitation of the hawk. He says further: "Steller's jay also has a true song of his own. I have heard it only a few times, but it is very sweet in tone. In many ways it resembles the 'whisper songs' that many birds indulge in in winter. Because of the extreme shyness of these birds, and the softness of the song, it is very hard to hear. Only when the bird is entirely unaware of observation will it be given. I would compare it with the 'whisper song' of the American robin, as I have heard that bird on cold winter days singing in red cedar tangles in the East. In it are also some tones that suggest the song of the ruby-crowned kinglet, but not so loud. Heard without seeing the performer, it could easily be mistaken for the kinglet. Altogether it is a very interesting and surprising performance."

Theed Pearse writes to me that he has heard it mimicking the crow's spring falsetto song, as well as the cry of the red-tailed hawk; and has heard one "really singing a song of its own, and a very delightful one; I could not recognize any other bird's notes, except perhaps the trill of the junco. When first heard it was a song that could not be identified as that of any local species, a strong warble, consisting of various notes with some trills; one feature was the number of different notes that the bird could go through without repetition."

Mr. Rathbun tells me that one of this jay's notes "is a gritting, rasping one, as rough as the edge of a saw," and unlike any other of the bird's notes. Dr. Samuel S. Dickey (MS.) adds the following to the bird's vocabulary: "Ordinarily the birds vented raucous, blue jay-like *cahs,* but they would vary such outbursts with *kirk-kirk, kirk-perk, perk-er, perk-er,* or wheezy magpie-like notes, such as *ca-phee, ca-phee, pheeze-ca.*"

Fall.—These jays are supposed to be resident all the year round in the region where they breed. They probably do not make any regular migration, although Mr. Swarth (1922) says that, late in August, "at Sergief Island many were seen, under circumstances suggesting migration. They were frequently in small gatherings, seven or eight together, and often on tidal marshes, far from timber, apparently traveling in a definite direction. When thus seen they were flying by easy stages from one drift log to another, in a southerly direction."

During fall and winter they are given to erratic wanderings, probably in search of food, throughout the open country and about the farms and villages. They may be very common during some seasons at certain places and scarce or entirely absent there at other seasons. Though quiet, retiring, and secretive during the nesting season, they are much more noisy, bolder or tamer, and more aggressive during the fall and winter, traveling about in family parties or small groups.

J. A. Munro tells me that Steller's jays were very abundant on Vancouver Island during the fall of 1913; on September 30 they were industriously carrying acorns from the Garry oaks; one collected on this date had two in its gullet and one in its bill. During the winter of 1921-22 they were also unusually numerous; several hundred were caught in quail traps. On February 1, 1923, there was an invasion of these jays at Victoria; 50 were strung on a wire at the game farm, and the operator mentioned catching seven at one time in a quail trap.

DISTRIBUTION

Range.—Western North America and Central America south to Nicaragua; nonmigratory.

The range of Steller's jay extends **north** to Alaska (Lake Aleknagik and Northeast Bay); British Columbia (Flood Glacier, Poison Mountain, Parsnip River, Moose River, and Yoho Park); and Montana (McDonald Lake and Big Snowy Mountains). **East** to central Montana (Big Snowy Mountains); Wyoming (Yellowstone Park and Torrington); central Colorado (Fort Collins and Colorado Springs); New Mexico (Halls Peak, Capitan Mountains, and Guadalupe Mountains); western Texas (Guadalupe Mountains and Davis Mountains); Chihuahua (Tomochic and Pinos Altos); Durango (La Ciénaga de las Vacas and Arroyo del Buey); Veracruz (Mirador and Orizaba); Honduras (Seguatepeque and San Juancito); and southeastern Nicaragua (Greytown). **South** to Nicaragua (Greytown); El Salvador (Chalatenango); and Guatemala (Tecpam and Volcán de Fuego). **West** to western Guatemala (Volcán de Fuego and Quelzatenango); western Oaxaca (Cieneguilla); western Sonora (Sonoyta); casually northern Baja California (San Pedro Mártir Mountains); western California (Palomar Mountains, Santa Barbara, Santa Lucia Mountains, San Geronimo, and Turner); western Oregon (Pinehurst, Prospect, and Dayton); western Washington (Camas, Grays Harbor, and Seattle); western British Columbia (Nootka Sound and Massett); and Alaska (Baranof Island, Sitka, and Lake Aleknagik).

The range as outlined is for the entire species, which has been separated into eight currently recognized geographic races. The northern part of the range along the Pacific coast (except the Queen Charlotte Islands) is occupied by the typical race *(Cyanocitta s. stelleri)* from the Alaskan Peninsula south, probably to northwestern Oregon; the Queen Charlotte jay *(C. s. carlottae)* is found only on the Queen Charlotte Islands, British Columbia; the coast jay *(C. s. carbonacea)* occupies the coastal zone from northern Oregon south to the Santa Lucia Mountains and Napa Valley in California; the blue-fronted jay *(C. s. frontalis)* is found from the Mount Shasta region of northeastern California, south through the Sierra Nevada and San Bernardino Mountains to northern Baja California; the black-headed jay *(C. s. annectens)* occurs in eastern British Columbia and south through the Rocky Mountains to Wyoming, Idaho, and casually northern Utah; the long-crested jay *(C. s. diademata)* is the form found in the Rocky Mountain system from northern Utah and southern Wyoming south to central Mexico; the Aztec jay *(C. s. azteca)* is found in south-central Mexico; and the blue-crested jay *(C. s. coronata)* occurs from southern Mexico south to Nicaragua.

The Nevada crested jay *(percontatrix)* is found in the Sheep and Charleston Mountains, Clark County, Nevada.

Casual records.—Among the cases where Steller's jays have been recorded outside the normal range are the following: There are a few records for western Nebraska, some of which have been recorded as the race *annectens,* but two specimens, one taken at Mitchell in October 1916 and the other at Oshkosh on March 5, 1920, proved to be *diademata.* A specimen *(annectens)* was taken at Indian Head, Saskatchewan, on May 24, 1923; one *(diademata)* was shot in Lincoln Park, Chicago, Ill., on June 12, 1911; and a specimen *(diademata)* was taken at Cap Rouge, Quebec, on November 8, 1926.

Egg dates.—Alaska: 3 records, May 12 (2) and July 7.

California: 103 records, April 12 to June 24; 51 records, April 30 to May 15, indicating the height of the season.

Colorado: 29 records, April 23 to June 3; 15 records, May 8 to 24.

New Mexico: 4 records, April 27 to June 6.

Oregon: 16 records, April 4 to June 5; 8 records, April 11 to May 4.

Washington: 20 records, April 1 to June 20; 10 records, April 19 to May 3.

CYANOCITTA STELLERI CARLOTTAE Osgood

QUEEN CHARLOTTE JAY

This island form was named by Dr. Wilfred H. Osgood (1901) and described as "similar to *C. stelleri,* but larger and darker colored; abdomen and flanks deep Berlin blue instead of Antwerp or China blue as in *C. stelleri;* frontal spots much reduced; black of head extending on breast and merging into blue of abdomen without sharp demarcation. * * *

"The large size and dark color of this jay were noticed in the field, and subsequent comparison of specimens in the museum showed these characters to be amply sufficient to distinguish it from the mainland form *C. stelleri.* * * * Jays are not very common on the islands. They were seen only occasionally and were generally in family parties of four to six adults and young" [June 13 to 25].

Almost nothing seems to have been published on the habits of this jay, as very little ornithological work has been done on the Queen Charlotte Islands, to which the subspecies seems to be confined. Though I have no notes on the subject I have no reason to think that its habits differ in any respect from those of the mainland from, which lives in a similar habitat. So far as I know, there are no authentic eggs of this race in collections.

Clyde A. Patch (1922) found it fairly common on Graham Island, "usually moving about in family parties. Frequently seen feeding on green fruit of the Skunk Cabbage which they manage to remove from its stem and carry to a comfortable spot on a trail, roadway or log. On one occasion a Jay was observed to capture a young wood mouse."

CYANOCITTA STELLERI CARBONACEA Grinnell
COAST JAY

The coast jay, or Grinnell's jay, as Ridgway (1904) calls it, is very evidently quite intermediate in characters between *stelleri* on the north and *frontalis* on the east and south, for Dr. Grinnell (1900b) in naming it described it as "intermediate in size * * * between *C. stelleri* and *C. stelleri frontalis.* Dorsal surface sooty-black as in *stelleri,* but with blue on forehead nearly as extended as in *frontalis.* Tint of blue of posterior lower parts paler than in *stelleri,* and extending further forward into pectoral region, as in *frontalis."* Furthermore, its range, the "coast region of Oregon and California, from the Columbia River south to Monterey County," is just where one would expect to find the two previously named forms to intergrade. This is just another case, like *annectens,* where the naming of an intermediate immediately produces two more sets of intergrades. Dr. Grinnell (1900b) says further: "*C. stelleri annectens* from Idaho resembles *carbonacea* somewhat closely, but the white spot over the eye distinguishes both *C. s. annectens* and *C. s. macrolopha* [= *diademata*] of the Northern and Southern Rocky Mountain regions, respectively, from the parallel Pacific Coast races, *carbonacea* and *frontalis,* neither of which has any trace of such a marking."

What has been written about the nesting habits, eggs, plumages, food and general habits of the other Pacific coast races of the species would apply very well to this subspecies. The measurements of 40 eggs average 30.6 by 22.5 millimeters; the eggs showing the four extremes measure 33.1 by 22.4, 31.1 by 24.0, and 26.6 by 21.2 millimeters.

CYANOCITTA STELLERI FRONTALIS (Ridgway)
BLUE-FRONTED JAY

PLATE 12

HABITS

This is the "crested blue jay" of the Sierra Nevadas and the inner coast mountain ranges of northern California. Ridgway (1904) gave it the common name of Sierra Nevada jay, which seems a more appropriate designation than blue-fronted, as the blue stripes on the forehead are not conspicuously more prominent than in some of the other races of the species. He describes it as "much lighter colored, and average size decidedly less" than in *C. s. carbonacea,* which, in turn, he calls "paler throughout and averaging slightly smaller" than *C. s. stelleri.*

The chosen summer haunts of the blue-fronted jay are in the coniferous forests of the Transition and Canadian Zones of mountain ranges, mainly in California. In the Lassen Peak region, according to Grinnell, Dixon, and Linsdale (1930), these jays "in summer were found in and about clumps of closely growing small coniferous trees, often as forming dense thickets of undergrowth in old forest that is thinning out, or at edges of forests. Kinds of trees that formed such suitable clumps and which were frequented by the jays were white fir, red fir, yellow pine, and hemlock. At the western frontier, the occasional pairs seen were usually in tracts of small yellow pines. The birds were seen most often at heights of close to four meters above the ground."

The range of this jay in the mountains extends upward to about 8,000 or 9,000 feet, or to the lower limit of the Hudsonian Zone, where Clark's nutcracker is found. It finds the lower limit of its range where the coniferous mountain forest gives way to the foothill oaks and chaparral; here it mingles to some extent with the California jay, but sticks mainly to the pines.

Professor Beal (1910) says: "It sometimes ventures to the edges of the valleys and occasionally visits orchards for a taste of fruit, of which it is very fond, but in general it keeps to the hills and wilder parts of the canyons. It is fond of coniferous trees and is likely to be found wherever these abound. Where ranches have been established far up the canyons among the hills, this jay visits the ranch buildings."

Nesting.—J. Stuart Rowley writes to me: "I have located many nests of this bird in the Sierra Nevadas, from Tulare County in central California to San Bernardino County in southern California. The most frequently used nest site seems to be a young conifer, with the nest placed about 10 feet up near the main trunk and supported by horizontal branches. The incubating females are rather close sitters and make quite a fuss when flushed from the nests."

W. E. Griffee sends me the following note: "While cruising timber in the lower Sierras, about 20 to 30 miles east of Placerville, Eldorado County, Calif., I found several nests of this subspecies. All were high on dry hillsides in rather dense reproduction of ponderosa and sugar pines and incense cedar, at elevations of 8 to 12 feet from the ground. Nests were, of course, easy to see and readily accessible, but to find them, had I not been climbing over the timbered hills as a part of my work, would have required a tremendous amount of walking."

J. G. Suthard tells me that he found a nest containing four fresh eggs on April 21, 1940, in the San Bernardino Mountains. "The nest was situated 8 feet up in a willow along a mountain stream at 9,000 feet elevation. It was shielded from view by a cluster of branches growing up from the slanting trunk of the willow. There were plenty of pine and fir trees in the vicinity, but the jays seemed to prefer the willows, which are possibly less frequented by squirrels. At the time, there were numerous patches of snow along the stream, and a few hundred yards higher the whole range was completely blanketed in white. The willows were still dormant. As will be noted from the photograph (pl. 12), the nest is lined with pine needles, which are those of the Jeffrey pine (*Pinus jeffreyi*)."

Rollo H. Beck wrote to Major Bendire (1895) : "I have found about a dozen of their nests, placed in oaks, buckeye, laurel, and holly bushes, at various distances ranging from 7 to 40 feet from the ground." Some unusual, or unexpected, nesting sites have been recorded. Col. N. S. Goss (1885) found quite a number of the nests near Julian, Calif., "and in all cases but one in holes and trough-like cavities in trees and stubs, ranging from four to fifty feet from the ground, generally ten to twenty feet up. The nest found outside was built upon a large horizontal limb of an oak close beside a gnarl, the sprout-like limbs of which thickly covered the nest overhead, and almost hid it from view below. * * * The nests are quite bulky, made loosely of sticks, stems of weeds, and lined with fibrous rootlets and grasses, and as they are all built at or near the opening, the tell-tale sticks project and make the findings of their nests an easy matter."

Walter E. Bryant (1888), on information received from A. M. Ingersoll, writes:

A strange departure from the usual habits of jays was noticed in Placer County, Cal., where they had persisted in building within the snow-sheds in spite of the noise and smoke of passing trains. The destruction of their nests by the men employed on the water train, which makes two trips a week through the sheds during the summer, sprinkling the woodwork and tearing down the nests of jays and robins with a hook attached to a pole, seemed not to discourage them. So accustomed do the jays become to the passing of trains, that they will often remain on their nests undisturbed. In one season more than two hundred nests of jays and robins were destroyed, so the train men say, between Cisco and Summit, a distance of thirteen miles.

These, like all jays, are very secretive in their nesting activities and use the greatest stealth in approaching the nest while building it or when it contains eggs or young. But Grinnell and Storer (1924) were able, under favorable circumstances, to observe a pair building their nest. They say:

One of the jays was seen to fly into a black oak, obtain a twig, and carry it off, upward, through the adjacent trees to the nest site, at the top of a yellow pine, fully 40 feet above the ground. Then the other member of the pair came, broke off a twig, dropped it, evidently by accident, and sought another. * * * Pieces dry enough to break off readily, and a little longer than the jay's body, were chosen, and twisted off by a wrench with the bill. The twig would be worked along between the mandibles until held across the middle and then the jay would ascend by the usual vertical hopping and short flights to the nest. Following the taking of black oak twigs the two jays, together, flew across the river which flowed close by the nest tree, and there, descending quickly to the ground, sought material in an azalea thicket at the edge of the water. Each took a quantity of twigs and grass and apprently also some mud, and flew again to the nest tree. Again they took twigs from the black oak.

They say of a nest examined in the Yosemite region:

It was solid in construction, with a large external basal framework of dead and more or less weathered twigs of irregular shape and small diameter (2 millimeters or less). Many of these were black oak twigs while others were of a very furry herbaceous plant. All of the material of this outer framework, as was attested by the clean, fresh-appearing ends of the pieces, had been freshly broken off by the jays. This suggests that, save for the small amount of herbaceous material, all the outer constituents were gathered above the ground. The outside framework measured about 300 millimeters (12 inches) in one direction and 400 millimeters (16 inches) in the other.

The inner cup of this nest was composed of dry needles of the yellow pine, held together by enough mud to give the structure a firm resistant feel. The mud, however, did not extend to the inner surface. The interior of the cup consisted solely of pine needles, which crossed and recrossed so as to make a porous interior lining. This cup was 100 millimeters (4 inches) in diameter at the rim and 68 millimeters (2⅝ inches) deep at the center.

Eggs.—The blue-fronted jay lays three to five eggs, usually three or four; Mr. Rowley, who has examined a number of nests, tells me that sets of four are found as frequently as three but that he has found only one set of five. The eggs are usually indistinguishable from eggs of Steller's jay, but Rollo H. Beck (1895) describes some variations, as follows: "In a series of these eggs now before me there is considerable variation in shape and markings. One set closely resembles those of the California Thrasher, another is marked exactly like the eggs of the Yellow-billed Magpie, and others the eggs of the California Jay. Some have but few spots, principally about the larger ends, while others have the ground color nearly obscured, so thickly are they spotted. The usual ground color is light-blue, which is spotted with various shades of brown and not infrequently with lavender and purple."

The measurements of 52 eggs in the United States National Museum average 30.22 by 22.61 millimeters; the eggs showing the four extremes measure **34.0** by **24.0**, **27.6** by 23.2, and 29.5 by **21.2** millimeters.

Young.—Bendire (1895) says that "an egg is deposited daily, and incubation lasts about sixteen days. The male assists in these duties, and usually but one brood is raised in a season." Grinnell and Storer (1924) say: "During the nesting season the jays are to be seen in devoted pairs, and after the broods leave the nest the full-grown young and their parents remain for a time in family parties. With the coming of fall, the parental and filial instincts wane, these family parties break up, and the individuals scatter out rather uniformly through the forest."

Food.—Prof. F. E. L. Beal (1910), in his study of the food of this jay, examined 93 stomachs and found that the animal food amounted to 28 percent and vegetable matter to 72 percent. The animal food consists largely of insects; beetles, a little more than 8 percent; Hymenoptera, about 11 percent, the largest item of animal food; grasshoppers and crickets, about 3.5 percent; caterpillars and moths, a little more than 2 percent; other insects were found only in insignificant amounts. Of the Hymenoptera, he says: "They were found in 30 stomachs altogether, and 2 were entirely filled with them. Ants were found in only 2 stomachs. Three honey bees were identified, one in each of three stomachs. One was a worker, another a drone, and the third indeterminate. None of the smaller parasitic Hymenoptera were identified. The greater part of this item of food consisted of wasps and wild bees, which would indicate that this bird is an energetic and expert insect catcher." Miscellaneous creatures identified were spiders, sowbugs, raphidians, hair and skin of a mammal, "two bits of bone, probably of a frog," and eggshells were found in 13 stomachs. "Only 6 of these egg-eating records occurred in June, the nesting month. All the rest were in September or later and were probably old shells picked up in abandoned nests or about ranch buildings or camp grounds."

Of the vegetable food, "fruit amounts to 22 percent and was found in 55 stomachs. Prunes were identified in 2 stomachs, cherries in 2, grapes in 2, Rubus fruits in 15, strawberries in 1, elderberries in 15, bay laurel fruit in 1, unknown wild fruit in 2, and fruit pulp, not fully identified but thought to be of cultivated varieties, in 16 stomachs. Thus 38 stomachs held fruit supposed to be cultivated. This number contains all containing Rubus fruits, which probably were not all cultivated— perhaps none of them were. * * *

"Grain amounts to 5 percent, and was found in 15 stomachs, distributed as follows: Wheat in 7, oats in 9, and barley in 1. * * * The chief food of this jay, however, is acorns, though occasionally it eats other nuts or large seeds. Mast amounts to 42.5 percent of the yearly diet, and was found in 38 stomachs. * * * In October and November it amounted to 76 percent, in December to 90, and in January to 99 percent."

He considers the economic status of this jay as of minor importance:

In destroying beetles and Hymenoptera it performs some service, but it destroys only a few. Of the order of Hemiptera, which contains most of the worst pests of the orchardist and farmer, it eats scarcely any. The Orthoptera, which are almost all harmful insects, are eaten only sparingly, and the same applies to the rest of the insect food. The destruction of birds' eggs is the worst count against the jay. But none were found, except in June, until September, when it was too late in the season for fresh eggs to be obtainable. In June 17 birds were taken, and 6 of them, or 35 per cent of the whole, apparently had robbed birds' nests. Now, it is evident that if 35 per cent of all the Steller jays in California each rob one bird's nest every day during the month of June the aggregate loss is very great.

So far as its vegetable food is concerned, this bird does little damage. It is too shy to visit the more cultivated districts, and probably will never take enough fruit or grain to become of economic importance.

In his paper on Modoc County birds, Joseph Mailliard (1927) writes:

In September, 1924, this jay was so numerous in Eagleville as to be a pest in the many small apple orchards of the settlement. These orchards are small, for home supply only, and the inroads made by the jays upon the apple crop assumed serious proportions. With the crop limited as it was by the drought of that year, the owners of such orchards as were bearing fruit waged incessant warfare upon the jays, both of this species and of the following one. Hundreds were shot, but those that were left soon became expert in dodging their pursuers and the slaughter lessened.

In fall and winter, while wandering about in the foothills and valleys, these jays become quite omnivorous, picking up any scraps of food, bread, crackers, meat, or anything edible, that they can find around the camps or ranches; what they cannot eat on the spot they carry off and hide; they have even been known to steal a piece of soap. They probably store some acorns and other nuts for future use and are suspected of robbing the stores of the California woodpecker.

Behavior.—There seems to be nothing in the behavior of the blue-fronted jay that differs materially from that of other races of the species, to which the reader is referred.

Voice.—Its vocal performances are apparently similar also to those of other races, though some different descriptions of its various calls have appeared in print. Ralph Hoffman (1927) says that "besides the ringing *tchek,* a little lower in pitch than the cry of the California Jay and generally given in flight, the Crested Jay utters from its perch a loud *kweesch, kweesch, kweesch.* It has besides a deeper *chu-chu-chu* and a note resembling a squeaking wheelbarrow, *kée-lu, kée-lu.* * * * Occasionally from the cover of dense foliage, it utters a formless succession of liquid, pleasing notes quite unlike its usual discordant notes, or a purring or rolling note."

Grinnell and Storer (1924) give slightly different renderings of what are apparently the same as the above notes, and add that "when two jays of a pair are hunting close together a low crackling or growling *ker'r'r'r'* is uttered."

Field Marks.—Any of the jays of the *stelleri* group may be easily recognized by the long, brownish-black crest, so conspicuous at all times and giving the bird an entirely different outline from that of the flat-headed jays of the genus *Aphelocoma*. The dark brownish-black head, neck, upper breast, and upper back, contrasting with the blue of the lower back and abdomen, are also distinctive; and the blue of the wings and tail is conspicuous in flight.

Winter.—In winter these jays desert to a large extent their summer haunts in the mountain forests and wander about in the foothills and valleys, visiting camps and ranches in search of food. John G. Tyler (1913) says that "during the winter of 1900-01 large numbers of these jays invaded the valley, being found literally by hundreds everywhere eastward from Fresno, where they frequented the trees bordering the vineyards, roadsides and ditches. Their large size and gay plumages rendered them very noticeable, and no doubt not a few of their number were missing when the blue-coated host returned to its Sierran home. The species has not been observed in the valley since that time."

CYANOCITTA STELLERI ANNECTENS (Baird)

BLACK-HEADED JAY

The crested jay of the northern Rocky Mountain region is apparently a connecting link between the long-crested jay *(diademata)* to the southward and Steller's jay *(stelleri)* to the westward, as it combines some of the characters of both races, in about equal proportions in the center of its range. Baird recognized this fact when he suggested the appropriate name of *annectens* (Baird, Brewer, and Ridgway, 1874). However, as it is an abundant form, covering a considerable range, it may be well to give it subspecific status, rather than to consider it as merely an intermediate, which, in fact, it really is.

Ridgway (1904) describes it as "similar to *C. s. stelleri,* but with a distinct (though sometimes small) elongated spot of grayish white immediately above the eye; streaks on forehead (if present) paler blue or bluish white; chin and upper throat more conspicuously streaked (the streaks grayish white rather than gray); back and scapulars rather paler and grayer, and the blue of rump, upper tail-coverts, and under parts of body paler and greener (nearly verditer or china blue)."

The 1931 Check-list gives the range of this race as the "Boreal and Transition zones of the Rocky Mountains from British Columbia south to eastern Oregon, Idaho, and Wyoming." This is probably the main breeding range of typical *annectens,* but it evidently intergrades gradually into typical *stelleri* from eastern British Columbia westward, and into *diademata* from southern Wyoming southward. Major Bendire (1895) sent 11 skins, taken near Walla Walla, Wash., to William Brewster, "who pronounced five of them typical *Cyanocitta stelleri annectens,* and two nearly typical *Cyanocitta stelleri,* and four intermediate between these two forms."

I cannot find that the black-headed jay differs materially in its haunts or in any of its habits from other races of the species. J. A. Munro, who has sent me some notes on it, says that in British Columbia it breeds in the Canadian Zone above 3,500 feet and comes down to the lake region in October, remaining until May. Seldom more than three or four are seen in a day's walk. There is apparently a limited migration from the northern part of its range, both southward and eastward, perhaps nearly or quite to the coast. He has heard it give the tremolo call of the loon and a perfect imitation of the redtail's scream, as well as the call of the raven. He says that black-headed jays were common all through the winter of 1921-22 about Okanagan Landing, wintering in the shore brush and coming to the kitchen door for scraps that were thrown out. He says that they are very curious and come readily to the pygmy-owl call.

The eggs are indistinguishable from those of other races of the species. The measurements of six eggs in the United States National Museum average 30.7 by 22.0 millimeters; the eggs showing the four extremes measure **31.8** by 21.6, 30.3 by **23.1, 29.5** by 21.6, and 31.3 by **21.1** millimeters.

CYANOCITTA STELLERI DIADEMATA (Bonaparte)

LONG-CRESTED JAY

PLATE 13

HABITS

The long-crested jay is the representative of the species that is found in the southern Rocky Mountain region, from southern Wyoming and Utah southward throughout a large part of Mexico. It is described by Ridgway (1904) as "similar to *C. s. annectens,* but lighter colored, with white superciliary patch much larger (or else purer white), forehead more conspicuously streaked with bluish white, greater wing-coverts distinctly barred with black, and the deep black crest very strongly contrasted with the clear brownish gray (nearly mouse gray) of the back and scapulars; rump, upper tail-coverts, and under parts of body light glaucous-blue."

Coues (1871) pays the following tribute to the long crest of this jay, from which it derives its name:

The imposing crest of this jay merits more than a passing allusion. * * * It grows to be two inches and a half long, and is composed of many slender feathers with loosened barbs. The longest ones grow from the crown, while shorter ones fill in from behind and before, to make an elegant pyramid when standing close together, or a bundle of plumes when shaken apart. * * * The crest can be raised or lowered, and opened or shut at pleasure; and its rapid movements, when the bird is excited, are highly expressive. The jay seems to be proud of his top-knot, and generally holds it pretty high, unless he happens to be on a birds'-nesting expedition, which I am sorry to say is not seldom, when he lowers his standard, and makes himself as small as possible, as he skulks silently about, looking, and no doubt feeling, like the thief that he is.

The haunts of the long-crested jay during the breeding season, at least, are in the coniferous forests of the mountains, ranging up to 10,000 or 11,000 feet among the pines. In the Huachuca Mountains, Ariz., in May, we found the long-crested jays very common from 6,000 feet upward. We frequently saw them about our cabin in Ramsey Canyon, evidently foraging for scraps in the little group of summer camps; this was far below the pine belt where the tree growth consisted mainly of sycamores, maples, walnuts, and other deciduous trees. But their main summer haunts were on the steep hillsides that rose abruptly from the sides of the canyon, where there was an open growth of large and small pines, and from there up to the pine-clad summit at 9,000 feet. H. S. Swarth (1904), referring to the same locality, says that "up to the middle of April they were most abundant in the oak regions and along the canyons from 5,000 to 7,000 feet, usually in flocks of a dozen or more; but after that time they gradually withdrew to the higher parts of the mountains to attend to their domestic duties."

Fred M. Packard tells me that in Estes Park, Colo., this jay is a permanent resident, "most common in the upper Transition zone, not uncommon in the lower Canadian, and occasionally seen in the Hudsonian in late summer."

Nesting.—The nesting habits of the long-crested jay are practically the same as those of the blue-fronted jay of the mountains of California. The only nest I have seen was found in the Huachuca Mountains, Ariz., on May 30, 1922; it was well up toward the summit, above Ramsey Canyon, and was placed near the end of a branch of a "bull pine," 8 feet from the ground (pl. 13); it was the usual nest of sticks, reinforced with mud, and was lined with rootlets. My companion, Frank C. Willard, records in his notes three other nests found in the same region; one was 15 feet up in a small oak, another on a horizontal branch of a large fir tree, about 25 feet from the ground, and the third was between 50 and 60 feet above ground in the top of a pine tree. All these nests were at altitudes above 7,000 feet.

Bendire (1895) says that "their nests are usually placed in small bushy pines or other conifers, at no great distance from the ground, varying mostly from 8 to 15 feet." But he mentions a nest, taken by

Denis Gale in Boulder County, Colorado, that was "in a black willow, 9 feet from the ground, at an altitude of 5,500 feet." In his description of a nest he says that "the inner lining consists mostly of small rootlets, in one instance considerable horsehair being intermixed, while in another the lining consists principally of grass and pine needles."

Aiken and Warren (1914) tell of a Colorado nest that "was 6 feet from the ground in a Douglas's fir sapling, only 2 inches in diameter at the base, and on a branch close to the stem of the tree. The outside diameter of the nest was about 10 inches, and it was 5 deep, the nest cavity being 4½ inches in diameter inside, by 3 deep."

Eggs.—The long-crested jay lays three to six eggs, usually three or four, though five is not a rare number. These are practically indistinguishable from those of other races of the species. The measurements of 40 eggs average 31.1 by 22.5 millimeters; the eggs showing the four extremes measure **34.5** by 22.9, 34.0 by **24.0, 27.9** by 21.6, and 28.8 by **21.2** millimeters.

Plumages.—The sequence of plumages and molts is the same as in other races of the species, but Mr. Swarth (1904) calls attention to some points in which the plumages seem to differ from those of *stelleri*. He says that in the young male in juvenal plumage, "there is some whitish on the chin, an indistinct whitish line over the eye, and the faintest suggestion of bluish white markings on the forehead. A juvenile female is essentially the same in coloration but lacks the whitish markings about the head." Of the adults he says: "Specimens in fresh, unworn plumage have the upper parts of a decidedly bluish tinge, in marked contrast to the brown dorsum of late spring and summer birds."

Food.—What has been written about the food of the blue-fronted jay will apply equally well to the long-crested. Clinton G. Abbott (1929) writes entertainingly of watching these jays at a feeding shelf: "Soft food would be gobbled on the shelf, but the roughly broken pieces of toast were invariably carried in the bill to a distance. Here, either on a branch or on the ground, the jay would place the morsel under one foot (the other foot sometimes also adding its grasp) and then with strong pecks would break off fragments. It is evident that this bird cannot swallow without raising its bill, and, also, its gullet must be surprisingly narrow. I have seen the upward jerk of the bill several times repeated, and each time the piece of toast was returned, to be whittled a little smaller, before finally disappearing out of sight."

Of its feeding on the ground he says: "Hopping, hopping methodically the bird would seem to examine every square inch over which it passed. Sometimes the head would be held high and the gaze directed downward, the long crest almost bobbing forward; at other times the attitude would be more one of sneaking and peering, with head near the ground and crest drawn back. With incomprehensible intuition, a certain spot would be selected, and a hole dug with powerful strokes of the bill, each stroke accompanied by a side motion of the head. In this way the miniature mattock would make quite a little excavation (sometimes as deep as the bird's bill was long) and something edible would be found, as the up-jerk of the bill would plainly show. * * * The bird's bill is its constantly used tool. It turns over small stones with its bill and, especially, it scratches among dead leaves with its bill."

Dr. Coues (1871) says that "in the mountains where the Long-crested lives, pine-seeds contribute in large part to his nourishment. I have often watched the bird hammering away at a cone, which sometimes he would wedge in a crotch, and sometimes hold with his feet, like a hawk with a mouse. Though most at home in the depths of the pines where the supply is pretty sure, he often strays into the adjoining patches of scrubby oak and juniper after the acorns and berries, or to pick a quarrel with Woodhouse's jay, and frighten the sparrows."

Dr. Walter P. Taylor tells me that in Texas these jays do considerable damage to strawberries.

Behavior.—In a general way the habits of the long-crested jay are similar to those of other members of the species, or of most other jays as well. Dr. Coues (1871) gives us a good sketch of jay character, as follows:

All the jays make their share of noise in the world; they fret and scold about trifles, quarrel over nothing, and keep everything in a ferment when they are about. The particular kind we are talking about is nowise behind his fellows in these respects; a stranger to modesty and forebearance, and the many gentle qualities that charm us in some little birds and endear them to us, he is a regular fillibuster, ready for any sort of adventure, that promises sport or spoil, even if spiced with danger. Sometimes he prowls about alone, but oftener has a band of choice spirits with him, who keep each other in countenance—for our jay is a coward at heart like other bullies—and share the plunder on the usual principle in such cases, of each taking all he can get. * * * But withal our jay has his good points, and I confess to a sneaking sort of regard for him. An elegant dashing fellow, of good presence if not good manners; a tough, wiry, independent creature, with sense enough to take precious good care of himself, as you would discover if you tried to get his skin.

Mr. Abbott (1929) was evidently impressed with his vigorous character, for he says: "In fact the word 'vigorous' aptly fits most of the activities of the Long-crested Jay. He will alight in a tree and hop up, up, up as though ascending the rungs of a ladder, from sheer energy. He wipes his bill on the branch with the utmost vigor. He loves to 'flick' his wings and tail. When he launches himself into flight from a small tree, he leaves it trembling with the force of his push-off. Even during the noonday siesta, when I have seen the jays resting like balls of blue in the branches on all sides, the head is never still; there is no hint of sleepiness."

Winter.—Mr. Packard tells me that, in Estes Park, Colo., these jays spend the winter from the upper Transition Zone (9,000 feet) to as low as 5,000 feet. "During the winter these birds frequent the feeding stations and cabins of Estes Park village, where they obtain food to supplement their forage. They do not associate as closely with man as do the camp robbers, but can be induced to feed from a person's hand."

At Cragmore, near Colorado Springs, at an elevation of 6,300 feet, in January, Mr. Abbott (1929) found the long-crested jay "to be the tamest and most abundant bird inhabitant of the open, landscaped grounds of this institution. I have learned that these beautiful jays may commonly be seen in the parks of Colorado's high-lying cities. * * * At Cragmore, they make themselves so thoroughly at home that they pay practically no attention to the passing motor-car or pedestrian, and settle as readily on buildings or electric wires as on the branches of trees. * * *

"Even when water is available, the Long-crested Jays seem to prefer to drink snow. I have seen one perch on a branch covered with soft snow and literally 'guzzle' the snow beside him, billful after billful. On the ground, too, I have watched them gobble far more fresh-fallen snow that [sic] seemed to be necessary. After thaws, when the snow remains only in frozen patches in sheltered spots, it is a different story. I have observed a jay at the edge of such a patch hammer away with all the energy of a woodpecker, raising his whole body with each stroke, in order to add strength to his efforts, and thus break off icy fragments, which he eagerly swallowed."

CYANOCITTA STELLERI PERCONTATRIX van Rossem

NEVADA CRESTED JAY

A. J. van Rossem (1931) obtained four specimens of crested jays in southern Nevada, three from the Charlestons and one from Sheep Mountain, to which he gave the above scientific name and which he describes as "similar in head markings and in general body coloration to Arizona, New Mexico, and Colorado specimens of *Cyanocitta stelleri diademata* (Bonaparte), that is with the supra-orbital region extensively white, the lower eyelid narrowly white and frontal streaks white or bluish white, but differing from that form in having the back and sides of neck 'deep neutral gray' (color terms in quotations from Ridgway, Color Standards and Color Nomenclature, 1912) instead of 'mouse gray.' Differs from

Cyanocitta stelleri annectens (Baird) of the northern Great Basin in decidedly paler coloration throughout, more extensively white eyelids and longer crest."

He gives the known range as "Transition Zone in the Sheep and Charleston Mountains, Clark County, Nevada." This race seems to be closely related to the long-crested jay, which it probably resembles in habits.

APHELOCOMA COERULESCENS COERULESCENS (Bosc)
FLORIDA JAY

PLATES 14-16

CONTRIBUTED BY ALEXANDER SPRUNT, JR.

HABITS

Some birds are so thoroughly typical of certain habitats that one looks for them almost automatically when passing through such places. Perhaps of no species is this more true than the Florida jay. Indeed, so true is it that the local term for the *habitat* is applied to the bird itself, and thus we have the "scrub jay," the universal name of the species in Florida.

No visitor to that fascinating State can have failed to notice the topographical divisions that distinguish it, and the "scrub" is essentially Floridian. The scrub consists, according to Arthur H. Howell (1932), of a type of vegetation peculiar to Florida that occupies scattered areas of whitish sand in the lake region, a narrow strip along the east coast, and smaller tracts on the west coast from Manatee County south to Collier County. The characteristic plants of the scrub are the sand pine *(Pinus clausa)* and shrubby oaks of several species *(Quercus myrtifolia, Q. geminata, Q. catesbaei)*. These oaks, with saw palmetto and rosemary *(Ceratiola ericoides)*, form dense and almost impenetrable thickets.

Proceeding south from Jacksonville one encounters the scrub just south of St. Augustine on the seacoast. Along the Ocean Shore Boulevard the great stretches of saw palmetto behind the dunes of the sea beach reach away illimitably in front of the car.

Here and there roadside signs, advocating the advantages of hotels, camps, and fishing guides, rear themselves above the gray-green fronds, and on these structures, as well as on the lines of telephone wires, one is almost certain to see that characteristic blue and gray dweller of the low growth perched in plain view of pedestrian or motorist, its crestless head and long tail in sharp silhouette against the sky. As many as two dozen "scrub jays" may be seen between St. Augustine and Daytona Beach any day from a speeding car, as an introduction to Florida's thrilling bird life.

Yet, a person could very well spend a lifetime in Florida and never see a single specimen of this bird. It is so partial to the type of vegetation it inhabits that it is utterly useless to look for it anywhere else. In former years it was possible to meet with it almost from the State line at the St. Marys River, southward along the entire east coast, but this is the case no longer. There has been a gradual recession of the range to the north and south of Jacksonville probably because of the elimination of the typical habitat—as S. A. Grimes (MS.) says "to make room for beach houses." This recession is to be noted in even short periods of time, for, as he adds, "the northern limit of the range has receded 20 odd miles within the past year (1939-40). I am no longer able to find a single jay in Duval or northern St. Johns Counties. Ten years ago there were five or six pairs in Duval County."

The present northern limit of the bird's distribution, therefore, is St. Augustine on the east coast. From that point southward along the coastal scrub it is quite common. There is considerable scrub on Merritts Island south of New Smyrna, and Hugo H. Schroder (MS.) states that he has "found more of these birds on Merritts Island than anywhere else in the State." The narrow scrub area between the Indian River and the tracks of the Florida East Coast Railway is doubtless the best part of the State (including Merritts Island) for the visitor to study this interesting species. Quoting Schroder again, "Florida jays are quite numerous south of Indian River City between the highway (U. S. No. 1) and the railway tracks." In my monthly trips to Florida throughout the year, with the exception of midsummer, I have found this to be invariably true. However, in 6 years of intensive field work on the Kissimmee Prairie I have yet to see a single specimen. This is strange, as much of that country seems well suited to their needs and inclinations. Nevertheless, they do not occur there. Records exist only in one area about Lake Okeechobee, that of the Fish-eating Creek section in Glades County on the west side of the Lake. On the east coast, this jay is found as far south as Miami, Dade County, but stops at about that point. Many observers have not noted them that far. The southernmost record comes from what was once known as Rockdale, a station on the Florida East Coast Railway, 10 or 12 miles south of Miami (Howell, 1932).

On the west coast, doubtless because of the abundant mangroves and scanty scrub, it occurs only as far south as Naples, Collier County, according to all records but one. This one, representing the southernmost point of the west coast, is an observation by Edward J. Reimann, a former Audubon warden of the Southwest Coastal Patrol. He writes me that on nearly 2 years' duty in the field from Fort Myers to Cape Sable he saw the Florida jay but once, and that was on Marco Island (Collier County) on October 27, 1936. Marco is about 15 miles south of Naples. Concerning this occurrence he states: "I saw this individual near the cemetery on the north end of the island and am inclined to believe it was a straggler. I searched the same locale numbers of times and also the piny woods a great deal, with the sole purpose of digging up resident birds. Near Caxambas (southern end of Marco) are wonderful live-oak thickets where I hunted them to no avail."

Here and there throughout Florida in suitable areas, inland as well as coastal (some in the very middle of the State), one can find this species up to Gainesville (interior) and Pine Point (west coast) just to the north of the mouth of the Suwannee River. It does not occur at all in the western "handle" of Florida. It is also absent from the open Everglades as well as the Kissimmee Prairie—Lake Okeechobee region. It has been noted sparingly in the Big Cypress Everglades about the village of Immokalee.

There are no records of this jay outside of Florida. I can find but one instance of a sight record beyond the confines of that State and that is considered unreliable by contemporary and present ornithologists. Not only is this jay confined to Florida exclusively, but very definitely to certain portions of that State.

Courtship.—Nothing in the literature I have seen throws any light on the courtship of *coerulescens*. Even those who live in its range and know the bird intimately say nothing about it. Personally, I have seen no evidence of it, and cannot speak from experience. S. A. Grimes, of Jacksonville, who knows the bird as well as any ornithologist living, states that it is his belief that pairs remain mated throughout the year. This is very probably the case and would account to a large degree for the lack of any literature on this phase of the bird's habits.

Nesting.—The Florida jay is gregarious in its nesting habits to the extent of gathering in small, scattered colonies. Perhaps half a dozen pairs will sometimes occupy a tract of scrub of limited extent, but again a nest may be found at some distance from any other pair.

Material is usually the same in all cases, viz, oak twigs of varying shapes and thickness, formed into a substantial, thick-walled cup lined with fine rootlets. It is much like the nest of the blue jay *(Cyanocitta cristata)* in appearance and structure but, unlike that species, does not occupy such elevation, for it is usually constructed at 4 to 12 feet above ground. Probably a high Florida jay nest would be about at the elevation of a low blue jay's. Necessarily, it is rather limited in the choice of a site because of the sameness of the scrub, but the myrtle (*Myrica cerifera*), sand pine (*Pinus clausa*), and various oaks (*Quercus*) are the shrubs and trees most used. S. A. Grimes (MS.) states that the wild olive (*Osmanthus*) "seems to be the favorite site, for it affords the best cover. It is a thick-branched and densely foliaged plant when the dune vegetation is in the 'scrub-jay stage'."

The seasonal range of nesting is extensive, a characteristic of many of the Florida forms, and this jay may be found any time between late March and late May, with eggs. Strange discrepancies in dates may be noted in the same locality, fresh eggs being possible in a nearly 2 months' range of time.

Both parents are assiduous in all domestic duties. Grimes (MS.), who has paid much attention to the scrub jay, writes that "both gather nest material and work it into the nest; both incubate; both brood; both feed and attend the young in and out of the nest. I have seen the adults swallow the cloacal sacs of the nestlings and at other times carry them away and drop them. The female probably does the greater part of the incubating, but the male sees to it that she does not want for food while she is so engaged."

Incubation occupies a little more than 2 weeks, 15 to 17 days. Again quoting from Grimes' notes: "One nest that I kept under observation was in use 45 days, including the ten it was under construction. The last egg in this set of five was laid on April 1, and the three eggs that hatched did so in the night of April 16-17. The young left the nest on May 5."

One interesting fact noted by Grimes in the northern limit of the range (Duval County) is that there is always a percentage of unhatched eggs. "In fact," he writes, "I have never known all the eggs to hatch in a set of scrub jay. If that condition is general, it must indicate some form of decadence in the species. Perhaps it is a normal condition at a border extremity of range, due to inbreeding."

In his comments on the recession of this jay's range from its former northern limit about Jacksonville in the past few years, Grimes has noted another unusual condition. "When the Florida jays," he says, "were down to the last five or six individuals here, for two successive seasons I found three birds attending one nest. Two were males. Even so, in the nest that I followed up, only two eggs out of four hatched."

Though evincing tameness to a degree at times, under almost any conditions, the Florida jay is particularly indifferent to human beings about its nest. Its behavior under these circumstances is often remarkable. When investigating a nesting *coerulescens*, one is reminded strongly of the primitive unconcern displayed by the noddy (*Anous stolidus*) on the Dry Tortugas. It is quite possible to handle the bird freely, and in certain cases there is not even an attempt made to peck at the intruder. Neighboring birds occasionally show more concern than the sitting individual!

Well illustrative of this trait are some interesting notes sent to me by Hugo H. Schroder (MS.), who says that on "April 25, 1932, I found a female on nest in scrub oak and vines about 5 feet up, in Orange County, northwest of Orlando. She remained while vines were opened so nest and occupants could be photographed, and she allowed herself to be picked up and placed in a different position whenever we desired her to be in a better pose; she uttered no protest and made no attempt to bite when picked up. Even when she hopped from the nest she allowed us to replace her, when she remained. The male came to scold while we were handling his mate, and once he came within a foot of my head. A number of neighboring jays added their voices of protest and one of these allowed me to reach within a foot of his body without moving away.

"May 3. Same nest, two young nearly ready to leave. Female allowed herself to be handled but did make a weak attempt to peck at my finger. One of the youngsters wanted to leave the nest, and I held him down while a photo was made; the female was perched on the other side of the nest at the time, her feathers puffed out a little but otherwise giving no sign of resenting the effort to restrain her youngster. Several times when I picked her up she uttered a very soft, low-pitched sort of song."

The Florida jay sometimes shows a decided preference for the nest even after the young have left. Both adults and young return to it for varying periods, and observations on this trait should be more extensive. An interesting instance is furnished by Wilbur F. Smith (MS.), who has had 9 years of experience with this jay near Englewood, Fla., on the lower west coast. He says: "My most thrilling experience with it was about four years ago when a pair built their nest in a hedge of Cherokee roses in a friend's yard. The nest was placed well in the middle of the hedge where light conditions prevented a picture. Three young birds hatched, and when they were about grown I took a friend to see them. We found the nest empty and no birds in sight, though the young had been in the nest the day before. The old birds had been fed all winter and were very tame. The owner of the place had left for his Kansas home, and no doubt the jays missed the daily supply of food, so it was not so surprising that one of them appeared on a wire above us, looked down expectantly, and dropped to proffered food in an outstretched hand. Then the other bird (adult) appeared, and on looking again at the nest we found that two of the young had climbed through the vines and were sitting on the edge of it, while the third was nearby.

"One of the old birds went to the nest with the young and resented my trying to so part the vines as to let light in for a picture. So I braved its displeasure by bringing the nest forward about 2 feet to the outside of the hedge on the chance of the birds following. The inclosed photo shows both birds sitting on the nest in the changed position and one of them taking food from the hand, when we stood, without any effort at concealment, about 3 feet away. We ran out of film, when the nest was returned to its old site, and before we left two young had climbed back into it."

Eggs.—According to Bendire (1895), "the eggs of the Florida Jay range from three to five in number, and their ground color varies from pea green to pale glaucous green. They are blotched and spotted with irregularly shaped markings of cinnamon rufous and vinaceous cinnamon, these being generally heaviest about the larger end of the egg. They are usually ovate in shape, though an occasional set may be called elongate ovate; the shell is smooth and compact, and shows but little gloss."

The measurements of 46 eggs average 27.5 by 20.3 millimeters; the eggs showing the four extremes measure **30.8** by 20.6, 26.9 by **21.3, 24.6** by 20.1, and 27.0 by **18.6** millimeters.

Plumages.—Immature Florida jays are much like the adults in appearance, but the colors are duller, with less blue on the breast, and the top of the head is lighter. The sexes are alike in all plumages.

Food.—The Florida jay maintains the family tradition for a rather wide choice of food, deserving the term omnivorous, but leaning toward selections of animal matter to an extent of somewhat more than 60 percent. The tendency of this bird to become familiar with humanity and accept its offerings leads to the inclusion of many items that would not otherwise appear, notably such food as bread, cake, and peanuts, which are invariably accepted with apparent avidity. Any such food, however, is highly artificial in nature and should not enter strictly into any summary of normal consumption. So strongly has the bird become entrenched in many parts of its range as a semidomestic species that these items are mentioned because of their frequent offering and equally accepted status.

Dr. Clarence Cottam, of the U. S. Fish and Wildlife Service, has kindly furnished me with a detailed account of the stomach findings of 16 specimens of *coerulescens* taken in January, March, April, May, and September. The conclusions from this study reveal that the food is: "Animal matter 60.63 percent, plant matter 39.37 percent, gravel 6.38

percent, trace of feathers." The breakdown of the above is worthy of note. Though the exact percentages are not given, the findings include the remains of grasshoppers, locusts, crickets, termites, burrower-bugs, squash bugs, leafhoppers, earwigs, beetles, weevils, butterflies, moths, caterpillars, cutworms, bees, wasps, ants, anglewings, flies, millipeds, and centipedes. Also included were spiders, scorpions, ticks, mites, mollusks, snails, turtles, frogs, and lizards. Vegetable matter was represented by wheat *(Triticum)*, crowfoot grass *(Dactyloctenium aegyptium)*, acorns *(Quercus)*, purslane *(Portulaca)*, milkwort *(Polygala)*, huckleberry *(Gaylussacia)*, blueberry, cranberry *(Vaccinium)*, and fogfruit *(Lippia)*. Portions of vegetable debris and indeterminate matter (mast?) and wood pulp were also present.

Audubon (1842) states that the seeds of the saw palmetto are a favorite food, so much so, indeed, that "no sooner have the seeds of that plant become black, or fully ripe, than the Florida jay makes them almost its sole food for a time." He adds that the method of feeding is like that of the blue jay, for *coerulescens* "secures its food between its feet, and breaks it into pieces before swallowing it, particularly the acorns of the *live oak,* and the snails which it picks up among the *sword palmetto.*" Nuttall (1832) also gives the seeds of the saw palmetto as being eaten "largely."

Bendire (1895) adds another item in his summary of the food as "offal." He also mentions wood ticks specifically, as does Maynard (1896), the latter stating that "upon examining the contents of its stomach, found that it was filled with ticks or jiggers which infest the skin of all quadrupeds in this section of Florida." These references to ticks substantiate, without saying so, of course, the observations of N. B. Moore on the habit of this jay of alighting on the backs of cattle and securing ticks in that manner. "Jigger" is the universal name of the red-bug in the southeast, an even worst pest than ticks in many ways.

Another food habit of this jay, not hitherto mentioned and something of an indictment against the bird, is its fondness for the eggs and young of other birds, and even of poultry. Just how much this is indulged in does not seem clear, but there is certainly abundant evidence that predation of the sort occurs. Bendire (1895) states that this jay is "charged with being very destructive" in this way. A writer whose name I am unable to determine, but whose initials are C. S. C., writing in the Chicago Field, says that they "eat and drink with poultry, having an eye on eggs and young chickens." M. M. Green (1889) states: "Stomachs of two shot contained insect food. The birds' bills were smeared with yolk of eggs. Several people told me that the jays were nest robbers." Nuttall (1832) notes that it "destroys the eggs and young of small birds, despatching the latter by repeated blows on the head."

Grimes (MS.) says: "I know they like crickets for I saw a male pass up four, one after the other, to his sitting mate. * * * In the fall and winter they feed to a large extent on the little acorns of Chapman's oak."

Behavior.—The Florida jay is a true representative of its family in traits and character. Individual variations occur, but essentially it resembles its better-known relative *Cyanocitta cristata,* in actions and habits. As its local name implies, it is not a high-ranging bird in any sense. One of its outstanding characteristics is its love of the ground and low elevations, which must impress anyone observing the bird for any length of time. Along roadsides it is frequently seen on the "shoulders" of the highway, particularly in sandy stretches, where it feeds commonly. Passing cars often flush it from such situations, whence it dashes off amid the scrub palmetto or ascends to a convenient telegraph wire. The flight is strong and without particular character unless the frequent sweeps with wide-open wings could be called such. The long tail is often fully expanded. On the ground it hops with strong, sure jumps, planting the feet firmly. In searching for food under such conditions it is given, according to Howell (1932), to probing the loose sand with the bill.

One often sees the moods of the bird expressed in the action of the tail. Usually, in repose, it hangs fairly straight down, offering a good field mark, but under stress of excitement this member is jerked and twitched in a highly expressive manner. Approach is not difficult most of the time, though easier during the nesting period. Sometimes an almost utter disregard of the human intruder is evidenced. In former years these birds were caged, and they proved easy to keep. Audubon (1842) gives an account of a pair he saw in captivity at New Orleans (!), which he states "had been raised from a family of five, taken from the nest, and when I saw them had been two years in confinement. They were in full plumage, and extremely beautiful. The male was often observed to pay very particular attentions to the female, at the approach of spring. They were fed upon rice, and all kinds of dried fruit. Their cage was usually opened after dinner, when both immediately flew upon the table, fed on the almonds which were given them, and drank claret diluted with water. Both affected to imitate particular sounds, but in a very imperfect manner. These attempts at mimicry probably resulted from their having been in company with parrots and other birds. They suffered greatly when moulting, becoming almost entirely bare, and required to be kept near the fire. The female dropped two eggs in the cage, but never attempted to make a nest, although the requisite materials were placed at her disposal."

A reference to the adaptability of this species to captivity is referred to by Nuttall (1832) when he states that it is "easily reconciled to the cage." Since caging of wild birds is now a thing of the past, the above may probably be all we will know about this species in private captivity, but successful attempts to tame it at large have been often accomplished. A striking example is noted by Howell (1932) just 100 years after Nuttall's observation, as follows:

Miss Edith Werner, who in the spring of 1923 was operating a tea house on the shore of Lake Jackson, near Sebring [Fla.], has been remarkably successful in taming the Florida Jays, which are abundant in the scrub close to her house. She whistles a bright little tune and in a few minutes the Jays appear from all directions and without hesitation alight on her arm or shoulder to take the pieces of bread she offers them. She told us she had been a year or more taming the birds, and that it was a month or more before she could get them near her. At the time of our visit however, they had become so used to strangers that they allowed us to feed them and even alighted on our heads and shoulders. On hearing a note of alarm from one of the Jays in the brush, they all deserted us and flew into the scrub. Miss Werner says the birds always have a lookout posted on a high bush, which sentinel remains there while the rest are feeding and gives warning of danger. She added that they often frolicked together in the morning, at which times they snap the bill continuously as they shake their bodies. Occasionally they sing very softly, under their breath, "like a canary."

The indifference of the Florida jay to human presence is alluded to by Hugo H. Schroder (MS.) in the following note: "While I was eating lunch beside the road south of Indian River City, Fla., a male jay landed on ground near my car. When I threw down some bread he picked it up and flew off with it. As soon as he returned, I threw more pieces of bread; each time the bird would fly off with it. More than a half dozen pieces were taken away; whether each one was eaten I could not see."

Wilbur F. Smith (MS.) states that "Florida jays become tame about the houses of winter visitors, taking peanuts and bread from the hand or on the head, or even from between the lips of some."

This bird appears to run true to corvine traits in its predilection for making away with odds and ends of property. This is a characteristic overlooked by many, or at least not referred to. Such articles are, as usual with avian thievery, bright and shiny as a rule, easily seen and attractive. Buttons, tops of small tins, spoons, bits of glass, china, and the like are among the hoards. A reference to this habit, the only one in fact that has come to my attention from the literature, appears in the Chicago Field of May 1880 and states that these birds "bury such food as they cannot immediately consume, and also spoons, thimbles, or any shining object that attracts their attention."

Another interesting habit is also apparently not well known and may have been more frequently indulged in during past years than now, though I know of no reason why it should have now ceased. This concerns the picking of ticks from cattle, a habit shared by some of the Florida herons. I have never observed it, nor can I find anything in the literature about it, but N. B. Moore (MS.) in writing of this jay says: "A common habit of this species during the time when cattle have many ticks upon them, and this happens through the greater part of the year, is to perch upon their backs, move or hop upon their rumps and hip bones, and pick them off and eat them, or, if they have young, carry them to the nest or to a tree or fencepost, where the young are perhaps waiting for food. It reminds one of the habits of the *Buphaga* of Africa to see this jay riding about on the backs of cattle and feasting on these disgusting parasites. The jay often obtains the ticks by hopping on the ground about the legs of the cows jumping by the help of its wings up to the buttocks, flanks, or brisket and seizing the most palatable ones. The cattle seem not in the least annoyed by those on their backs, and yet the pretty constant switching of their tail and throwing back their horns keep the jays constantly on the alert, and they often quit their place to avoid a blow, perching either on another cow or on a tree or a fence."

With the even greater prevalence of cattle in Florida today than when Moore wrote (about 1870), it seems strange that this habit has not been commented on more by recent observers. To many persons' surprise Florida is one of the greatest cattle-raising States in the Union, but in recent years there has been a definite effort, attended by marked success, to eliminate ticks, and this may have resulted in such a sharp decrease in the parasites that the jays have largely abandoned this source of food and the method of obtaining it.

On monthly investigations on the Kissimmee Prairie, I see literally thousands of cattle, but as mentioned previously the jay does not occur on the open prairie and therefore could not be expected in the largest cattle concentrations. It is known that the Florida crow (*Corvus brachyrhynchos pascuus*) procures ticks and other insects from the backs of cattle, and occasionally some of the smaller herons do the same thing, which reminds one of the African cow heron.

Somewhat contrary to the accepted opinion that jays are domineering and quarrelsome, there is evidence that *coerulescens* is an exception to the rule. Though at times seen to drive off such species as blackbirds and mockingbirds, it appears to live in considerable harmony with its avian neighbors, with little bickering and interference. Wilbur F. Smith (MS.) in noting this trait says: "The Florida jay has far better manners than other members of the family. I have photographed it with quail (*Colinus virginianus floridanus*), ground doves (*Columbigallina pas-*

serina), meadowlarks *(Sturnella magna argutula)*, red-winged blackbirds *(Agelaius phoeniceus mearnsi)*, and grackles and have never seen it bully or disturb these birds, a fact worth noting in view of the family reputation. In the section where I have known it for nine years [Englewood, Fla.] it is a general favorite, giving ground only to the quail that feed about the homes." It is supposed that in his expression "giving ground" Mr. Smith refers to the popularity of the quail over the jay, not that the jay retreats before the other.

Voice.—Notoriously noisy as are most of the jays, this species is not unusually so. Compared at least to *Cyanocitta* and its forms, it is decidedly less vocal. The notes are essentially jaylike, which is not too general a term to employ for quick recognition, but are given at greater intervals and not so constantly. Certain calls are loud and have a harsh, rasping quality, and it is probably some of these that Howell (1932) likens to notes of the boat-tailed grackle *(Megaquiscalus mexicanus major)* and that he terms "churr." I cannot say that they ever impressed me in such a way, but bird calls sound different to different hearers.

The song, if one can designate the attempt as such, is widely at variance with the call or alarm notes. It is a rather surprising performance really, and would puzzle many not seeing the singer. Wetmore (MS.) describes it as "a mixture of low, sweet-toned calls, high in pitch, mingled with others that were variously slurred or trilled in utterance." It is next to impossible to describe most bird notes in words. However, the above seems to me to be as good an interpretation as can be given. Not in character or similiarity, but in that one would not expect such a song from such a bird, it recalls some of the performances of the loggerhead shrike *(Lanius ludovicianus)*! On some occasions, I have heard low, subdued notes that cannot be described otherwise than as a chuckle, delivered rather rapidly and having an abrupt quality. It is an agreeable delivery and imparts the distinct impression that the bird is in a thoroughly contented mood at the time.

Field marks.—The outstanding field marks of this species, aside from the characteristic color pattern, are the crestless head and the long tail. The name *"Aphelocoma"* is from the Latin meaning "smooth hair," referring, of course, to the lack of a crest in a crested family; *"coerulescens"* refers to the prevailing color, blue.

DISTRIBUTION

Range.—The peninsula of Florida; nonmigratory.

The range of the Florida jay extends **north** in that State to **Port**

Richey, Fruitland Park, and Ormond. **East** along the Atlantic coast from Ormond south to Lemon City. **South** to Lemon City, Immokalee, and Fort Myers. **West** along the Gulf coast from Fort Myers north to Port Richey.

Egg dates.—Florida: 49 records, March 21 to June 14; 25 records, April 10 to 30.

APHELOCOMA COERULESCENS SUPERCILIOSA Strickland

LONG-TAILED JAY

PLATES 17, 18

HABITS

The California jay of the interior is now known by the above name. Under its former name, *Aphelocoma californica immanis,* the 1931 Check-list gives its range as "extreme southern Washington, valleys of Oregon between the Cascades and the Coast ranges, and the Sacramento and San Joaquin valleys of California and adjacent mountain slopes."

Dr. Grinnell (1901) in describing it, from specimens taken near Scio, Oreg., gave as its characters, "in coloration similar to *Aphelocoma californica,* but size greater and tail proportionately much longer." This description was apparently based on only four birds, at least the measurements of only four are given, all from the Willamette Valley, Oreg. Mr. Swarth (1918), with a much larger series from a much larger area does not agree exactly with Grinnell's description; he says that *immanis* is "distinguished from *A. c. californica* both by large size and *pale* [italics mine] coloration; from *oocleptica* by pale coloration, size being about the same." At the time that Dr. Grinnell described *immanis* the characters and the distribution of the California races of *Aphelocoma* were not so well understood as they are today, and the fact had not been recognized that the two coastal races are dark colored and the interior race is paler. Ridgway (1904) does not recognize *immanis* but lists it as a synonym of *californica.*

Grinnell, Dixon, and Linsdale (1930) call this bird the interior California jay, an appropriate name. They say of its haunts in the Lassen Peak region: "This species, belonging to the brush-covered portions of the section, found suitable surroundings on the western slope of the section where the following kinds of plants grew: buck-brush, scrub oak, elderberry, hazel brush, manzanita, red-bud, grapevine. Individuals were also often seen in trees, but, as a rule, in their lower portions. The kinds of trees thus frequented were: blue oak, willow, living or fire-killed digger pine, knobcone pine, cottonwood, valley oak, sycamore, box elder, and orchard trees. In the eastern part of the section the jays frequented the slopes that were juniper covered. In addition to the junipers they were seen in mountain mahogany, sage-brush, and willows (in the canons)."

Nesting.—The nesting habits of the long-tailed jay are apparently similar to those of the other California races, and the eggs are practically indistinguishable. The measurements of 40 eggs average 28.4 by 21.0 millimeters; the eggs showing the four extremes measure **31.2** by 21.3, 27.4 by **22.0**, **25.0** by 20.0, and 26.5 by **19.5** millimeters.

Young.—Grinnell and Storer (1924) have written quite fully on the habits of this subspecies, some of which may well be quoted here. While watching the two parent birds feeding their young, they noted that—

the parent birds had a particular route in approaching and leaving the nest, and this route was adhered to strictly. They would always approach through the trees of a wooded slope to the east, and then, having reached the nest tree, hop by easy stages to a position on the west side of the nest. From there the nestlings would be fed, and then the nest cleaned. After that the bird would work out of the south side of the willow, fly to a digger pine across the creek immediately above our tent, hop upward until near the top of the pine, and from there would take off in a direct course to its next forage ground. Even when the jays had been hunting insects in the open area immediately west of our camp, they would circle about when ready to return to the nest and approach it from the east. Only one adult visited the nest at a time although they often followed one another in quick succession. Save for the low crooning given when standing over the young, no calls were uttered while the parents were in the vicinity of the nest. There was a "zone of quiet" about their home, within which the owners would not call or raise any alarm.

Behavior.—Of its behavior they say: "The Interior California Jay is notoriously bold and forward in its behavior; although it is counted as a nonflocking species, individuals and pairs will gather quickly in response to the excited calls of one of their kin. The birds seem never to be so busy with their own affairs that they cannot stop and investigate any object of an unusual nature. Ordinarily this jay is the picture of animation. Perched, it stands in an attitude of alertness, its head up, tail straight back or tilted slightly upward, and feet slightly spread. Just after alighting a jay will often execute a deep bow involving the entire body, and this may be repeated a number of times and in different directions. The purpose of this bowing is not clear to us."

Mrs. Ruth Wheeler writes to me of her experience with this jay: "I had a very interesting experience last year photographing a family of the California jay. We found the parents to be extremely wary. I have never worked with birds that appeared to show as much intelligence. We set up our bird blind near their nest, which was in a young oak, and only about 4 feet from the ground. Although the birds had become used to the blind and were nowhere to be seen when we entered, still they appeared to know that we were there. They came back very quietly, slipping through the trees and alighting near the blind. Then one of them leaned over and peered through the small opening through which the camera was focused. After looking very carefully, he saw us and set up a great outcry. We were able to get only one picture of the nest, which we took with a flash. After that the birds would not come near while we were in the blind."

Voice.—Grinnell and Storer (1924) describe the notes of this jay as only slightly different from those of the other subspecies, but they add to our knowledge of the bird's varied vocabulary, perhaps a limited language. Grinnell gives *"cheek, cheek, cheek,* etc., staccato, 3 to 10 times in rapid succession; *chú-ick, chú-ick, chú-ick,* etc., usually in 3's slowly; *schwee-ick,* higher-pitched, 2 to 6 times, uttered still more slowly." Storer adds: "A series of mildly harsh notes, *kwish, kwish, kwish,* uttered usually 3 to 5 times in quick succession; a more protracted softer note, *kschu-ee,* or *jai-e,* usually given singly. Birds of a pair when foraging together, and young and adults when in family parties, utter a subdued guttural *krr'r'r'r'r.* When attending young still in the nest, the parent birds utter a low crooning, impossible of representation in syllables; and the young birds, after leaving the nest and before gaining their living independently, have a 'teasing scold' which they utter almost incessantly, in keeping their parents apprised of their need for food."

APHELOCOMA COERULESCENS OOCLEPTICA Swarth
NICASIO JAY

HABITS

Harry S. Swarth (1918) gave the above name to the flat-headed jays of "the coast region of northern California, west from Mount Diablo and the coast ranges. North to Humboldt Bay, south to the Golden Gate and the east side of San Francisco Bay." Of its distinguishing characters, he says: "Of large size and dark coloration. In color closely similar to *A. c. californica,* but size measureably greater throughout. In measurements *oocleptica* is equal to the maximum of *immanis,* from which subspecies it is distinguished by its dark coloration. Differs from *hypoleuca* both in greater size and much darker color."

Nesting.—There is not much to be said about the nesting habits of the Nicasio jay, which are practically the same as those of the other California subspecies. John W. Mailliard (1912) says that this jay is an abundant resident in Marin County and that their "nesting notes upon this species established the following sites for the eighty-three nests observed: oaks 69; bay 3; wild coffee 4; elder 2; madrona 1; gooseberry 1; toxon 1; poison oak 2. And yet in Belvedere, Marin County, where live-oaks are most plentiful, a nest has been built almost yearly, for seven or eight years, in a clematis which climbs up the side of our summer home. The nest has usually been placed within reach of, as well as observation from, the window of a constantly occupied bed room, a window opening out and frequently opened and closed daily."

Eggs.—The eggs of the Nicasio jay are practically indistinguishable from those of the California jay and show the same interesting variations. The measurements of 40 eggs average 27.8 by 20.5 millimeters; the eggs showing the four extremes measure **30.8** by 21.8, 29.0 by **22.4, 24.4** by 19.3, and 25.4 by **18.8** millimeters.

Food.—The notes that Charles A. Allen, of Nicasio, Calif., sent to Major Bendire (1895) evidently refer to this race. He writes:

No bird is more destructive of the smaller species building open, unconcealed nests than this Jay. I have seen one alight on a limb near a nest, eat the eggs that it contained, and, not satisfied with this, give the nest a down and inward stroke with its bill, ripping it open. They are especially destructive to the nests of the Black-chinned and Anna's Hummingbirds and the Ground Tit. They also become altogether too familiar about the poultry houses, and will eat the eggs as fast as the hens lay them. As soon as they hear a hen cackle after laying, three or four of these birds go to the spot at once. Even the chicken house affords no protection against these robbers, if they can find a way of entering it; shooting is equally ineffectual, for they are too numerous. They destroy vast quantities of fruit in apple, peach, pear, and plum orchards, as well as many smaller fruits. Shooting them by hundreds and hanging their carcasses in the fruit trees as scarecrows is of no avail; they do not know enough to be frightened at anything. I have tried to poison them, but never saw a dead one except when shot. They also destroy a great deal of young wheat when first sown, until it is 2 or 3 inches high. They pull it out of the ground and eat the soft, swelled grains; after the stalks begin to grow they will not molest it.

One cannot help feeling that the above bitter invective is somewhat overdrawn and perhaps a bit prejudiced. His statement that they "do not know enough to be frightened" is offset by the fact that he was never able to poison one; the truth of the matter probably is that they *know too much* to be frightened unnecessarily, and that they are crafty enough to avoid real danger. His statement that they pull up sprouting grain does not agree with Professor Beal's (1910) statement that "the jay is not known to pull up grain after it has sprouted."

But Professor Beal evidently overlooked Mr. Allen's statement, as well as the following from Joseph Mailliard (1900): "I have had acres of peas * * * practically destroyed by these birds. * * * I remember one spring when a patch of about an acre and a half was sown with a mixture of peas and oats, and the peas were pulled up as fast as sprouted, by the jays, so that the crop consisted of oats alone. * * * Some years they destroy a lot of corn and other years almost none. * * * This year the Jays, in conjunction with Towhees, Juncos and a few Flickers, badly damaged some late sown oats beside the house." He watched them through glasses and saw them pull up the sprouting grain and eat the kernels.

Professor Beal (1910) adds the following observation in the jay's favor: "But the jays do not frequent orchards entirely for fruit. During May and June the writer many times visited an apple orchard, the leaves of which were badly infested with a small green caterpillar, locally known as the canker worm. When a branch is jarred, these insects let themselves down to the ground on a thread spun for the purpose. Many jays were seen to fly into the orchard, alight in a tree, and then almost immediately drop to the ground. Observation showed that the caterpillars, disturbed by the shock of the bird's alighting on a branch, dropped, and that the birds immediately followed and gathered them in. These caterpillars were found in the stomachs of several jays, in one case to the extent of 90 percent of the contents."

Voice.—Mr. Allen mentions some notes of this jay that are somewhat different from those recorded by others; he wrote to Major Bendire (1895): "One of their notes of alarm, uttered when they see something they do not like, especially an Owl asleep in a tree, sounds like 'cŭr, cŭr, cŭr'; as soon as this is heard by others in the vicinity they will commence to gather and join in the chorus. A sort of social note of recognition sounds like 'whŭze, whŭze', given while moving about among the trees and shrubbery, and one of their common call notes sounds like 'creak, creak'."

APHELOCOMA COERULESCENS CALIFORNICA (Vigors)

CALIFORNIA JAY

PLATES 19, 20

HABITS

The three subspecies of *Aphelocoma coerulescens* that are found in California are common, and in many places abundant, over almost all the State, except the desert regions and the mountains, but the subject of this sketch, *A. c. californica,* is confined to a comparatively narrow coastal strip along the southern half of the coast. The 1931 Check-list gives its range as "from the southern arm of San Francisco Bay to the Mexican line, east to the eastern base of the Coast ranges." But Swarth (1918), who does not recognize *A. c. obscura,* extends its range into northern Lower California, as far south as the San Pedro Mártir Mountains.

Roughly speaking, the characters distinguishing the three California races are size and color.

Swarth (1918) says that *californica,* as compared with *immanis* (now *superciliosa),* the interior form, "is of small size and dark coloration. The blue areas are of a deeper shade, the back distinctly darker brown, and the light colored under parts have a dusky suffusion. Lower tail coverts usually tinged with blue, sometimes conspicuously so. Coloration is about the same in *californica* as in *oocleptica* [the northern coast form], from which subspecies *californica* is distinguished by smaller size throughout." The other two races are larger than *californica,* and both about the same size, but *oocleptica* is dark colored and *superciliosa* is much paler.

The habitats of the three races and their general habits are all very similar. One life history might well do for all three. They all live mainly in the Upper Sonoran Zone, with some extension of range into the Lower Sonoran and Transition Zones. Their favorite haunts are the oak and brush-covered foothills of the mountains, the brush-covered sides of the canyons, the oak and digger-pine chaparral, thickets of *Ceanothus* and poison-oak bushes, and among the small trees and shrubbery along watercourses. In such places, where there is ample concealment among the thick foliage, this handsome, flat-headed, mischievous villain is quite sure to be found; if not immediately in evidence, the well-known squeaking sound, such as one uses to call small birds, will bring all the jays within hearing of it.

Nesting.—Major Bendire (1895) writes:

The nests are usually found on brush-covered hillsides or in creek bottoms, placed in low bushes and thickets, such as blackberry, poison oak, wild gooseberry, currant, hazel, hawthorn, and scrub-oak bushes, or in osage-orange hedges; occasionally in a small piñon pine or a bushy young fir, and quite frequently on a horizontal limb of an oak, varying in height from 3 to 30 feet from the ground. In the majority of cases the nests are located near water, but sometimes one may be found fully a mile distant. Externally they are composed of a platform of interlaced twigs, mixed occasionally with moss, wheat stubble, and dry grass; on this the nest proper is placed, which consists of a lining of fine roots, sometimes mixed wih horsehair. No mud enters into the composition of their nests. One now before me * * * measures 9 inches in outer diameter by 3½ inches in height; the inner cup is 4 inches in diameter by 2 inches deep. Outwardly it is composed of small twigs of sagebrush, and the lining consists entirely of fine roots; it is compactly built and well constructed. The nests are usually well concealed, and the birds are close sitters, sometimes remaining on the nests until almost touched.

In addition to the trees and shrubs mentioned above, nests of the California jay have been found in live oaks, elders, willows, apple trees, pear trees, junipers, cypresses, and honeysuckles. W. L. Dawson (1923) says:

Taking the country over, nests built in oak trees probably outnumber all others combined, yet the component members of the chaparral, ceanothus, chamissal, and the rest, must do duty in turn, and all species of the riparian sylva as well. The thick-set clumps of mistletoe are very hospitable to this bird, and since this occurs on oaks, cottonwoods, and, occasionally, digger pines, it follows that jay-heim is found there also. * * *

The lining varies delightfully, but is largely dependent, it is only fair to say, upon the breed of horses or cattle affected on the nearest ranch. So we have nests with white, black, bay, and sorrel linings, not to mention dapple gray and pinto. One fastidious bird of my acquaintance, after she had constructed a dubious lining of mottled material, discovered a coal black steed overtaken by mortality. New furnishings were ordered forthwith. The old lining was pitched out bodily, and the coal black substitute installed immediately, to the bird's vast satisfaction—and mine.

Eggs.—Four to six eggs generally constitute a complete set for the California jay; as few as two and as many as seven have been recorded. The eggs are usually ovate in shape, rarely elongate-ovate. They are very beautifully colored and show a wide range of variation, seldom, if ever, equaled and never exceeded among North American birds' eggs. In any series of these colorful eggs there are apparent two quite distinct types of coloration, the green and the red. Lawrence Stevens, of Santa Barbara, writes to me that about half of the sets that he takes are of the green type and half of the red type. He finds eggs of the green type mostly in the creek bottoms in willows, usually in sets of four, and finds eggs of the red type mostly on the hillsides, in sets of five. As several other collectors do not agree with him on these points, there is probably no correlation of color with the locality or the size of the set. He mentions one set that has a cream-colored background with red spots, that one would hardly believe to be jays' eggs.

James B. Dixon tells me that only about two sets in ten are of the red type. Dawson (1923) describes the colors very well as follows:

The red type is much the rarer. In this the ground color varies from clear grayish white to the normal green of the prevailing type; while the markings—fine dots or spots or, rarely, confluent blotches—are of a warm sepia, bister, verona brown, or Rood's brown. The ground color of the green type varies from pale sulphate green to lichen green, and the markings from deep olive to Lincoln green. In the Museum of Comparative Zoology we have a set kindly furnished by Mr. H. W. Carriger, whose markings are reduced to the palest subdued freckling of pea-green. In another set of the red type, fine Mars brown markings of absolute uniformity cover the egg; while the eggs of another set are covered as to their larger ends with an olive-green cloud cap, which leaves the remainder of the specimen almost free of markings.

Bendire (1895) describes the eggs somewhat differently as follows: "The ground color of the egg of the California Jay is very variable, ranging from deep sea green to pea and sage green, and again to dull olive and vinaceous buff. The eggs with the greenish ground color usually have markings of a dark bottle-green tint, mixed sometimes with different shades of sage green. The eggs having a buffy ground color are spotted, blotched, and speckled with different shades of ferruginous, cinnamon, rufous, and occasionally lavender. The markings are generally scattered over the entire surface of the egg, and are usually heavier about the larger end, but nowhere so profuse as to hide the ground color."

The measurements of 50 eggs average 27.6 by 20.5 millimeters; the eggs showing the four extremes measure **30.6** by 21.8, 30.2 by **22.4, 24.4** by 19.3, and 25.4 by **18.8** millimeters.

Young.—Bendire (1895) says that the male assists "to some extent in incubation, which lasts about sixteen days. The young are able to leave the nest in about eighteen days, and follow the parents for some time." Mrs. Wheelock (1904) says that "the male assists in the nest-building, but not in the incubation. The latter requires fourteen days. * * * One of the first lessons the young Jays learn is to love the water. It requires some coaxing for the first splash, but they seem to take to their bath as do little ducks, and to find it just as necessary as food."

Plumages.—The young jay is hatched naked and blind; probably some form of natal down appears in advance of the juvenal plumage, though I have not seen it. Ridgway (1904) gives the following detailed description of the juvenal plumage: "Pileum, hind neck, auricular and suborbital regions, sides of chest, rump, and upper tail-coverts uniform mouse gray, the pileum slightly more bluish gray; back, scapulars, and lesser wing-coverts deep drab-gray; lores dusky; a broad postocular and supra-auricular space, narrowly streaked with dusky gray; anterior portion of malar region, chin, throat, median portion of chest and under parts generally white, faintly tinged across upper breast and on anterior portion of sides with very pale brownish gray; wings (except smaller coverts) and tail as in adults."

The postjuvenal molt begins early in July, and I have seen a young bird beginning to molt on the throat and upper breast as early as June 29. This molt involves all the contour plumage and the lesser wing coverts, but not the rest of the wings and tail. I have seen no specimens showing the latter part of this molt, but it is apparently completed before September, when young birds become practically adult.

Adults have a complete postnuptial molt, which seems to be accomplished mainly in August; the plumage becomes much worn and faded during late spring and early summer, the blue wearing off on the head, exposing the dusky bases of the feathers, the brown of the back fading, and the under parts becoming soiled and browner; I have seen birds molting in August and others in full fresh plumage as early as September 24.

Food.—Prof. F. E. L. Beal (1910) examined 326 stomachs of the California jay, and found that 27 percent of the food consisted of animal matter and 73 percent vegetable, though the animal matter amounted to 70 percent in April. Among the insect food, he lists predaceous ground beetles, mostly beneficial species, 2.5 percent for the year and as much as 10 percent in April; other beetles, mostly harmful, 8 percent for the year and 31 percent in April; wasps, bees, and ants amounted to less than 5 percent; honey bees were found in 9 stomachs, and all, 20 in number, were workers; Lepidoptera, mainly in the caterpillar stage, amounted to 2.5 percent; this item included 12 pupae of the coddling moth, an unexpected service that would cover a multitude of sins in other directions; grasshoppers and crickets were eaten to the extent of 4.5 percent. Of other animal food, he says: "A few miscellaneous creatures, such as raphidians, spiders, snails, etc., form less than one-half of 1 percent of the food. * * * Besides the insects and other invertebrates already discussed, the jay eats some vertebrates. The remains consisted of bones or feathers of birds in 8 stomachs, egg-shells in 38, bones of small mammals (mice and shrews) in 11, and bones of reptiles and batrachians in 13 stomachs." In destroying small mammals the jay does good service, as most of them are injurious, but the same cannot be said about its appetite for the useful reptiles and batrachians. The damage to the eggs and young of small birds is a serious matter. Some 95 stomachs were collected between the middle of May and the middle of July, the height of the nesting season, "of which 17, or 18 percent, contained eggs or remains of young birds. If we may infer, as seems reasonable, that 18 percent of the California jays rob birds' nests every day during the nesting season, then we must admit that the jays are a tremendous factor in preventing the increase of our common birds. Mr. Joseph Grinnell, of Pasadena, after careful observation, estimates the number of this species in California at about 126,000. This is probably a low estimate. If 18 percent of this number, or 22,680 jays, each robs a nest of eggs or young daily for a period of sixty days from the middle of May to the middle of July, the total number of nests destroyed in California by this one species every year is 1,360,800."

Mr. Dawson (1923) draws a still blacker picture; he figures, on the basis of suitable acreage and average population per acre, that there are 499,136 pairs of California jays in the State and says: "If we allow only one set of eggs or nest of birds to each pair of jays *per diem* for a period of two months, we shall be well within the mark of actuality. Yet that will give us in a season a total destruction of 29,948,160 nests, or, say, 100,000,000 eggs." These figures look appalling, but, in considering them, we must not lose sight of three important facts: First, jays and small birds have existed together for untold ages without any serious reduction in the number of the latter; second, the increase in small birds is limited by the amount of suitable area that will support them, and such area is probably kept filled to capacity; and third, it is a well-known fact that if a pair of birds is robbed of its eggs a second or third set will be laid; this is less likely to happen, however, if the young are taken.

But wild birds are not the only sufferers from the depredations of this jay; the eggs and young of domestic poultry are preyed upon. Professor Beal (1910) writes:

He is a persistent spy upon domestic fowls and well knows the meaning of the cackle of a hen. A woman whose home is at the mouth of a small ravine told the writer that one of her hens had a nest under a bush a short distance up the ravine from the cottage. A jay had found this out, and every day when the hen went on her nest the jay would perch on a near-by tree. As soon as the cackle of the hen was heard, both woman and bird rushed to get the egg, but many times the jay reached the nest first and secured the prize. * * * A still worse trait of the jay was described by a young man engaged in raising poultry on a ranch far up a canyon near wooded hills. When his white leghorn chicks were small, the jays would attack and kill them by a few blows of the beak, and then peck open the skull and eat the brains. In spite of all endeavors to protect the chicks and to shoot the jays, his losses were serious.

Of the vegetable food, mast, mainly acorns, is the largest item, and during the late fall and winter months made up one-half to three-quarters of the entire food; October showed the largest amount, 88.57 percent. Acorns and nuts are carried off and stored wherever they can be hidden in cracks and crevices, but since many are dropped on the way, or hidden on the ground, the jay may be considered useful as a tree planter.

Grain constitutes an important item; in March, when grain was being sown, it amounted to 45.50 percent; and again, during the harvesting season in September, it made up 24.26 percent of the food. "Grain was found in 95 stomachs, of which 56 contained oats; 34, corn; 2, wheat; 2, barley; and 1, grain not further identified. Many of the oats were of the wild variety.

"Fruit was found in 270 stomachs. Of these, cherries were identified in 37, prunes in 25, apples in 5, grapes in 2, pears in 2, peaches in 1, gooseberries in 2, figs in 1, blackberries or raspberries in 71, elderberries in 42, manzanita in 4, cascara in 1, mistletoe in 1, and fruit pulp not further identified in 76." He remarks, further, that "it is safe to say that half of the fruit eaten was of wild varieties and of no economic value." His table shows that fruit formed 22.05 percent of the total food for the year but averaged nearly half of it during the summer months and 61.41 percent in May. In addition to what fruit the jay eats, much more is damaged and left on the trees to rot and more falls to the ground.

Robert S. Woods writes to me: "The California jay is very destructive to almonds and finds no difficulty in cracking the harder-shelled varieties. Its raids begin before the nuts are ripe enough for human consumption and continue as long as any of the crop remains. The almond is held against a branch with the foot and vigorously pounded with the bill until an opening is made large enough to permit the kernel to be extracted piecemeal. English walnuts are broken into while still on the tree. However, the Eureka variety, at least, seems to be immune after the shell has thoroughly hardened, though some of the thinner-shelled strains or varieties could doubtless be successfully attacked even after maturity.

"Jays will often eat dry bread crumbs but greatly prefer food of a more fatty nature. When coarsely chopped suet is placed on a feeding table, it is ignored by most of the local dooryard birds, but the jays will diligently carry away and hide the pieces until all are gone."

From the foregoing evidence it may be seen that the California jay has more faults than virtues. It has few redeeming traits, and economically it does more harm than good. Its beauty and its lively manners make it an attractive feature in the landscape, but it may be that there are too many jays in California.

Behavior.—There is much in the actions of the California jay that reminds one of our familiar eastern blue jay; it is a handsome villain, but one misses the jaunty crest. It is far less shy, much bolder, more impertinent, and more mischievous. Its flight is just as slow and apparently laborious, accomplished by vigorous, heavy flappings of its wings on its usually short flights; it lives mostly at the lower levels among the trees and shrubbery and may often be seen sailing down over a brush-covered hillside with its blue wings and tail widely spread; as it glides upward to its perch it greets the observer with its harsh cries. It is quick and agile in all its movements, as it darts about through the underbrush, where it searches diligently for small birds' nests, or follows the little birds about to learn their secrets. It is not above picking a quarrel with the California woodpecker, whose stores it probably wants to steal, but, like most thieves, it is a cowardly bird and often needs the support of its fellow brigands. It is cordially disliked and dreaded by all the smaller birds. It is a nuisance, too, to the sportsman or the bird student, as its curiosity leads it to follow a human being about and proclaim his presence in such a loud voice that every creature within hearing is warned to disappear.

This jay seems to have a sense of humor or a fondness for play. Joseph Mailliard (1904) gives an amusing account of the behavior of California jays with his cats, stealing their food and teasing them. While a jay is attempting to steal food from a cat, "each has the measure of the other, and while a cat is watching, it is rarely that a jay approaches within reach of its business end, though it will do all it can to make the cat jump at it, or at least turn away. Grimalkin has learned to keep her tail well curled up when feeding, as a favorite trick of the jay is to give a vigorous peck at any extended tail and, when the cat turns to retaliate, to jump for the prize and make off with shrieks of exultation. * * * To find a cat napping, with its tail partially extended is absolute joy to one of these birds, which will approach cautiously from the rear, cock its head on one side and eye that tail until it can no longer resist the temptation, and, finally after hopping about a few times most carefully and noiselessly, Mr. (or Mrs.) Jay will give the poor tail a vicious peck and then fly, screeching with joy, to the nearest bush."

One day, after one of the cats had hidden her newly born kittens in the garden, "a faint mewing outside the window attracted the attention of someone in the kitchen when lo and behold there was a jay hauling a very young kitten out from under a young artichoke plant in the garden. The jay lugged the poor kitten along for a little way, seeming to enjoy its feeble wails, and then stopped and screeched in exultation over the find, only to repeat the process again and again. Needless to say the old cat was not present at the moment or things would have been made more lively. The bird certainly did not want to eat the kitten, and the affair seems to have been nothing else than a matter of pure mischief."

Voice.—Mrs. Bailey (1902) describes this jay's voice very well as follows: "The *Aphelocoma* voice differs strikingly from that of *frontalis,* having a flat tone and being uttered with unseemly haste. Its notes vary greatly in expression and are so emphatic and often peremptory that one cannot doubt that something important is being said. A favorite cry, used apparently to rouse attention, is quick '*quay-quay-quay-quay-quay-quay-quay.*' Another still more emphatic one is *boy'ee boy'-ee* while an inquiring *quay-kee?* is often heard. Sometimes when a jay flies down to a companion it gives its *quay-quay-quay-quay-quay* and is answered by a high-keyed *queep-queep-queep-queep*—however that may be interpreted."

Ralph Hoffmann (1927) says that "the California Jay utters a succession of harsh cries like the syllable *tschek, tschek,* slightly higher pitched

than those of the Steller Jay. Another note commonly uttered when the
bird is perched is a very harsh *ker-wheek.*" James B. Dixon tells me
that "the male has a very pleasing ventriloquial song, which he sings
during the mating season and which can be heard only a very short
distance."

Field marks.— A flat, crestless, blue head, a pale brown back, blue
wings and tail, and a white-streaked throat will serve to distinguish this
species from the much darker crested jays of the *stelleri* group. Its jay-
like behavior and its loud voice make it conspicuously different from
other birds.

Enemies.—Jays are probably sometimes attacked by predatory birds
and animals, but they are fairly well able to take care of themselves and
defend their eggs and young. Man seems to be their bitter enemy.
Large numbers are shot every year by farmers and fruit growers where
the jays are damaging their crops. Organized jay shoots are popular
in some parts of California, under the pretext of reducing the numbers
of a destructive bird, but largely, too, as a pleasant recreation and an
interesting competition for the shooters; dealers in ammunition also
find it profitable. Dr. Mary M. Erickson (1937) witnessed one of these
shoots and has published an interesting article on it. She says:

Jay shoots have been held in Calaveras County for many years. Two persons
reported that hunts have taken place about once a year during the eleven and
fourteen years they had lived in the vicinity. Two old-time residents said that
occasional shoots had been held thirty or forty years previously. Recently, one
or two shoots a year have been held, usually in the fall, sometimes in the spring,
but the time of year and the number are irregular. The last shoot had been held
on October 20, 1935, when, according to a local newspaper, 1368 jays were killed.
The shoots, at least in recent years, have been conducted as contests between
two teams, and after the count there has been a dinner, or as this year, a barbecue
in which wives and friends shared, at the expense of the losing side.

In the shoot that she witnessed, 398 California jays, 214 Steller's
jays, 1 red-tailed hawk, 1 Cooper's hawk, and 3 sparrow hawks were
brought in. She estimated that an area of approximately 200 square
miles was covered in the hunt, but probably not with systematic thor-
oughness. "On the day before the shoot, fifteen hours were spent by Mr.
Hooper and me in taking a census in three sample areas of typical jay
habitat, and every effort was made to get an accurate count. On this
meagre basis, the population is estimated as one jay, either California or
Steller, for every 5½ acres of suitable habitat, or 118 jays per square
mile of such habitat. * * * In comparison with these figures, an estimate
for Calaveras County of one jay for every 5½ acres, in an acre of
equally good or better habitat, does not seem excessive. Assuming that
only half of the total area is suitable for occupancy by jays, the jay

population of the 200 square miles in which the hunting was most concentrated, would be 11,636. On this basis, the shooting of 612 jays resulted in destruction of about 5 per cent of the jay population."

The shoot in which these 612 jays were killed was at the beginning of the nesting season, when it would have the maximum effect on the breeding population. She reasons that " the shoot held in the fall of 1935 when the population was near its maximum, probably did not eliminate more than 5 per cent of the next *breeding population* [italics mine], even though twice as many were killed, for part of the kill was composed of birds which in time would have been destroyed by natural forces."

Probably this 5 percent reduction in numbers, even if accomplished every year, would have no appreciable effect on the year to year population of jays. For it is a well-known fact that every suitable habitat is filled up to its capacity to support the species; and that the removal of a few individuals makes it just so much easier for others to survive, or to drift in from outside. Natural causes probably eliminate much more than 5 percent of the species each year, but any release of pressure enables the species to expand and fill in the gap. Any attempt at a wholesale and systematic elimination of the California jays, that would be effective, would prove very expensive and would probably not succeed.

DISTRIBUTION

Range.—Western United States and Mexico; not regularly migratory.

The range of the California jay extends **north** to southwestern Washington (Vancouver); southeastern Oregon (Malheur Lake); northern Utah (Ogden); and northern Colorado (Two Bar Springs and Sedalia). **East** to central Colorado (Sedalia and Fountain); northwestern Oklahoma (Kenton); eastern New Mexico (Santa Rosa and Capitan Mountains); western Texas (San Angelo and Kerrville); Coahuila (Sierra Guadalupe and Carneros); San Luis Potosí (Chorcas and Jesús María); Hidalgo (Real del Monte); Veracruz (Perote and Orizaba); and Oaxaca (Coixtlahuaca and Mount Zempoaltepec). **South** to Oaxaca (Mount Zempoaltepec and Ejutla); and southern Baja California (Cape San Lucas). **West** to Baja California (Cape San Lucas, Llano de Yrais, San Ignacio, and San Pedro Mártir Mountains); western California (San Diego, Santa Barbara, San Francisco, Red Bluff, and Mount Shasta); western Oregon (Waldo, Corvallis, and Dayton); and southwestern Washington (Vancouver).

As outlined, the range includes the entire species, of which 10 subspecies are currently recognized. The typical California jay *(Aphelocoma coerulescens californica)* occupies the coastal region of California from

San Francisco Bay south to the Mexican border; the long-tailed jay
(*A. c. immanis*) is found in the interior, from the San Joaquin and
Sacramento Valleys of California north to southern Washington; the
Nicasio jay (*A. c. oocleptica*) is found in the coast region of northern
California; Belding's jay (*A. c. obscura*) is found mainly in the Upper
Austral Zone of northwestern Baja California; Xantus's jay (*A. c.
hypoleuca*) occupies the Cape district of Baja California; Woodhouse's
jay (*A. c. woodhousei*) is found from southeastern Oregon and the
central Rocky Mountain region south to southwestern Texas and southeastern California; the Texas jay (*A. c. texana*) is found in central
Texas south to the Davis Mountains, and probably to northern Coahuila;
the blue-gray jay (*A. c. grisea*), occupies the Sierra Madre region of
southern Chihuahua and Durango; Sumichrast's jay (*A. c. sumichrasti*),
is found in the southeastern parts of the Mexican tableland, chiefly in
the states of Veracruz, Puebla, Tlaxcala, and Oaxaca; while the blue-
cheeked jay (*A. c. cyanotis*) occupies the Mexican Plateau from the
states of Mexico and Hidalgo north into Coahuila and Durango. There
is almost endless intergradation between some of these races. The
desert California jay (*A. c. cactophila*) occurs in central Baja California.

Egg dates.—California: 160 records, March 10 to July 11; 80
records, April 6 to 30, indicating the height of the season.

Mexico: 22 records, March 20 to June 24; 11 records, April 20 to
May 16.

Oregon: 4 records, April 20 to June 4.

Texas: 28 records, March 14 to May 18; 10 records, March 30 to
May 8.

WOODHOUSE'S JAY

Arizona: 9 records, April 5 to June 6.

New Mexico: 8 records, April 19 to May 27.

Utah: 26 records, April 6 to May 20; 14 records, April 25 to May 3.

SANTA CRUZ JAY

Santa Cruz Island: 27 records, February 6 to May 16; 13 records,
March 27 to April 7.

APHELOCOMA COERULESCENS OBSCURA Anthony

BELDING'S JAY

Belding's jay now seems to be recognized as a valid race of the
coerulescens species, inhabiting northwestern Baja California as far
south as latitude 30° N. It was named by A. W. Anthony (1889) and

described as "differing from *A. californica* in much darker colors and weaker feet." It was accepted by the A. O. U. committee in the 1910 and the 1931 Check-lists, and by Ridgway (1904), regardless of the fact that it is practically identical in coloration and size with the California jays found in the southern half of the coast region of California, though darker and smaller than the long-tailed jay *(immanis)* found in the interior of California, as shown by Swarth (1918). Mr. Swarth's remarks on the subject are worth quoting in full, as they throw some light on the status of this race. In his study of this genus, he says:

The present treatment of the races of the California jay differs from that in most recent literature covering the subject (e.g., A. O. U. *Check-list*, 1910, p. 225; Ridgway, 1904, pp. 327-331) in that it does not recognize the subspecies *obscura*. This race was described by Anthony (1889, p. 75) from specimens taken in the San Pedro Martir Mountains, Lower California. In a subsequent paper (1893, p. 239) the same writer asserts that birds from the San Pedro Martir Mountains and from San Diego County, California, are indistinguishable, and for some years past the name *obscura* has been generally used to cover the bird of the San Diegan region of California. * * * Comparison of series from these points, however, with specimens from various coastal localities as far north as San Francisco Bay (including the vicinity of Monterey, the type locality of *californica*), shows that all belong to the same race, that there are no characters serving to distinguish specimens from these several places. Hence the name *obscura* must be considered a synonym of *californica*.

Aphelocoma californica obscura was described as a smaller and darker colored bird than *A. c. californica*. Perpetuation of this error may have occurred through comparison of southern California specimens with others from the Sacramento Valley or the Sierra Nevada, in the belief that the latter were representative of typical *californica*. This assumption is wrong, however, and although jays from certain sections of California may readily be distinguished as, respectively, larger and paler, or smaller and darker, true *californica* and *obscura* both fall into the latter category.

It is significant, also, that Mr. Anthony (1893), in his subsequent paper, appears in doubt about the status of this race, for he says; "It seems, however, from the series now on hand as if *obscura* would have to be reduced to a synonym of *californica*."

The San Pedro Mártir Mountains have produced so many new subspecies, five described by Mr. Anthony (1889) and a number more by others, that it seems worth while to quote his description of them:

About one hundred and fifty miles south of the United States boundary, and midway between the Pacific Ocean and Gulf of California, lies a high range of mountains, which is marked upon the later maps of the peninsula as 'San Pedro Martir.' The region embraces a series of small ranges which rise from an elevated *mesa*, having a mean elevation of about 8,000 feet, and an extent of sixty by twenty miles. In these mountains are born the only streams that this part of the peninsula affords, and an abundance of pine timber is found throughout the region. Many of the ranges on the eastern side of the San Pedro Martir rise to an elevation of 11,000 feet, or even, in one or two places, to 12,000 (?) feet.

Arising as the region does from the dry, barren hills of the lower country to an elevation higher than any other on the peninsula or in Southern California, and presenting in its alpine vegetation and clear mountain streams features so different from the dry manzanita and sage-covered hills of the surrounding country, it is not unnatural to suppose that its animal life would be found to differ in some respects from that of the surrounding hills.

Mr. Anthony found this jay ranging up to 10,000 feet in these mountains. He says nothing about the habits of the bird, and nothing seems to be published on the subject elsewhere.

The measurements of 12 eggs average 27.8 by 20.8 millimeters; the eggs showing the four extremes measure 29.2 by 21.1, 26.4 by 20.6. and 26.8 by 20.2 millimeters.

APHELOCOMA COERULESCENS CACTOPHILA Huey
DESERT CALIFORNIA JAY

Laurence M. Huey (1942) gave the above names to the jays of this species found in the central portion of the peninsula of Baja California. In his description of it, he says that it "is closest to *A. c. hypoleuca* of the Cape District of Lower California. From that form it differs in the general tone of the back, which is darker, more slaty; also the under-parts are not as white as are those of *hypoleuca*, having a faint wash of gray color which is more highly exemplified in *Aphelocoma californica* [=*coerulescens*] *obscura* from the northernmost part of the peninsula and in the races farther north in upper California. The bib, or throat, and sides of neck are of a darker shade on both their blue and dusky aspects than are those of *hypoleuca*, and lighter than those of *obscura*."

Of its range, he says: "From near latitude 29° 20′, south over the width of the peninsula to the vicinity of Mulejé, on the gulf coast near latitude 27°. On the Pacific slope the range extends farther south, latitude 25° 40′ being reached before intergradation takes places."

This subspecies seems to be strictly intermediate in characters between the race to the northward of it and that to the southward of it, which might be expected in the intermediate territory that it occupies.

APHELOCOMA COERULESCENS HYPOLEUCA Ridgway
XANTUS'S JAY

HABITS

In the Lower Austral and Arid Tropical Zones of the southern half of Lower California, south of latitude 28° or 29° N., we find this smaller and paler form of the California jay. Not only is it decidedly smaller than the more northern forms of the species, but also the blue portions of its plumage are a lighter and more clearly azure blue, the under parts are more purely white, and the bill and feet are relatively larger.

William Brewster (1902) writes: "This, the only Jay known to inhabit the Cape Region, is very common and generally distributed there, being found almost everywhere from the sea-coast to the tops of the highest mountains. About La Paz it nests in March, but the birds seen by Mr. Frazar on the Sierra de la Laguna in May and early June were in flocks and showed no signs of having bred that season or of being about to breed. They probably leave the mountains before the beginning of winter and seek more sheltered haunts in the valleys and foothills at lower elevations, for Mr. Frazar did not find a single individual on the Sierra de la Laguna during his second visit, in the latter part of November, 1887."

Griffing Bancroft (1930) says of its haunts: "The habitat of these jays is arboreal associations other than those of the oases. The level country adjoining San Lucas Lagoon in places is heavily overgrown with mesquite and palo verde. The small cañons in the mountains support scattered trees. The large valleys are frequently dotted with them, especially where moisture is not too far beneath the surface. The riparian associations are almost uniformly accompanied by the taller growths. Within these limitations *hypoleuca* is common, for a jay." He also writes to me that he found it "most abundant in the vast mangrove swamps of Magdalena Bay, but did not observe it elsewhere in the mangroves."

Nesting.—Although eggs were collected by Xantus as early as 1860, Walter E. Bryant (1889) was the first to describe a nest, as follows: "A single nest of this new variety was found by myself a few miles southward from San Ignacio on April 12, 1889. The nest was built about three meters high in a green acacia near the trail. The female was sitting, and did not fly until preparations for climbing the tree had commenced. The nest was in quite an exposed situation amongst scant twigs on a horizontal branch. It is composed of small loosely laid dry twigs, and a shallow receptacle lined with fibre and horsehair."

Mr. Bancroft (1930) says of the nesting "The breeding habits of the Xantus Jay, however, are unlike those of the other races of its family, partly through choice and partly from necessity. Nearly all the nests we found were in the arrow tree whose dense growth of leaves afforded a maximum of concealment. The nest is usually in the heart of the foliage, six to ten feet above the ground. It consists of a foundation of fine twigs which support a semispherical cup. The foundation may be scanty or it may be quite pretentious, according to the requirements of its location. The cup is thin and neatly woven. It is composed of fine rootlets, tree yucca fibres, or cow-hair. It may be of one material only or the three may be used together. It is stiff enough to maintain its shape; the foundation merely serves to hold it in place."

Nesting dates seem to differ considerably in different parts of the peninsula, for J. Stuart Rowley (1935) says: "My notes show that on the last of April along the shore of Concepcion Bay on the Gulf, many nests of this jay were found, and without exception all contained newly hatched young. Then, after crossing the peninsula to the Llano de Yrais on the pacific slope, no nests were found occupied, but young were flying about in nearly full plumage (specimen of such juvenal collected there). When we reached Miraflores, in the Cape district, nesting activities were just beginning and from May 10 to 19, inclusive, at this locality eight sets of two eggs each and five sets of three eggs were taken. * * * To the northward, at San Ignacio, only one nest was found to hold even eggs, three fresh being taken on April 27; the majority of birds were apparently just building here."

One of the sets, now in the Doe collection, was taken by Mr. Rowley from a nest placed in the center of cardon growth 6 feet up.

Eggs.—Two or three eggs seem to be the usual complement for Xantus's jay, and oftener two than three constitute a full set. Mr. Rowley (1935) located over 50 occupied nests and never found more than three eggs or young in a nest, and he thinks three are "rather uncommon."

Major Bendire (1895) says that the two eggs in the United States National Museum, taken by Xantus in 1860, "have a pale bluish-green ground color and are spotted over the entire surface with small markings of grayish brown, which are slightly heavier about the larger end of the egg. The eggs are ovate in shape and slightly glossy."

Mr. Bancroft (1930) says that "laying begins in April, two eggs being the usual number. Reversing the customary order, as the season progresses the size of the clutch increases until, in June, we found three more often than two. That number represents the largest set of which we have knowledge. The eggs differ from those of any other subspecies of the California Jay in averaging a very much greener background and in being marked with decidedly finer spots."

Mr. Doe tells me that the eggs referred to above are "very dark emerald green, obscurely spotted with gray brown."

The measurements of 50 eggs average 27.2 by 20.2 millimeters; the eggs showing the four extremes measure **30.1** by **22.8**, 23.4 by 17.8, and 26.8 by **13.5** millimeters.

APHELOCOMA COERULESCENS WOODHOUSEI (Baird)

WOODHOUSE'S JAY

PLATE 21

HABITS

Woodhouse's jay has long stood on our list as a distinct species and was originally described as such. There are some reasons for thinking that the original designation may be more nearly correct than the present concept as a subspecies. Mr. Swarth (1918) says: "Compared with any of the subspecies of *Aphelocoma californica, A. woodhousei* differs in coloration and in proportions of bill. The blue areas are dull and pale, the back is strongly suffused with bluish gray, and the under parts and throat with gray; the under tail coverts are blue. The general effect of these modifications is to produce a much more uniformly and inconspicuously marked bird than *A. californica.* The bill of *woodhousei* averages longer than in *californica,* but is more slender." Believing this jay to be a distinct species, he says: "The range of the Woodhouse jay in California is restricted to scattered and disconnected areas of Upper Sonoran in the Inyo region, the arid desert section of the eastern part of the state. In the late summer and fall it is a visitant to the eastern slope of the Sierra Nevada, where it comes into direct contact with *A. c. immanis,* but it apparently does not breed in this section." He claims further that, although there is intergradation between the three California races where their habitats meet, "nothing of the sort can be detected along the boundary between *immanis* and *woodhousei";* and he says that "comparison of three California specimens at hand in fresh fall plumage, with individuals taken at the same season in southern Arizona, shows no difference between the two birds."

According to the 1931 Check-list, the wide range of Woodhouse's jay extends from "southeastern Oregon, southern Idaho, and southern Wyoming south to southeastern California (east of Sierra Nevada), southern Arizona, southern New Mexico, and southwestern Texas."

Woodhouse's jay is a bird of the foothills and the lower slopes of the mountains. In Arizona we found it rather local in its distribution, mainly in the oak belts about the bases of the mountains and on the steep, brush-covered hillsides; we never saw it below 3,000 or above 7,500 feet, but noted it mostly between 5,000 and 6,000 feet. We first saw it about the base of the Mule Mountains, where the blackjack oaks grew thickly in the little valleys and gorges or were scattered over the opener hillsides. About our camp in the foothills of the Dragoon Mountains, where blackjack and other oaks dotted the gently sloping hills and grew more densely in the brush-covered gulches well up into the mountains, these jays were really common. But they were very shy. We frequently saw them flying ahead of us or sailing from one oak to another, with blue wings and tail widespread, or heard their squawking cries, but to shoot one was another matter; a long shot at one on the wing obtained my only specimen.

In New Mexico, according to Mrs. Bailey (1928), this jay is widely distributed "among the nut pines, junipers, and scrub oaks of Upper Sonoran zone." Dr. Coues (1874) says that its preference "is for oak openings, rough, broken hill-sides, covered with patches of juniper, manzañita, and yuccas, brushy ravines and wooded creek-bottoms." Dr. Jean M. Linsdale (1938b) says that, in Nevada, "resident Woodhouse jay was found regularly in small numbers about every locality worked, from a little over 6,000 feet, near the base of the mountains, up to about 9,000 feet on the ridges. Individuals or family groups were found in the thickets of willow and birch along the streams and in the piñons and mountain mahoganies on the adjacent slopes and ridges."

In Colorado these jays range from 6,000 up to 9,000 feet, where Robert B. Rockwell (1907) says that "their favorite haunt is a gulch on an open hillside, which is heavily covered with scrub-oak, service-berry and pinyon, and here they are found in numbers, flitting thru the underbrush and keeping out of sight as much as possible, but continually uttering the coarse, grating cry characteristic of so many of this family."

Nesting.—We did not succeed in finding a nest of Woodhouse's jay in Arizona; they are said to be very well concealed, and probably we overlooked some, which might easily happen, as Robert B. Rockwell (1907) says that "in the location and concealment of the nests they are evidently adepts, as in five years' observations I found but two nests, one of which was unoccupied"; and this was in a locality in western Colorado, where the birds were abundant.

He describes the finding of his nest as follows:

As my pony brushed against a peculiarly thick clump of service-berry I heard a very slight flutter and not seeing a bird fly out, I dismounted and forced my way into the clump. As I did so the bird slipped quietly out on the other side and I caught a fleeting glimpse of her as she flew, barely a foot off the ground, into a nearby bush.

The nest, for such it proved to be, was built near the center of the clump and about four feet from the ground. It was held in place by a thick net-work of small angular twigs and two larger vertical branches none over ⅜ inch in diameter. The only concealment afforded the nest was the thick mat of leaves at the extremity of the branches which formed a sort of canopy about the exterior of the bush, not a leaf being near enough to the nest to afford concealment; but right here is where I discovered the secret of their concealment. The outer structure of course so nearly resembles the network of small twigs in the serviceberry bush that it was difficult to tell where the nest stopped and the twigs began.

The nest itself, which at first appeared to be a rather fragile structure, upon closer examination proved to be a remarkable piece of bird architecture. It was

composed of a platform of very crooked dead twigs, thickly interlaced to form
a basket-like structure, in which the nest proper was firmly placed. The latter,
which was entirely separate from the outer basket was a beautifully woven and
interlaced cup, composed of fine weed stalks on the outside, giving place to fine,
brown, fibrous rootlets toward the interior which was sparingly lined with
horsehair.

In general appearance the exterior was not unlike the nest of the white-rumped
shrike, while the interior or nest proper closely resembled a black-headed gros-
beak's nest. The entire structure, while not particularly artistic, exhibited a
high grade of bird architecture and was remarkably strong and durable.

The nest outside measured about six inches in diameter by six inches in depth,
and the interior structure measured outside 4½ inches in diameter by 2¾ inches
deep; inside 3¾ inches in diameter by 2¼ inches deep.

Dr. Linsdale (1938b) thus records two Nevada nests: "An occupied
nest of this bird was found on June 4, 1932, on the top of a ridge, at
9,000 feet, near Wisconsin Creek (Orr). A jay was seen to slip away
through mountain mahoganies and piñons. About 100 feet from there
and 30 feet down a south-facing slope a nest was found in a piñon.
It was 7 feet above the ground, resting on the outer part of a limb and
supported by small twigs. The outer part of the nest which was 10
inches in diameter was composed of small and medium-sized twigs of
sage brush. The inner part was 5 inches in diameter and 2½ inches
deep. It was composed of fine grass stems and lined with porcupine hair."

The other nest, from which the young had just flown, was found
"in a mountain mahogany, 5 feet above the ground, on the east side of
the tree and on a southeast-facing slope. The nest was about 9 inches
in diameter and was composed of small twigs. The cup was 5 inches
in diameter and an inch deep. It was made of small grass stems and
horsehair."

There are three sets of eggs of Woodhouse's jay in my collection,
all from Utah. Two were placed in sagebushes, one 4 feet and the other
20 inches above ground. The other was placed in a young pine next
to the trunk and about 6 feet from the ground. The construction of the
nests was similar to that of those recorded above from Nevada. Frank
W. Braund tells me that he has a nest in his collection, taken on a
cactus desert in Arizona, that was 4 feet up in a white cholla cactus.
There are two nests in the Thayer collection in Cambridge; one was
5 feet up in a scrub oak, lined with black horsehair; the other was 6
feet from the ground in a cedar, lined with fine grass.

Eggs.—Woodhouse's jay lays anywhere from three to six eggs to a
set, but oftener four or five. They are mostly ovate in shape, with
variations toward short-ovate or elliptical-ovate. They are only slightly
glossy. The ground color is light bluish green, "bluish glaucous," "pea
green," or pale "sage green." They are more or less evenly marked

with various shades of brown, pale shades of "ferruginous" or "tawny," in small blotches, spots or fine dots, and sometimes with a few underlying spots of pale drabs.   The measurements of 50 eggs average 27.8 by 20.4 millimeters; the eggs showing the four extremes measure 31.0 by 21.5 and 24.3 by 19.2 millimeters.

Young.—Bendire (1895) says that "incubation lasts about sixteen days, both parents probably assisting; and I think that but one brood is raised in a season." Dr. Linsdale (1938b) found a family of four young birds near one of the nests described above.   "Both parents," he says, "were present, and they were feeding the young ones. During this process the adult made no sound, but feeding calls were uttered by the young.   Once when a young one was preparing to fly to one of its parents following the other, a slight movement by the observer resulted in a sharp call from a parent jay.   Following this the young bird remained perfectly quiet for about a minute.   It then began to move about, but another warning call caused it again to become silent."

Mr. Rockwell (1907) says: "The young of the year are not very much in evidence until they are well matured, but during August and September by which time the young are all able to take care of themselves the birds are particularly conspicuous and noisy. * * * As soon as the young birds are able to travel there seems to be a sort of vertical migration, during which large numbers of the birds ascend a few thousand feet into the heavier timbered country."   But, he continues, "this vertical movement does not affect the entire number of the species."

Plumages.—The plumage changes of Woodhouse's jay are apparently similar to those of the California jay.   But the juvenal plumage seems to be somewhat different, which Ridgway (1904) describes as follows: "Pileum plain mouse gray; rest of upper parts (except wings and tail) plain brownish gray or deep drab-gray; an indistinct superciliary line, or series of streaks, of white; general color of under parts dull light brownish gray, paler on chin, throat, chest, and abdomen, deeper and more brownish on upper portion of breast, against pale grayish jugular area; wings and tail as in adults, but smaller wing-coverts gray and lesser coverts indistinctly tipped with the same."

Food.—Like its neighbors and relatives in California, Woodhouse's jay is quite omnivorous, and its food covers the same wide range. Where oaks and nut pines, or pinyons, are abundant, the fruits of these trees evidently make up the largest percentage of the food of this jay at the proper seasons. During the summer it is said to feed somewhat on grasshoppers and other insects. Mrs. Bailey (1928) says that "in some of the few stomachs examined, three-quarters of the food consists of pinyon nuts.   Acorns, wheat, ground beetles, grasshoppers, caterpillars, and ants are also eaten." This jay probably has the same bad habit as other jays of robbing small birds of their eggs and young, though perhaps not to such an extent as the California jay. Mr. Rockwell (1907) says: "I have never seen any indications of this and judging from the good feeling which apparently exists between these birds and other species I am inclined to think that their depredations are not as extensive as those of others of the jay family."

Behavior.—Based on my rather limited experience with it in the field, I should say that this is the shiest, most secretive, and most elusive of all the jays that I have seen in life. Even in its favorite haunts, where these jays are common, one is seldom seen except at a distance or as a fleeting blue shadow disappearing through the underbrush. We often saw one perched in an alert attitude on the top of some blackjack oak; but, if we attempted to approach, it bobbed its head and body, gave its harsh cry of alarm, and bounded off to a more distant tree; within about 50 yards was as near as we could come to it on the more open slopes. In the ravines and gulches, where the trees and bushes grew more thickly, we could get a closer view of it, but only for an instant, as it made an abrupt dive downward from its observation perch and faded away through the brushy tangle, not to be seen again.

The facile pen of Dr. Coues (1874) describes its flight and other movements much better than I can, as follows: "The flight of the bird is firm and direct. When going far, and high over head, in flocks, the wing beats are regular and continuous; among trees and bushes, the short flights are more dashing and unsteady, performed with a vigorous flap or two and a sailing with widely-spread wings and tail. The tail is often jerked in the shorter flights, especially those of ascent or the reverse, and its frequent motion, when the bird is not flying, is like that seen in *Pipilo* or *Mimus*. Among the branches the bird moves with agile hops, like all true Jays, and its movements when on the ground have the same buoyant ease; it never walks, like Maximilian's and other Crows."

Dr. Walter P. Taylor writes to me: "Mr. Colton, proprietor of a store at Grand Canyon, has a tame jay that he has been feeding for four years. He whistles in a certain way, and the bird flies either direct to his hand or to a nearby tree, from which it then flies to his hand. The jay stands on the hand, picking up pinyon nuts until it gets five or less. Five is the maximum. It then flies off down over the edge of the Grand Canyon with its load, returning, if called, about 10 minutes later. It ate not only from Colton's hand but also from Gilchrist's and mine."

Voice.—Dr. Coues (1874) gives the following attractive account of the vocal ability of this jay:

The ordinary note is a harsh scream, indefinitely repeated with varying tone and measure; it is quite noticeably different from that of either Maximilian's or Steller's, having a sharp, wiry quality lacking in these. It is always uttered when the bird is angry or alarmed, and consequently is oftener heard by the naturalist; but there are several other notes. If the bird is disporting with his fellows, or leisurely picking acorns, he has a variety of odd chuckling or chattering syllables, corresponding to the absurd talk of our Blue Jay under the same circumstances. Sometimes again, in the spring-time, when snugly hidden in the heart of a cedar bush with his mate, whom he has coaxed to keep him company, he modulates his harsh voice with surprising softness to express his gallant intention; and if one is standing quite near, unobserved, he will hear the blandishments whispered and cooed almost as softly as a Dove's. The change, when the busy pair find they are discovered, to the ordinary scream, uttered by wooer and wooed together, is startling.

Field marks.—Superficially, Woodhouse's jay looks and acts much like the California jay, and its voice is similar; but its coloration is much more uniform, appearing largely dull bluish gray, with less contrast between the brown of the back and the blue of the wings and tail. The under parts are much grayer, less whitish, and the blue of the flight feathers is duller.

Fall.—This jay is supposed to be nonmigratory, and it probably is mainly resident throughout the year over most of its range. Extensive fall wanderings in search of a food supply might easily be mistaken for true migration. Aiken and Warren (1914) report: "When Aiken was at his ranch on Turkey Creek in October, 1873, a migratory flight of Woodhouse's Jays was seen. They were not flying high, but making short flights from point to point, always in a southerly direction. It was estimated that there were at least 500 scattered over from 50 to 100 acres of ground, as they kept lighting after their short flights. After this flight had passed the species seemed to be fully as common during the following winter as it had been during the summer. The flight had undoubtedly come from a more northern locality. Local birds appear to be non-migratory and are found in the same localities throughout the year." Mr. Rockwell (1907) writes: "With the first frosts they congregate in small scattered flocks and perform whatever migration may be credited to them, which I am inclined to think amounts to very little, usually before the first big storm; but climatic conditions seem to have very little effect upon them, food supply alone being responsible for their migratory movements."

Winter.—Referring to their winter habits in Colorado, Mr. Rockwell (1907) says: "When the winter coat of white has entirely covered their food on the bleak hillsides, they return to their winter haunts nearer the inhabited sections where the waste from barn-yard and granary affords an abundant food supply until spring comes again. * * *

"During the winter months they are found in large numbers in the brush-clad gulches and ravines in the lower part of their range and usually not far from cultivated ground, where they feed largely upon grain and seed in the barn-yards, feedlots and fields. During this period they become very tame if not molested and will even occasionally slip into an open kitchen door in quest of some tempting morsel."

APHELOCOMA COERULESCENS TEXANA Ridgway
TEXAS JAY
HABITS

This race seems to be confined to central and central-western Texas, from Kerr and Edwards Counties to the Davis Mountains. It is a connecting link between *A. c. woodhousei* and *A. c. cyanotis,* intergrading with the former to the northward and with the latter to the southward. The blue-eared jay *(cyanotis)* was formerly supposed to occur casually in Texas, but subsequent investigation by Dr. Oberholser (1917) has shown this to be an error, and this race was dropped from our list.

The Texas jay differs from Woodhouse's jay in having the chest and lower throat very indistinctly, if at all, streaked with blue, by the paler gray of the under parts, and by the pure white under tail coverts, the latter being blue in *woodhousei.*

The type of this race was collected near the head of the Nueces River, in Edwards County, Tex., presumably by Howard Lacey (1903), who says: "In December, 1894, when deer hunting on the head of the Nueces Ricer, I shot and skinned one of these birds and sent it to the professor [H. P. Attwater]. He sent it on, I believe, to the late Captain Bendire, and it is now the type of the species." Attwater was credited with collecting the specimen.

Mr. Lacey was, evidently, the first to collect the eggs of this jay; in April 1898, near the head of one of the main branches of the Guadaloupe River. He says of the locality:

Numerous little valleys run down toward the rivers, becoming steeper and steeper as they approach the larger creek, and often forming narrow canyons with high bluffs on both sides. Large trees are not numerous, but the whole face of the country is covered with clumps of shin oak and scrubby live oak. In these clumps we found the jays' nests, generally placed near the outside of a thicket, at from four to six feet from the ground, and often conspicuous from quite a distance, as the shrubs were only beginning to put out their leaves at that time. As a rule the birds were setting and one nest contained young nearly ready to leave it. The nests were composed of an outer basket of twigs not very firmly put together, and lined rather neatly with grass, hair, and small root fibres. They were rather more bulky than mockingbirds' nests and the inner nest was saucer shaped rather than cup shaped. Most of them were placed in shin oaks, but some few were in live oaks, and I have since found several in cedar bushes. The birds are not so noisy as the common blue jay and are particularly silent when near their nests.

They have a habit of hopping upwards through a thicket from twig to twig until they arrive at the top of it, when they fly off with four or five harsh squeaks to the next clump of brush, into which they dive headlong.

Austin Paul Smith (1916) has this to say about the Texas jay:

This very local form keeps well within the Upper Sonoran, except on occasions when it descends to the streams to drink, mostly after dry weather has set in; but it quickly returns to its natural haunt—hillsides covered with a mixed growth of cedar and oak. It was found to congregate in flocks, even during the breeding season which, as Lacey has correctly stated, occupies late March and early April, so perhaps only a portion of its numbers nest annually. The Texan Jay while affecting a varied diet is very fond of the acorns of the Spanish and shin oaks, searching these out and eating them after they have sprouted. Until the plumage of this Jay is much worn, it closely resembles *A. woodhousei*, for the brown on the back is much obscured by a slaty cast in the fresh plumage while many of the adults have the under tail coverts strongly tinged with blue.

The measurements of 44 eggs average 27.0 by 20.4 millimeters; the eggs showing the four extremes measure 31.0 by 21.3, 26.0 by 21.5, 23.4 by 18.7, and 23.6 by 18.6 millimeters.

APHELOCOMA COERULESCENS INSULARIS Henshaw

SANTA CRUZ JAY

HABITS

Santa Cruz Island, one of the Santa Barbara group, off the coast of southern California, has developed this large, handsome, dark-colored jay, which once stood on our list as a full species, though it is evidently very closely related to the mainland forms of the California jay. It is confined entirely, so far as we know, to the island for which it is named. It is larger than the largest race and darker than the darkest race of *californica,* and it has definitely blue under tail coverts, which the neighboring mainland jays of the California species do not have. Mr. Swarth (1918) says: "From *A. woodhousei,* which it resembles in its blue under tail coverts, *insularis* is distinguished by greater size, darker coloration, and (like *A. californica*) in more strongly contrasted markings. * * * The Santa Cruz jay is one of the most sharply differentiated of any of the island species, and it is hard to appreciate the possibility of the development of the form under the given conditions. * * * The most striking feature of the Santa Cruz jay, as compared with the mainland species is its enormous size, so in this case a marked restriction of range, with the consequent probability of inbreeding of closely related individuals has not been productive of the dwarfed stature which such conditions are supposed to engender."

Santa Cruz Island is the only one of the group on which any jays are to be found. It is one of the larger islands, over 20 miles long and up to 5 miles in width at its wider parts; it lies about 21 miles due south across the channel from Santa Barbara on the mainland. It is a rugged, steep, mountainous island, with some of its peaks said to rise from 1,800 to 2,700 feet above sea level. The coast line is irregular and largely precipitous, with few suitable landing places except on the beaches at the mouths of the streams. A. B. Howell (1917) says: "The eastern part is very irregular, barren and almost destitute of water. The western part, however, is, in certain localities, especially near Prisoners Harbor, plentifully besprinkled with forests of Santa Cruz pine, which, in the higher parts, gives a distinctly boreal impression. At the lower edge of the pines are oaks and considerable grass land. The larger canyons are well wooded with a variety of deciduous trees, some of them quite large, and there is good water in many of them."

It was in this latter locality that we landed on June 5, 1914, and spent parts of two days exploring the vicinity of our camp. Here the deep valleys, watered by rocky streams, were well wooded with ancient live oaks, willows, and other deciduous trees and shrubs. There were scattering oaks, or small groves of them on the less exposed portions of the steep hillsides; and the opener hills were covered with wild oats, scattering bushes, and some cactus. But it was in the wooded valleys that we found the main object of our search, the grand Santa Cruz jay. Most of the other birds, towhees, vireos, flycatchers, wrens, warblers, and hummers, were concentrated with the jays in these valleys or canyons. The jays were common enough here, but were rather shy and were oftener heard than seen. We did not explore the pines at the higher elevations, but Mr. Howell (1917) says that these jays "are not equally common over the entire island, but seem to prefer the neighborhood of the pines and heavy brush."

Nesting.—Mr. Howell (1917) writes: "It is truly surprising to note the number of old jays' nests upon the island. These must either last for a greater number of years than is the case elsewhere, or else the birds are in the habit of building extra or dummy nests. The favorite sites seem to be in the tops of the local 'palo fierro' (ironwood) trees, though many were noted in low oaks or large bushes, mostly on the sides of the canyons. Construction is the same as that employed by the mainland form. The latter part of April, 1911, all the females shot had already laid, and I believe that a large majority of them had small young. Two nests that I examined on the 28th were some twenty feet up in ironwoods, and held, respectively, two small young and an addled egg, and three young, half grown."

W. L. Dawson (1923) says:

The Santa Cruz Jay nests early. The last week in March is the height of the season, counting always by fresh eggs. We have found them as early as March

10th. For nesting sites the California live oaks are leading favorites, but the birds nest indifferently throughout the scrub * * * to the tops of the ranges. Manzanita, Christmas berry, hollyleaf cherry, ironwood, mountain mahogany, scrub and Wislizenus oaks, and Monterey pines, all serve as hosts, therefore, with little preference save for shade. Nests, although bulky, sometimes being as large as a crow's, are placed at moderate heights, usually from eight to twelve feet; and are, habitually, so well made that they may be lifted clean of their setting without injury. The jays evidently have assigned beats, or ranges, of mutual adjustment, and they are very loyal to a chosen locality at nesting time. Thus, the nests of succeeding years are grouped in a single tree, or scattered narrowly in a small section of the scrub.

He says that the nest is "a bulky mass of interlaced twigs of live oak tree, into which is set neatly and deeply a cup of coiled rootlets with some admixture of grasses and, rarely, horsehair."

Eggs.—Three or four eggs, rarely five, constitute the full set for this jay. They vary in shape from rounded-ovate nearly to elliptical-ovate but are mostly ovate, with only a slight gloss. They do not show the wide variation in colors exhibited in the eggs of the California jay.

Mr. Dawson (1923) remarks on this subject: "It is in the uniform coloring of the egg that the Santa Cruz Island Jay most surely reveals its isolation, and its consequent inbreeding. The ground color of fresh eggs is a beautiful light bluish-green (microcline green), and this is lightly spotted with olive (Lincoln green to deep grape green). The green element fades quickly, however, so that eggs advanced in incubation are of a pale Niagara green color. Among a dozen sets there are no color variants worth mentioning; nor have I seen a single example of the 'red' type, which is so pleasing a feature of the mainland form."

Dawson's colored plate shows some variation in the size and shape of the markings, in pale olives and light browns; some are finely sprinkled with faint dots, others more clearly marked with small spots, and one has pale olive-brown blotches of fair size. He gives the average measurements of 140 eggs in the Museum of Comparative Zology at 29.0 by 21.3 millimeters; they range in length from 25.4 to 31.7, and in breadth from 19.6 to 22.6 millimeters.

The measurements that I have collected of 50 eggs average 29.2 by 21.6 millimeters; the eggs showing the four extremes measure 32.0 by 21.5, 29.0 by 23.0, 26.2 by 20.6, and 28.5 by 20.5 millimeters.

Plumages.—The plumages and molts of the Santa Cruz jay probably follow the same sequence as in the California jay, to which it is so closely related. The juvenal plumage seems to be only slightly different; Ridgway (1904) describes it as follows: "Pileum, hindneck, auricular and suborbital regions, and sides of chest dull slate color, slightly tinged with dusky blue; back, scapulars, rump, and smaller wing-coverts dark brownish mouse gray; upper tail-coverts dull grayish blue; chin, throat, and median portion of chest white, the last somewhat streaked with gray; under parts of body pale smoke gray, separated from the white of the chest by a narrow collar of bluish slaty, connecting the two slaty areas on sides of chest; under tail-coverts and thighs smoke gray; wings (except smaller coverts) and tail as in adults."

Food.—Practically nothing has been published on the food of this jay, which probably includes the same wide range as that of other jays. Dawson (1923) implies that it is a robber of small birds' nests and that it even invades the poultry yard. As much of its habitat is thinly settled, or entirely uninhabited by human beings, its feeding habits are not of great economic importance.

Behavior.—Its habits suggest those of the mainland forms of the genus.

During the breeding season it is quiet and secretive, but at other times it is bolder and more inquisitive, coming readily in response to the squeaking call and watching the intruder at short range in silence. Pursuing it through the brushy valleys leads to only passing glimpses of it, but its curiosity often leads it to reward the patient waiter.

J. Stuart Rowley writes to me: "It was my good fortune to be able to spend the day of April 18, 1937, on the western side of Santa Cruz Island. Here, in the scrub oak on the hillsides and in the ravines, is the home of this large, dark-blue-colored jay. Since this was my first experience with these jays, I had expected them to behave much like the mainland species. However, they were extremely shy and quiet and would duck down into the bushes as I walked along, remaining hidden from view until I was well beyond them. I was able to collect a nice series of birds by concealing myself in the brush and making a squealing distress sound with my lips on the back of my hand. This procedure brought the birds up promptly, without any voiced protest, but with wide-eyed curiosity.

"I found one nest that day, it being placed about 8 feet up in a scrub oak. When located, no sign of either bird was seen or heard; and, until I had climbed the tree and just reached into the nest, no jays would seem to be in the vicinity. However, when I started taking the four eggs from the nest, both birds burst forth with the most vociferous scolding I have ever had administered. This retiring behavior by a species of jay was a new experience for me. After the nest was reached, their restraint exploded."

Voice.—The various notes of the Santa Cruz jay are much like those of its relatives but rather harsher and suggestive of the notes of Steller's jay.

Dawson (1923) mentions a note that is strikingly like "the *rickety rack rack rack* or *shack shack shack shack shack* of the Magpies." And "exquisite warblings have I heard at a rod's remove, so delicate that a Wren's outburst would have drowned them utterly, but so musical that I had hoped the bird was only tuning his strings in preparation for a rhapsody."

APHELOCOMA SORDIDA ARIZONAE (Ridgway)

ARIZONA JAY

PLATES 21, 22

HABITS

This is the northernmost race of a Mexican species that extends its range into southern Arizona and southwestern New Mexico. Major Bendire (1895) says of its haunts in these localities: "The Arizona Jay is a common resident throughout the oak belt of southern Arizona and New Mexico which generally fringes the foothills of the mountains and ranges well up among the pines. In suitable localities these Jays are very abundant, especially so along the slopes of the Santa Catalina, Huachuca, Santa Rita, and Chiricahua mountains, in southern Arizona, and the ranges adjacent to the Rio Mimbres, in southern New Mexico. They are rarely seen any distance out on the arid plains; but after the breeding season is over small flocks are sometimes met with among the shrubbery of the few water courses, several miles away from their regular habitat."

Around the base of the Huachucas, especially where the mouths of the canyons open out toward the plains, are several large groves, or open parklike forests of large blackjack and other oaks; where the oaks extend upward into the foothills, they form a thicker growth of smaller trees, mixed with scrub oaks and other thick brush. Here, especially among the larger and opener growth at the lower levels, we found Arizona jays abundant and noisy, traveling about in groups of four to eight birds all through the nesting season. I was glad to make the acquaintance of this interesting jay, the only jay I have met that shows a tendency toward communal nesting and gregarious behavior. We saw none above 7,000 feet and found them most abundant from the base of the mountains up to 6,000 feet. W. E. D. Scott (1886) found them in the Santa Catalinas between the altitudes of 3,000 and 7,000 feet.

Nesting.—In the region referred to above we found numerous nests of the Arizona jay; nests containing eggs were found during the first three days of May, and nests containing young were seen on May 1 and May 11. On May 1 we found two occupied nests in one tree, one with eggs and one with young; in both cases the parent bird was on the nest, incubating the eggs or brooding the young. I climbed the tree to examine the nests, which caused both birds to leave and begin scolding; as soon as I retired, the bird returned immediately to the nest containing eggs, though it held but two, an obviously incomplete set. Others have seen these jays sitting on the completed nests some time before the eggs were laid.

The nests that we examined were all placed in oaks at heights ranging from 10 to 25 feet above ground, though my companion, F. C. Willard, told me that he found one as low as 6 feet in a scrub oak, and another at 9 feet. The nests were all very much alike, quite bulky and conspicuous. The base of the nest usually consists of a rough, scraggly platform, or basket, of large, coarse sticks, held in place by their crooked shapes, mixed with a mass of smaller twigs. In this basket and strongly supported by it, is a well-made cup of closely woven rootlets, lined with fine dry grasses, or with horsehair or cow's hair. Although apparently loosely built, the foundation is really very firm, and the whole structure can be removed without falling apart.

The nests we found were placed at various situations in the tree, usually on a horizontal branch or an upright crotch, but occasionally out near the end of a branch. We always saw several birds in the vicinity of the nests, and Mr. Willard told me that they live in loose colonies on a communal basis, and that three or four birds often assist in the building of a nest. Most of the nests we saw were not far apart, and all the jays in the group showed their mutual interest by flocking, with loud cries of protest, about any nest that was being investigated.

Mr. Scott's (1886) experience with the nesting of this jay is interesting and is thus related by him:

About the last of February, 1885, I noticed the birds mating, and on the 16th of March found a nest, apparently completed, but containing no eggs. There were at least half-a-dozen pairs of the birds in the immediate vicnity, but a close search did not reveal any other nests. The nest was built in an oak sapling about ten feet from the ground, and is composed of dry rootlets laid very loosely in concentric rings, and with little or no attempt at weaving together. There is nothing like a lining, and the walls of the structure have an average thickness of about three-quarters of an inch. The interior diameter is five inches, and the greatest interior depth an inch and three-quarters. The whole fabric recalls to mind a rather deep saucer. The nest was not built in a crotch, but where several small branches and twigs leave the large branch (an inch and a half in diameter) which forms the main support. All the other nests I have seen resemble this one so closely that this description will answer for them.

I did not visit the nest again until the 25th of the month, and was then rather surprised to find another nest, precisely similar to the first, only about a foot away from it on the same branch, further out from the main stem of the tree. The female bird was sitting on the nest first built, and remained there until I was about to put my hand upon her; no eggs had been laid. * * *

On the 1st of April I again visited the two nests first mentioned, and though the old bird was sitting on the nest earliest completed, it still contained no eggs. A visit to the same spot on April 7 was rewarded by finding five fresh eggs in this nest. * * * The other nest did not, at this time or afterward, contain eggs; though I visited it for several weeks, at intervals of five or six days.

The striking features developed by these observations are, first, the long period after the nest was built before eggs were laid (the nest being evidently complete on March 16, and having no eggs until later than April 1), though the old birds, one or the other, were sitting on the empty structure; and, second, the building of another nest in every way identical with the first, and very close to it, which was of no obvious use, for I never noticed either of the old birds sitting on it, as was so constantly their habit in the nest close by.

Lt. H. C. Benson, according to Bendire (1895), found this jay breeding abundantly in the vicinity of Fort Huachuca, Ariz., during April and May 1887. "All of the nests taken by him, some thirty in number, were placed in oaks, from 12 to 30 feet from the ground, usually about 15 feet high, being generally only moderately concealed." The Major describes one of his nests as follows: "It is composed outwardly of small sticks and twigs; next comes a layer of fine rootlets, well woven together—this mass is alone over half an inch in thickness—and, finally, the inner nest is lined with a liberal supply of horsehair. It is well constructed, and measures about 10 inches across externally by 4 inches in depth; the inner diameter is about 4½ by 2 inches in depth."

A nest I collected in Arizona, and afterwards presented to the United States National Museum, is somewhat larger than those described above and apparently was made with larger sticks. The outside diameter is 13 inches, or 18 inches, if the longest extruding twigs are included; the outside height is 6 inches; and the largest sticks in the foundation are from ⅕ to ¼ of an inch in diameter, rather large and long for a jay to handle.

Eggs.—The number of eggs in a set varies from four to seven; perhaps three sometimes constitute a full set; four is the commonest number, and five is not a rare number. In the United States National Museum there are 34 sets, with only one set of six and one of seven among them. The eggs are unique among jays' eggs, in being entirely unspotted. They vary in shape from ovate to elongate-ovate and are somewhat glossier than the eggs of other jays. They have been said to closely resemble eggs of the robin and the crissal thrasher, but they are larger than either of these birds' eggs and of a somewhat different color, greener than either. Bendire (1895) calls the color glaucous green. I should call it "Niagara green." The measurements of 136 eggs in the United States National Museum average 30.28 by 22.26 millimeters; the eggs showing the four extremes measure 35.1 by 22.1, 28.7 by 24.6, 26.9 by 21.6, and 30.5 by 20.3 millimeters.

Young.—Bendire (1895) says that "but one brood appears to be raised in a season, and incubation lasts about sixteen days." Whether both sexes assist in incubation and in the care of the young does not seem to have been stated, but probably the care of the young, at least, devolves on both. Swarth (1904) says that "soon after the first of June young birds begin to appear, and by the middle of the month are very much in evidence everywhere in the oak region; first sitting in the trees squalling to be fed, but very soon descending to the ground and rustling for themselves."

Dr. Walter P. Taylor tells me that he once "saw an adult feed a full-grown juvenal by regurgitation."

Plumages.—I have seen only small naked young, none with natal down. The young bird in juvenal plumage is not strikingly different from the adult in general appearance, though less blue above the browner below. The top and sides of the head are dark gray, with hardly a trace of blue; the rest of the upper parts are lighter and browner gray, including the lesser wing coverts; the rest of the wings and tail are as in the adult: the under parts are dull grayish brown; the base of the upper mandible and most of the lower mandible are yellowish horn-color in the dry skin, probably flesh-color in life. I have seen specimens in this plumage from June 2 to August 2, when the postjuvenal molt begins; this molt involves the contour feathers, but not the wings and tail; it is sometimes completed in August and sometimes not until October, but I have seen young birds in fresh, first winter plumage in September. The first winter plumage is worn until the first postnuptial molt the following summer; it can always be recognized by the yellowish base of the lower mandible, which persists through the winter and spring; I have seen it as late as May. Furthermore, young birds are always duller colored than adults, less blue above and browner below, with hardly a trace of blue on the breast; the wings and tails are also much worn by spring. Young birds become fully adult, in plumage, at their first postnuptial molt in August, but I think that some are able to breed in their first winter plumage.

Adults, with their bright blue plumage and wholly black bills, have a complete postnuptial molt, between August and October. I have seen them in worn plumage from June to August, and in wholly fresh plumage in September.

Food.—Major Bendire (1895) says: "Their food consists of grass-hoppers and insects of various kinds, animal matter when obtainable, wild fruits, seeds, and especially acorns. The latter probably form the bulk of their subsistence throughout the greater portion of the year. In the Suharita Pass, between the Santa Catalina and the Rincon mountains, near Tucson, Arizona, I noticed about twenty feeding on the fig-like fruit of the suahara, of which, like many other birds, they seemed to be vary fond."

Mr. Swarth (1904) writes: "Acorns form a staple article of diet with these birds, and they can be seen everywhere under the oak trees searching for their favorite food, progressing by means of strong, easy hops; and poking under sticks and stones, eating what they can, and hiding more for future use. On finding an acorn, a retreat is made to some near-by limb or boulder, where the prize is held between the two feet, and opened by a few well directed blows."

Mrs. Bailey (1928) adds to the list of insects eaten "beetles, true bugs, gray tree moths, and alfalfa weevils." And I once saw one at a tent caterpillar's nest, picking out and eating the caterpillars. In their fall and winter wanderings, Arizona jays come readily to feeding stations and become quite tame. Mr. Scott (1886) says that "a bone or piece of meat hung in a tree that shades my house, induced daily visits as long as the severer weather of the past year lasted." Earl R. Forrest has sent me some fine photographs (pl. 21) of these jays that came regularly to his feeding station at Oracle, Ariz. Doubtless Arizona jays, like other jays, sometimes rob the nests of small birds and eat the eggs or young, but very little positive evidence of this has been published. It apparently does little, if any, harm to cultivated fruits, or other human interests; it helps to reforest barren areas by planting acorns; and it destroys some harmful insects; its economic status is neutral, or perhaps beneficial. Dr. Taylor tells me that they do some damage to deer carcasses, or other meat hung up outdoors and unprotected; he saw them also eating and carrying off sausages that he had thrown out.

Behavior.—The Arizona jay is one of the most interesting birds of the family, unique in more ways than one. It is the only one of our jays that is markedly gregarious at all seasons, traveling about in scattered flocks of 6 to 20 or more birds; even in the breeding season it lives under semicommunal conditions, with mutual interest in all the nests in the community, helping to build and defend its neighbors' nests and young, shrieking loud invectives at the intruder, with much bobbing of heads and twitching of tails. All this is in marked contrast with the solitary and secretive habits of other jays during the breeding season. Mr. Swarth (1904) writes of its behavior:

Noisy, fussy and quarrelsome as all the jays are, I know of no other species which possesses to such an eminent degree the quality of prying into all manner of things which do not concern it, and of making such a nuisance of itself in general, on the slightest provocation or on none at all, as the Arizona Jay does. * * * A Red-tail or Swainson Hawk sitting on some limb, furnishes a little excitement until he removes to some quieter locality; but the crowning joy of all is to find some wretched fox or wild cat quietly ensconced on some broad, sheltered, oak limb. In such a case the one that finds the unhappy victim takes care to let every jay within half a mile know from his outcry that there is some excitement on hand; and it is nothing unusual to see thirty or forty birds gathered about the object of their aversion, letting him know in no undecided terms just what their opinion of him is. It is a curious sight also to see a dozen or more gathered around some large snake, which they seem to fear nearly as much as they hate. On one occasion I had an excellent opportunity of watching about twenty Arizona Jays protesting at the presence of rather a large rattlesnake which was leisurely travelling down a dry watercourse which passed our camp. The jays seemed imbued with a wholesome fear of their wicked looking antagonist, and though they surrounded it, kept at respectful distance; they were not as noisy as they often are, but kept uttering low querulous cries, quite different from their usual outbursts. Some of the boldest lit a short distance from the snake and strutted before it in a most curious fashion, head and body held bolt upright, and the tail pressed down on the ground until about a third of it was dragging. * * * Besides his vocal outbursts, the Arizona Jay makes when flying a curious fluttering noise with his wings, loud and distinct enough to be heard some little distance producing a curious effect; especially when, as often happens, a troop of them comes swooping down some steep hill side to the bottom of the canyon. Though wary and cunning to a marked degree, so that it is usually impossible to get within gun shot of them, still their curiosity leads to their destruction; for it is a simple matter for the collector, by hiding behind a bush and making any squeaking or hissing noise, to get all the specimens desired.

Bendire (1895) says: "Their flight appears to me far less laborious than that of the California Jay. It reminds me of that of some of our Raptores, rising now high in the air, partly closing their wings, and then darting suddenly down, then up again, and repeating these movements for some time."

Voice.—Herbert Brandt (1940) records the call of the Arizona jay as "a rather rasping, nasal 'wait-wait-wait', given as rapidly, and in such a key, as the occasion may warrant." My own brief field notes record a loud and incessant alarm note sounding like *wack, wack, wack;* I have also heard a soft, cooing note, like *cŏot, cŏot, cŏot,* in a conversational tone. Dr. Taylor writes to me that "one conspicuous call-note is a *weent! weenk! weenk!,* with rising inflection."

Field marks.—Within its limited range in the United States, there is no other bird with which this bird is likely to be confused. It is a large jay, much larger than its neighbor, Woodhouse's jay. It has a dull-blue head, bluish-gray or dull-blue back, wings, and tail, and bluish-gray or dull-gray under parts.

The brown or gray back and the streaked throat of the other species of *Aphelocoma* are conspicuously absent; it is decidedly more uniformly colored than the other jays, with no very conspicuous markings. It can be distinguished from the long-crested jay by the entire absence of any crest.

Winter.—It is resident practically all winter long throughout its range, though it wanders about more or less, in large or small flocks, visiting the ranches, farms, and houses to pick up what scraps of food it can find, and it will become quite familiar and friendly where it is fed regularly.

DISTRIBUTION

Range.—Southern Arizona, southwestern New Mexico, and Texas south to the southern part of the Mexican tableland; nonmigratory.

The range of this species extends **north** to central Arizona (Payson, Strawberry Valley, and Fort Apache); southwestern New Mexico (Silver City and Fort Bayard); southwestern Texas (Chisos Mountains); and northern Neuvo León (Parras). **East** to Nuevo León (Parras and Monterey); Tamaulipas (Realito and Galindo); and southeastern Veracruz (Jalapa and Mount Orizaba). **South** to southern Veracruz Mount Orizaba); Puebla (Texmelucan and San Pedro); Mexico (Toluca); Michoacán (Patzcuaro); and Colima (Sierra Madre). **West** to Colima (Sierra Madre); Jalisco (Sierra Nevada); Nayarit (San Sebastián and Santa Teresa); Durango (Salto, Arroyo del Buey, and Providencia), northeastern Sinaloa (Sierra de Chaix); eastern Sonora (Oposura, La Chumata, and Saric); and Arizona (Baboquivari Mountains, Tucson, Oracle, Salt River Refuge, and Payson).

The range as outlined includes the entire species, which has been separated into several subspecies, only two of which are found in the United States. The form known as Sieber's jay *(Aphelocoma sordida sieberii)* is found on the southern parts of the Mexican Plateau; the Colima jay *(A. s. colimae)* occupies the southwestern portion of the Mexican tableland; the San Luis Potosí jay *(A. s. potosina)* is found in the northeastern portion of the Mexican Plateau; and the Zacatecas jay *(A. s. wollweberi)* occupies the central and northwestern parts of the plateau. The Arizona jay *(A. s. arizonae)* is found from Arizona and New Mexico south to the northern parts of Sonora and Chihuahua, while Couch's jay *(A. s. couchii)* occurs from the Chisos Mountains of southwestern Texas south to the southern part of Nuevo León.

Egg dates.—Arizona: 87 records, March 25 to July 4; 43 records, April 17 to May 8, indicating the height of the season.

Texas: 3 records, April 27 to June 13.

New Mexico: 4 records, April 24 to June 2.

APHELOCOMA SORDIDA COUCHI (Baird)

COUCH'S JAY

HABITS

This is another of the *sordida* group of jays that extends its range northward from Mexico into the Chisos Mountains in central-western Texas. Van Tyne and Sutton (1937) report the capture of a specimen near Alpine, which is near the northern end of Brewster County, Tex., and about 85 miles north of the Chisos Mountains, "the only record for Couch's Jay in the United States outside of the Chisos Mountains."

Referring to the subspecific characters of this race, they write: "Since the published descriptions of this subspecies provide no very satisfactory comparison between *couchii* and *arizonae* we offer the following comments: *couchii* is brighter, richer blue above than *arizonae*, especially on the head, rump, wings, and tail; in *couchii* the gray-brown of the back is darker and more contrasted with the blue of the head and neck than in *arizonae;* in *couchii* the throat is white in rather sharp contrast with the gray of the breast, while in *arizonae* the throat is gray, shading gradually into the gray of the breast; the thighs of *couchii* are gray or blue-gray but in *arizonae* they are practically concolor with the flanks; the bill of young *arizonae* is mottled with yellowish, and this often persists for at least a year, but in *couchii* the bill becomes entirely black soon after the young bird leaves the nest."

They found this jay "common everywhere above the lower limit of trees (about 5000 feet)" in the Chisos Mountains. Herbert Brandt (1940) also found Couch's jay very common in these mountains and has written considerable about it. As to its relationship to the Arizona jay he says: "The geographically connecting link between these two birds is said to be far south in Mexico, so the territories occupied by these two distantly related subspecies are the terminals of a long, horseshoe-shaped range. The habitats of the two birds, instead of being separated by but four hundred miles—or the distance from the Big Bend to Arizona—are in reality some eighteen hundred miles apart. This may be seen by following south their respective mountainous territories—one along the western highlands of Mexico, the other on the eastern side—until these mountains blend into each other on the plateau of lower mid-Mexico. The evidence, however, from the standpoints of dissimilar eggs, nest, voices, and size, perhaps explains in part the reason for the view of the older ornithologists that the Couch and Arizona Jays were two distinct species."

Nesting.—Van Tyne and Sutton (1937) report the following nests observed in the Chisos Mountains: "On April 27, 1935, Semple found a nest and four eggs in a willow oak that stood along a dry stream bed at the lower margin of the Basin, * * * at about 5000 feet. The nest, which was compactly built, was about fifteen feet from the ground on a bough that extended over the stream bed. The eggs were fresh. The parent birds were noisy in defense of their nest. * * * On May 1, 1935, Sutton found two nests, the first in the process of construction, in a pine tree not far from the trail to Laguna at an elevation of 6000 feet; the second with two eggs, an incomplete set, in an oak near Boot Spring. Both nests were well built, with an ample cup which was neatly lined with rootlets. On May 17, 1932, Peet found a nest with three well-fledged young ten feet from the ground in a small oak tree near Boot Spring."

Mr. Brandt (1940) found a number of nests of this jay in the same region and says: "The Couch Jay of the Chisos Mountains appears to have but little individuality in its nest building, for one abode seems just like the other, and evidently it is perfectly satisfied with the appointments and furnishings of its home. The noteworthy feature of each nest is the thick horsehair lining, which is woven concentrically into a smooth, springy mattress of trim saucer shape. * * * The builder is very particular in this respect, because it never seemed to use any other lining in the nests we saw than the long black or white tail or mane hairs of horses."

He remarks that horses are scarce in that region and that the jays must work hard to procure enough hair; but he suggests that, as he found no hair lining in the old nests, the birds may rob the old nests to line the new. He describes a nest that they found in a small oak, 12 feet up toward the top, in a tricleft crotch of a level limb. "It was typical in every way of a jay's home, as it was made up of two distinct parts, the outer portion having a well-laced platform of twigs neatly laid at various angles, and the inner structure composed, to a depth of half an inch, of curly white grass, this lined in turn with a mat of circularly woven, black-and-white horsehair to the thickness of about an inch, and giving to the structure a soft gray color."

He mentions another nest, at least 30 feet from the ground in a tall pine tree. One was found "in an oak sapling, not over three feet from the ground and fully exposed to view. Another nest was revealed in an upper crotch of a pinyon, in which the sitting bird was at home, its beautiful blue tail protruding colorfully over the side until I was able almost to touch it, when it left headlong, to reveal four purple-skinned jaylets."

Eggs.—Four eggs seem to constitute the normal set for Couch's jay. One would expect this jay to lay eggs like its Arizona subspecies, but this is not so. Such an occurrence is unusual among subspecies. I have not seen any of its eggs, but they have been well enough described by others to show the difference. Mr. Brandt (1940) says: "All ten sets of Texas eggs that we observed were invariably dotted with dark, greenish spots on a paler greenish ground color, closely resembling the eggs of the California Jay group."

Van Tyne and Sutton (1937) say: "The eggs are Pale Nile Blue speckled and blotched with pale brownish markings, ranging from mere specks to blotches one and two millimeters in diameter. The markings tend to be concentrated more about the large end, and on one egg there is a distinct wreath of marks about that end."

The measurements of 28 eggs average 28.6 by 21.9 millimeters; the eggs showing the four extremes measure **30.3** by 21.3, 29.0 by **24.0, 26.0** by 22.0, and 28.5 by **20.7** millimeters.

Plumages.—The plumage changes of Couch's jay are probably similar to those of the Arizona jay, except that, as mentioned by Van Tyne and Sutton (1937), the young bird acquires an entirely black bill soon after it leaves the nest, whereas in the Arizona bird the base of the bill remains light colored for about a year. Also, whereas the Arizona bird begins the postnuptial molt about the first of August, they found that Couch's jay was "molting heavily at least a month earlier."

Food.—What small scraps of information we have on the food of this jay indicate that it does not differ materially from that of the Arizona jay, or from that of the *Aphelocoma* genus in general. Its haunts are so far removed from human settlements and agricultural regions that it is probably of little economic importance. Van Tyne (1929) says: "Their food consisted mainly of coleoptera and orthoptera, together with a few nuts and seeds. They probably also raid the nests of small birds, for I saw them repeatedly pursued by Scott's Orioles and Mockingbirds whose nests they had approached."

Mr. Brandt (1940) emphasizes the latter trait, saying: "At nesting time this winged coyote is the most competitive of all egg collectors as it moves wantonly through the wild countryside, sly, observant, and alert. It is when the callow young are in the cradle that it is most insatiable, and levies a heavy toll wherever the slightest opportunity offers."

Behavior.—Mr. Brandt (1940) noted that these jays "traveled about in scattered groups numbering up to a dozen birds, which usually moved forward through the trees by short flights, one bird flying over the other and then alighting until those in the rear repeated the maneuver. Their more extended flight is direct, and performed by quick wing-beats, with brief cessations at intervals." He found it an easy matter to call up an unseen flock of these jays, almost anywhere within their habitat, by using the well-known squeaking call. "If the caller be concealed beneath a tree the bird flies directly to it; its decurved wings then produce an air-drumming that in its rapidity results in a peculiar, hollow, booming whir. The birds may soon discover the human source of the unusual noises, and thereupon depart, but will return again and again to the place, each time apparently as excited and bubbling over as at the first experience. Here we find a strange anomaly, for this bird has a reputation as the most cunning, wise, and wary of the mountain dwellers, yet it is the one most easily duped by confused squeaks, usually making a ridiculously entertaining show of itself."

Voice.—Comparing the voice of this jay with that of the Arizona jay, he says: "The much different, and more agreeable, call of the Couch Jay is made up of groups of from three to six notes, and to my ear may best be written as 'oint-oint-oint,' being delivered more slowly, and evenly, in a high pitch. We learned that the Texas bird has, too, an additional and entirely different note which I have never heard from the Arizona jay; it is a loud, rattling, throaty cackle, resembling somewhat that given by the Blue Jay, although only an occasional individual in a flock seems to render this call. This particular bird, when the flock is agitated, will issue its gurgling scream repeatedly, but the others make no attempt to join."

Dr. Van Tyne (1929) noted that "they were very noisy, constantly repeating a shrill, rasping *scree, scree, scree.* I also heard them give a peculiar rattling note, not unlike the call of *Dryobates pubescens.*"

Enemies.—Baird, Brewer, and Ridgway (1874) relate the following incident, apparently quoted from the notes of Lt. D. N. Couch, for whom the subspecies was named: "Near Guyapuco a large snake *(Georgia obsoleta)* was seen pursued by three or four of this species. The reptile was making every effort to escape from their combined attacks, and would, no doubt, have been killed by them, had they not been interfered with. The cause of so much animosity against the snake was explained when, on opening its stomach, three young of this species, about two thirds grown, were found."

XANTHOURA YNCAS GLAUCESCENS Ridgway

GREEN JAY

HABITS

This brilliantly colored jay brings to that favored region of the lower Rio Grande Valley in Texas a touch of tropical color that adds much to the many thrills one feels as he meets for the first time the many new forms of Mexican bird life to be found only in that unique region.

As I sat on a log near the edge of a stream in a dense forest along one of the resacas near Brownsville, I caught my first glimpse of a green jay, a flash of green, yellow, and blue, as it flitted through the thick underbrush and the trees above me. In spite of its brilliant colors it was surprisingly inconspicuous among the lights and shades of the thick foliage. I had just been admiring the dainty little Texas king-fisher that flew down the stream and perched on a fallen snag, had been lulled almost to sleep by the constant cooing of the many white-winged doves, and awakened again by the loud calls of the gaudy Derby flycatcher. The curious chachalaca and the red-billed pigeon had their nests in the vicinity, and there were a host of other interesting birds all about me, but the green jay was the gem of the forest.

I am wondering how much longer this bird paradise will last, for I have read that huge tractors have been uprooting the forest trees, clearing up the chaparral, and plowing up the rich land to make room for the rapidly growing citrus orchards and other expanding agricultural interests. Thus will soon disappear the only chance we have of preserving on United States soil this unique fauna and flora; and all these interesting birds will have to retreat across the Mexican border, leaving our fauna that much poorer.

According to Baird, Brewer, and Ridgway (1874), "Colonel George A. McCall, Inspector-General of the United States Army, was the first person to collect these birds within our limits. He obtained them in the forests that border the Rio Grande on the southeastern frontier of Texas. There he found them all mated in the month of May, and he felt no doubt that they had their nests in the extensive and almost impenetrable thickets of mimosa, commonly called chaparral."

We learn more about it from the writings a number of years later of Dr. James C. Merrill (1876 and 1878) and George B. Sennett (1878 and 1879). The latter writes (1878): "It was first met with on April 2nd, in the vicinity of Brownsville; but it was not until we reached the heavier timber about Hidalgo that we saw it in full force. They were there April 17th in pairs, and busy constructing homes. They are most frequently seen during the breeding season in the densest woods and thickets, but at other times I am told they are common visitors of the camp, the ranche, and the huts in the outskirts of towns, to the annoyance of all on account of their thieving propensities."

The subspecies *glaucescens* is smaller and its coloration is paler and duller than in the other four races of the species found in Mexico and Central America. Its range extends from the lower Rio Grande Valley southward into northern Tamaulipas and Nuevo León.

Nesting.—Most of the information we have on the nesting of the green jay comes from the two observers mentioned above. Mr. Sennett's (1878) first nest was taken on April 28 "from a mezquite-tree standing in a dense thicket not far from the river-bank, and contained four fresh eggs. It was situated in a fork about fifteen feet from the ground, and was composed of sticks lined with fine stems, and a rather bulky affair." He tells of a nest, found on April 30, that "was some nine feet from the ground on the outer branches of a small tree, and composed wholly of sticks and fine twigs. The sticks were so full of thorns that when they were crossed about among the lining branches more firmness was given to the nest than usual, and by cutting off the branches I could readily take it entire. The outside diameter is nine inches one way by eight the other; its depth is four inches; inside, three and a half inches wide by two inches deep."

Dr. Merrill (1876) reports a nest, taken on May 27 near Hidalgo, Texas: "It was placed on the horizontal branch of a waican-tree, about twenty-five feet from the ground, and was built of twigs and rootlets; the cavity was slight, and the entire structure so thin that the eggs could be seen through the bottom. These were three in number, and were quite fresh. * * * A second nest, found in the same vicinity May 8, was on a sapling seven feet from the ground; it closely resembled the first one, and contained four eggs, three far advanced in incubation; the fourth * * * was quite fresh."

Major Bendire (1895) says of the nests: "The nests are generally placed in dense thickets and well hidden among the branches at heights varying usually from 5 to 10 feet from the ground, and rarely in large trees. They are frequently found in retama, anacahuita, brasil, and hackberry bushes or trees. The outer nest consists usually of a slight platform of small thorny twigs and branches, sparingly lined with fine rootlets, small pieces of a wire-like vine, bits of moss, and occasionally dry grass and leaves. The Green Jay apparently does not use mud in the construction of its nest. * * * It is probable that two broods are sometimes raised in a season."

Eggs.—Major Bendire (1895), with a large series of eggs before him, writes: "The number of eggs laid by this species is from three to five; sets of four are most often found. The prevailing ground color of these eggs is grayish white, occasionally pale greenish white or buff color. They are profusely spotted and blotched—but never heavily enough to hide the ground color—with different shades of brown, gray, and lavender; these markings are generally more abundant about the larger end of the egg. The shell is close grained, moderately strong, and shows little or no gloss. Their shape is mostly ovate, and sometimes short ovate."

The descriptions of the eggs, as given by others, are not very different. Mr. Sennett (1878) says that "the ground-color is usually light drab, tinged faintly with green, but I have one egg out of a set of four with the color dull yellowish-white. The markings are brown, sometimes distinctly spotted or speckled or streaked, and sometimes quite indistinct and clouded." Dr. Merrill (1876) mentions one that "differed in having the markings most numerous at the smaller end." The measurements of 70 eggs in the United States National Museum average 27.31 by 20.43 millimeters; the eggs showing the four extremes measure 30.8 by 21.8, 24.9 by 20.3, and 25.9 by 19.1 millimeters.

Plumages.—Dr. Herbert Friedmann (1925) found a nest containing four young birds about four days old. "The young were still blind but the primary and secondary quills were beginning to sprout and were dull bluish in color. The top of the head and the spinal tract (both the skin and the neossoptiles) were greenish gray in color."

I have seen no very young birds, but Ridgway (1904) describes the juvenal plumage as follows: "Pileum, hindneck, and malar patch greenish blue, the forehead and palpebral spots similar but paler, and the nasal tufts darker; black of chin, throat, chest, etc., much duller than in adults; under parts of body very pale yellowish green or greenish yellow anteriorly, fading on flanks, abdomen, under tail-coverts, etc., into very pale creamy yellow; otherwise like adults."

Food.—Austin Paul Smith (1910) charges the green jay with feeding on the eggs and young of various small birds, such as thrashers, orioles, sparrows, wrens, chats and mockingbirds, and that, outside of the nesting season, it feeds "mostly on seeds and insects. In winter the seeds of the Ebony *(Siderocarpus)* is the main reliance; also in less quantity the fruit of the Palmetto, to secure which they will travel far into the open."

Cottam and Knappen (1939) have given us the most detailed account of the food of this jay as follows:

Smith's indictment is not confirmed by the only previous record of stomach contents with which the writers are familiar—that from Vernon Bailey's field notes for April-May 1900, at Brownsville, Texas: 'Stomach contained one grasshopper, beetles, small insects, and part of a kernel of corn.' Except for the corn this food listed by Bailey is similar to that found by us in the stomach of a Green Jay collected by Dr. Francis Harper near Norias, Texas, on August 17, 1929. One per cent of the food consisted of fragments of two seeds of a bristlegrass *(Setaria ? grisebachii)*, seed fragments of pricky-ash *(Xanthoxylum clava-herculis)*, and undetermined plant fiber. The remainder of the food was animal in origin, including fragments of: sixteen or more stink bugs *(Brochymena* sp.), 79%; several coreid bugs *(Acanthocephala* sp.), 8%; finely ground indeterminable bugs (Heteroptera), trace; a short-horned grasshopper nymph (Acrididae), 1%; a field cricket nymph *(Gryllus assimilis)*, 1%; a hymenopteran, trace; indeterminable insect, trace; and a fragment of a spider, 1%. Gravel formed 1% of the gross contents.

Behavior.—All jays are more or less alike in their behavior, and the green jay is no exception to the rule. It is a noisy and conspicuous bird, making itself known by its harsh notes and its gaudy plumage. As a rule it is not at all shy and has the usual supply of jay curiosity, and the collector should have no difficulty in obtaining all the specimens he needs. Dr. Merrill (1878) says that "it is often very tame and bold, entering tents and taking food off plates or from the kitchen whenever a good opportunity offers. Large numbers are caught by the soldiers in traps baited with corn, but the plumage is their only attraction as a cage-bird."

Austin Paul Smith (1910) says that the green jay—

ranks above all its North American cousins in plumage, tho not in bearing. I have yet to find a species of crestless jay that is free of cowardly disposition and sneaky manner. It is born in them. The crested members of this group, as most of us well know, are no disciples of uprightness, but they can hide their faults, in a large degree, by a dignified appearance. Unluckily, for the Green Jay, his feathers seem to accentuate his sins. * * * It is another resident species, most at home in heavy growth along the river; altho from there it will often wander on foraging expeditions, even inspecting rural barnyards when hunger be pressing. The Green Jay is the worst gourmand in its family; and this failing often causes it to lose its liberty. Its plumage makes it very attractive as a cage bird, and to secure one only requires a wicker cage, set in a conspicuous place and baited with meat of some kind; fitted with a trap door worked by a string held by some hidden Homo, who possesses the instinct to pull the string at the opportune moment. Captivity does not curtail the Jay's appetite, and they have been known to accept food immediately after being trapt. Indeed, this bird will eat all the time if food be accessible; and the indulgent owner finds it a matter of difficulty to keep the bird alive more than a week, but such individuals as are fed with discretion, will live to make interesting, altho noisy pets. In a wild state, the Green Jay is suspicious as becomes the tribe, tho as a rule it falls to a ruse quitely easily. If one be shot, the balance set up a din that can ordinarily only be stopt, either by shooting them all or decamping from the neighborhood.

DISTRIBUTION

Range.—Lower Rio Grande Valley south to Guatemala; nonmigratory. The range of the green jay extends **north** to northern Jalisco (San Sebastián); and southern Texas (Rio Grande, Lomita, and Brownsville). **East** to Texas (Brownsville); Tamaulipas (Río Cruz); Veracruz (Tampico, Jalapa, and Presidio); Yucatán (Río Lagartos and Chichen Itzá); Quintana Roo (Chunyaxche); British Honduras (Belize and Mantee); eastern Guatemala (Santa Tomás); and northeastern Honduras (Omoa). **South** to northern Honduras (Omoa, Santa Ana, and Chamelicon); southwestern Guatemala (Zapate, Naranjo, and Patio Bolas); and Oaxaca (Santa Efigenia, Guichcovi, and Pluma).

West to western Oaxaca (Pluma); Guerrero (Rincon); and north-western Jalisco (San Sebastián).

The range as outlined is for the entire species, which has been separated into several subspecies. One race *(Xanthoura yncas luxuosa)* occupies the eastern edge of the Mexican Plateau from Veracruz and Puebla north to southern Tamaulipas and Nuevo León; the Rio Grande green jay *(X. y. glaucescens)* is found in the lower Rio Grande Valley in Texas and south into the Mexican states of Nuevo León and Tamaulipas; the Tehuantepec green jay *(X. y. vivida)* is found in south-western Mexico and northwestern Guatemala; the Guatemalan green jay *(X. y. guatimalensis)* occupies the country north and east from northern Honduras to the Yucatán Peninsula; while the Jaliscan green jay *(X. y. speciosa)* is apparently confined to the state of Jalisco.

Egg dates.—Texas: 47 records, April 2 to May 29; 25 records, April 15 to 30, indicating the height of the season.

Mexico: 2 records, April 23 and 30.

PICA PICA HUDSONIA (Sabine)

AMERICAN MAGPIE

PLATES 23-25

CONTRIBUTED BY JEAN MYRON LINSDALE

HABITS

The magpie has been closely associated with man for many centuries in many parts of the Northern Hemisphere, and the lore concerning it has developed in great amount. Sometimes hated for its disagreeable traits, sometimes admired for its attractive ones, this bird has remained one of the best-known to people who live near it. And wherever it occurs, the magpie tends to favor lands also occupied by man.

In America only persons living in the North and the West have opportunity to become intimately acquainted with magpies in their normal haunts. Of the close to 20 distinguishable kinds of magpies in the world, two occur in northwestern North America. The black-billed one, most like its relatives in Europe and Asia, occupies much of the mountainous country west of the prairies and north of the deserts even to the Alaska Peninsula. It avoids the deep forests and the dry, open plains, but it is at home in the canyons and on streamsides where tall thickets and scattered trees provide cover from pursuit, sites for nests, and clearings for foraging on the ground.

The magpie is one of the larger birds in any locality in which it is found. Its structure and inherited habits enable it to feed upon a wide variety of foods, including both plant and animal matter. A bird of its size is able, probably, in the region it inhabits, to find food of this nature in sufficient quantity most easily by foraging on the ground. The most productive ground is in the open where there is low-growth vegetation. A magpie's wings are short and rounded and so shaped that it cannot fly rapidly or far. Therefore, if it is to escape from pursuit, it must stay in places where it can move rapidly into thick clumps of brush. These two circumstances, then, tend to restrict magpies to places where there is open forage ground and where clumps of bushy trees and bushes are scattered over the landscape. Further limitation requires trees and bushes of sufficient strength to support the bulky nest. These suitable nesting trees are oftenest found along the streams.

A rather striking relation to climate exhibited by this bird has not been clearly explained. On the map of the dry climates of the United States published by Russell (1931) the region marked as Cold Type Steppe Dry Climate is almost exactly the range of the black-billed magpie. The boundaries coincide everywhere within a few miles. In this type of climate the mean January temperatures furnish the greatest contrast with the climate of the region occupied by the yellow-billed magpie.

Magpie, the name for this bird now used almost universally among English-speaking people, is a contraction of Magot Pie, a Middle English name for the bird. According to Swann (1913) the first part of the name appears to have no reference to the bird's habit of picking maggots from the backs of sheep (as some persons have supposed), but it is "derived from the French Margot, a diminutive of *Marguerite,* but also signifying a Magpie, perhaps from its noisy chattering, in which it is popularly supposed to resemble a talkative woman." The second part of the name is supposed to come through French from the Latin *pica,* which refers to the black-and-white coloration of the bird.

Throughout the range of the group the many allusions to magpies in folklore and the superstitions concerning them demonstrate widespread familiarity with the bird in early times. The same tendency is reflected in the large number of vernacular names, more than 400, that have been applied to the magpie.

Because a long account of all the magpies, which I once assembled, was published so recently (Linsdale, 1937) and only a little additional information has been available, this entire story has been mainly extracted from the earlier one, which may be consulted for more extensive detail.

Courtship.—The study of courtship in magpies is especially difficult because their gregarious habit, their marked shyness, and aversion to entering small traps ordinarily used for birds make it practically impossible to distinguish individuals in a natural group and then to keep track of them for any considerable length of time. The screen of their habitat further complicates any attempt to study this part of magpie life. Repeated glimpses, however, result in a composite notion that must approximate the true story. The most important items have come from observers in Europe, but they seem to apply equally as well to the American form. The available information indicates that many magpies remain together in pairs through the year, and the changes consist mainly in the replacement of lost mates and the entering of young birds into the life of the flock.

Aretas A. Saunders reports (MS.) that he saw birds going through what he believed were courting actions, on March 12, 1911, in Montana. Three he took to be males were following one supposed female.

Nesting.—Nests of magpies are substantial structures that ordinarily endure several seasons of weathering. They are so characteristic of the species that they are useful as certain indicators of the nesting of the birds in any locality where they may be found. In some instances the nests remain long after the birds have given up nesting in a place or have been driven out by human interference.

Observers generally have agreed that only a single brood is reared in a season. Bendire (1895) found that whenever a set of eggs was destroyed a second and sometimes even a third set would be laid. These were frequently in the same nest or in one close by. The second set usually contained a smaller number of eggs, five or six.

Many observers have concluded that a pair of magpies builds a whole series of nests each season, of which they actually use only one. This impression possibly resulted from the tendency of the birds to desert a nest upon slight disturbance at an early stage of its construction. Then, too, these conspicuous structures are more impressive than is the case with smaller birds which may exhibit the same trait.

Actual building in the Western States usually begins in March and requires about six weeks. Before this for several weeks the birds show indications of the coming nesting. Early stages are interrupted often by late snows, but the birds ordinarily come back and resume their work with the return of mild weather. A nest found in Washington by Averill (1895) and started on March 22 had beginnings of a roof on April 10 and held the first egg on May 1. In Colorado nests half completed by the end of March contained partly incubated eggs on April 28 (Gilman, 1907).

Black-billed magpies nest in small colonies at sites separated and strung out along some stream course or over some area of woodland or thicket. Such a group of nests may occupy an area half a mile across or a line a mile or more in length. Kalmbach (1927) found 26 broods of young within a mile along a creek in Utah. Each group of nesting pairs is separated from the next group, often by an intervening area of unfavorable habitat, but sometimes the vacant places result merely from lack of birds to fill them. At any rate the favorable habitat is seldom filled and the nesting pairs tend to be clustered rather than spread evenly.

The nest of the magpie is noteworthy for the large quantity of material contained in it. Ordinarily the structure measures about 2 feet in height by 1 foot in diameter, or slightly larger. A nest found by Silloway (1903) in Montana was 4 feet high, 4 feet long, and 40 inches wide. Dawson (1909) found one in Washington 7 feet from bottom to top, the upper one-third being the dome, and another not over a foot in diameter and scarcely that in depth.

The base and outer walls of a nest are composed of coarse material, heavy sticks, often thorny ones. The materials vary greatly, depending mainly upon the nature of the available supply. The sticks may be 2 feet long, and often they are pulled from sagebushes or cottonwood trees. Sometimes they are picked up from the ground. Inside the base is a heavy cup of mud held together with some vegetable material. Fresh cow dung sometimes is substituted for the mud. Within the cup is a lining, installed after the construction of the dome and after the nest appears completed. It is composed of rootlets, fine plant stems, or horsehair.

The dome or canopy built over the whole structure gives the magpie nest its bulky appearance and provides questions of special interest in the life of this bird. This canopy is usually made of thorny twigs, pulled from nearby plants, and it has one or more openings in its side for the birds to enter and leave. Sometimes there is no dome, but this is rare. A nest found by Potter (1927) was in a railroad bridge, directly under one of the rails and between two ties. There was no room for a dome and none was needed. The track was used by at least one train each day.

Apparently this dome serves as a protection against the raids of predators, especially birds. Throughout the range of magpies their old nests are used also by raptorial birds, often night-hunting owls. Protection from owls may be a chief function of the dome on a magpie nest. An example of this use was observed in Nevada (Linsdale, 1937). On June 6, 1933, at dusk when the long-eared owls became active, magpies near camp showed much concern. Alarm notes were heard at three different magpie nest locations, and birds were seen in flight. Whenever an owl flew up it was followed closely by a magpie. In the vicinity each owl nest was situated close to an occupied magpie nest. The owls did practically all their foraging at night when the magpies probably slept, and hence they most likely needed some special protection just as might be provided by the thorny canopy over the nest. This was near the nest-leaving time for both species.

The black-billed magpie nests sometimes in tall trees, but oftener in tall bushes, especially in thorny ones. In trees the nests are placed often on low horizontal limbs sometimes close to the trunk and nearly always less than 25 feet from the ground. In bushes the nest may be in the extreme top, and nearly always it is far enough above ground to be out of reach of large foraging mammals.

Preference for certain kinds of bushes or trees to hold the nest seems to depend largely on what ones are available in each locality. In various places the following kinds of plants have been recorded as providing sites for nests of black-billed magpies: Alder, aspen, birch, buffaloberry, cottonwood, fir, hawthorn, juniper, pine, scrub oak, and willow.

Both birds of a pair take an active part in nest-building; both carry materials and place them on the nest. However, one of the pair, probably the female, gives more attention to the actual shaping of the nest.

In some localities magpies regularly use the same nests year after year. In this case the old nest is repaired and new material is added to it. Sometimes a remarkably large structure is thus built. In other localities the birds seem never to use a nest for a second brood but always build an entirely new one or, at most, build upon an old one, using it mainly as a base. Repair of nests is not limited to reoccupation. The birds see to it that the nest is kept in repair during the incubation and brooding of the young. If a part of the canopy is torn away, it is likely to be replaced quickly.

The use of magpies' nests by other birds has been discussed fully by Rockwell (1909). The abandoned nests furnish protection during severe rain or hail storms, or other severe weather, for robins, blackbirds, bluebirds, warblers, and other species that live along the timbered streams. Some birds, the horned owl, long-eared owl, and screech owl, make use of these nests almost continuously for daytime hiding retreats. These birds, especially the first two, also lay their eggs in old magpie nests. The sparrow hawk uses these nests for laying, but nearly always it chooses nests that still have their roofs intact. Rockwell noted that sparrow hawks that utilized old magpie nests always appeared timider than the ones that nested in cavities of trees. Other species reported as using these nests for their eggs or as bases for nests of their own are the sharp-shinned hawk, at Fort Lewis, Colo., the mourning dove, at Fort Harney, Oreg., and the bronzed grackle, at Littleton, Colo. At Barr, Colo., a brood of young magpies left a nest early in May, and within a week a pair of English sparrows started to build within the structure. Afterward a cowbird's egg was found in this nest. Nearly all the birds found laying eggs in these used nests chose ones between 15 and 30 feet above the ground.

A dilapidated magpie nest 8 feet above the ground in a willow near Pyramid Lake, Nev., held a nest of a gadwall, built of down and containing nine eggs (Ridgway, 1877). Near Denver a magpie's nest found by Bradbury (1917a) held seven fresh eggs, and on its flattened roof were three eggs of the black-crowned night heron. Apparently both pairs of birds had started about the same time to nest in the same structure. Another magpie nest 50 feet away contained five long-eared owl's eggs that were being incubated.

A peculiar association between nesting magpies and other kinds of nesting birds, mainly hawks, has been detected by many observers in many localities. In Alberta Taverner (1919) found magpie nests invariably in the neighborhood of, or not more than a hundred yards or so from, nests of red-tailed or Swainson's hawks. Bowles and Decker (1931) report that almost invariably one finds a nest of the magpie in the same tree only a few feet from that of the ferruginous roughleg; there is a continual supply of food to be had from the leavings of the hawks. Rhoads (1894) cited Captain Lewis as observing "that the nests of the Bald Eagles, where the Magpies abound, are always accompanied by those of two or three of the latter, who are their inseparable attendants." On the Columbia River a magpie's nest was once found by Dawson (1909) in the "basement" of an occupied osprey's nest. He intimates that the magpies derived benefit in having access to surplus food brought in by the ospreys.

Mammals, of fairly large size, have been found occupying old nests of the magpie. In New Mexico, Gilman (1908) reported four young house cats living in a nest 16 feet up from the ground. A gray fox found resting in the daytime in an old magpie nest near Colorado Springs, Colo., was reported by Warren (1912) on authority of C. E. Aiken.

Aretas A. Saunders sends the information that magpies sometimes use their old nests as shelter in winter in stormy or windy weather, and he thinks that possibly they use them regularly at night in winter.

Eggs.—Seven is the usual number of eggs in a set; sets of 8 and 9 are not uncommon, and as many as 10, 11, and even 13 have been found in one nest. Small sets in a nest are likely to be the result of some accidental destruction.

Concerning the time of egg laying, Kalmbach (1927) writes that "in Colorado, Utah, California, and southern Oregon, egg laying begins before the middle of April, in Washington and Montana about two weeks later, while in the extreme northern part of the magpie's range it does not begin before June or even July."

Coloration of the eggs varies, but the ground color is usually greenish gray, and this is profusely blotched with different shades of brown, sometimes completely hiding the ground color. Bendire (1895) describes the majority of the eggs as ovate. Others are short-ovate, rounded, elliptical, and elongate-ovate. The shells are close grained and moderately strong and show little or no gloss. Measurements given by him of 201 eggs in the United States National Museum are as follows: Average 32.54 by 22.86 millimeters; largest 37.84 by 26.42; smallest 27.94 by 21.59.

The average weight of 17 eggs was given by Bergtold (1917) as 0.34 ounces, or 9.64 grams. Weights of 13 eggs, in two sets, given by the same writer ranged from 132 to 155 grains (8.58 to 10.07 grams). The average for the whole lot of 13 eggs was 9.39 grams. An egg studied by me in Smoky Valley, Nev., which contained a well-developed embryo, measured 31 by 24 millimeters and weighed 7.2 grams. Another (incubation estimated at 14 days) measured 37 by 23 millimeters and weighed 8.2 grams.

Young.—Bendire (1895) gives the length of the incubation period as 16 to 18 days. He observed that one egg is deposited daily, and that incubation does not begin until the full set is nearly completed. Wheelock (1904), apparently on the basis of original observations, wrote that the female incubates for 18 days.

Opportunity came to me in several seasons to study young magpies in various stages of development in Smoky Valley, central Nevada. Three young, just hatched on May 16, had colorless skins that appeared pinkish because of the blood showing through them. Each was weak and barely able to raise its head and open its bill. When first taken from the nest they made a few weak squeaks. The brooding parent allowed approach to within 50 yards and then flew off with a series of about eight loud, harsh calls. It did not return, but this one or another continued the alarm from a spot 150 yards away. At another nest in similar stage the brooding bird flew off silently at approach within 75 yards.

When removed from a nest two young magpies that had grown to more than ten times their bulk at hatching at first uttered loud food calls and opened their bills. Soon an adult came and gave sharp calls, whereupon the young became quiet and the parent moved away. Later, however, the young again gave food calls. When placed in a cardboard box they worked their legs rather violently and grasped with their claws, apparently in an attempt to raise their bodies. At the same time they opened their bills and gave cries. They were unable to support their bodies above the flat surface, but they raised their heads the full length of their necks.

A bird one-third larger than the two just described (133 grams) was able to support itself on its tarsi, and, when placed on the ground, it immediately began to move off through the brush. Through most of the day this bird was kept it was silent, but it became hungry and uttered calls in the afternoon. Other young magpies of about this size kept perfectly quiet and made no sound or move during the whole time they were being examined.

When disturbed on June 6, five large young in a nest crawled upward inside the tall dome and clung to sticks in its wall. One went through to the outside, but later it returned. Several times these young uttered alarm notes nearly as loud and harsh as those of the parent birds. The next day at noon when this nest was approached the young birds crawled out of it and perched among the branches of the surrounding thicket.

Wheelock (1904) watched a brood of young magpies through the period of nest-leaving. For several days before time to come out of the nest the four young ones poked their heads out the doorways. On the twenty-second day one hopped out and perched on a branch. The parents meanwhile showed great excitement. When the young bird was approached closely it jumped off its perch and flew or was blown out of the tree. It could not control its long tail, which opened and acted as a sail in the wind. One parent followed this bird while the other one remained with the rest of the brood in the nest.

A late time for nest-leaving was observed at 6,500 feet in Yellowstone Park by Skinner (MS.), who saw a fully feathered young magpie perched outside a nest on June 22. By July 7 there was no sign of any birds about the site.

At midday on May 18, 1932, in Nevada, I watched another group of five young magpies out of the nest and able to fly a little. Four were in one thicket and the other was 50 feet away, but all had difficulty in maintaining a balance. Except for their tails being only about 4 inches long, I could scarcely distinguish them at a distance from adults on the basis of feathering. When approached closely the birds moved off through the thicket by short flights and by hopping, and they kept up a series of harsh notes of alarm. When I was still 100 yards off I saw one parent fly away quietly, and no adult was seen while I was near the young. But as soon as I left there were feeding calls; probably one of the parents had arrived.

At noon on May 22 this brood was seen at the same place. The birds were closer to the ground and a little more scattered than they had been the first time. When they moved they were a little more sure-footed. One of them allowed me to approach within 10 feet before it flew.

In the same vicinity, late in the afternoon of June 7, I watched about 25 magpies about a spring. They were in brush clumps and willows and evidently were mostly young, representing 3 or 4 families. They did not fly off so quickly or so well as adults would have. Most of them permitted approach to within a few feet, while adults at the same time remained as shy as ever and kept well out of sight. When I approached them these young birds moved off in several directions through the buffaloberry thickets. This was the earliest group noted that season, which included more than one family. Judged from the numbers of young seen, nearly all were then out of the nest and had left their home surroundings. Magpie calls were heard much more frequently than they had been early in May.

Out of close to 50 nests examined in one season in Smoky Valley, Nev., the birds at only three were so bold as to return to the nest, even on repeated visits by persons, and to give alarm notes. Usually these pairs kept close to the nest while it was being examined. At one nest especially, which contained large young, the female would come within 3 or 4 feet of an intruder and, uttering alarm notes, would stay as long as the person remained. The male came within 15 or 20 feet but did not stay so long. At the time for the young to leave, the parent often picked at branches of the buffaloberry bush on which it perched, breaking off thorns and pieces of bark with its beak.

Plumages.—Nestling magpies have skins at first nearly free of color except that which comes from the blood near the surface, and they have no down. This evidently is an adaptation to the enclosed type of nest. The skin soon assumes a yellow tinge and then becomes grayish as the birds begin to fledge. When they leave the nest their tails are not more than 5 inches long.

Juvenal birds are much like the adults except for the loose texture of the body feathers. The black parts of the body plumage are browner and the white parts creamier, while the wings and tail are less brilliant. The wing feathers and tail feathers and primary coverts of juvenal magpies are not molted in the first autumn. The body feathers and the wing coverts are molted. The young bird then has browner and less glossy wings and tail than adults, and this distinction becomes marked in the following spring and summer.

Also, adults may be distinguished from young birds up to the time of their second molt by differences in the form of the outer primary. The white area is less extensive on the inner web of the primaries in the young than in the adults, and the black terminal borders are larger. Often also the delimitation of the white and black is not sharp in the young where it is distinct in the adult. The outer (reduced) primary is shorter in adults than in young, and all the primaries are more pointed in young than in adults. The rectrices, especially the outer, vary according to age. The lateral one is narrow and rounded at the end in the young; it is large and square at the end in the adults.

The time and order of replacement of the feathers seem to be nearly the same in Western United States as given for western France by Mayaud (1933). There the juvenal molt of body plumage takes place from July to October. The complete annual molt commences near the first of July, reaches its height in August, and ends from mid-September to late in October. Molt of body plumage is very rapid. Molt of the tail commences early and ends sooner than that of the remiges. The two median rectrices fall first, and the replacement proceeds regularly to the lateral ones. The upper and lower caudals fall a little after the beginning of the molt of the rectrices. The molt of the primaries begins very soon and ends very late. Its direction is from the inside out, from the first to the tenth (and eleventh). The secondary remiges molt in three series; the two proximal ones with the ninth and tenth falling in the external-internal direction and the eighth and seventh in the internal-external direction, and a third series, the first to sixth, falling in the external-internal direction. The molt of the secondaries commences after that of the primaries and that of the distal series ends a little after that time.

Abnormal plumages in the magpie attract more than ordinary interest because of the possibility, which seems almost probability, that some of the existing geographic forms arose by the preservation of this kind of character. Several examples of freakish plumage in the black-billed magpie have been reported: DuBois (1918) on July 20, 1918, near Collins, Mont., saw one "entirely of a grayish-white, or very pale gray color," but exhibiting no definite markings. Rockwell (1910) found two albino magpies in a brood, the balance of which appeared to be normal. Both were pure white except for a slight creamy tint. A specimen mentioned by Svihla (1933) from near Nampa, Idaho, has normal pattern, but the feathers, bill, tarsus, and claws, which are usually black, are rusty-brown in this one.

Food.—E. R. Kalmbach has made extensive study of magpie food in North America. His published report (1927) is based upon the examination of 547 stomachs, of which 313 were adults and 234 were nestlings. This material is fairly representative of the bird's range and is well distributed throughout the year. Chief points of interest in this report are included in the following abstract.

Food of nestlings differed from that of adults at the same time of year and was decidedly different from that of adults at other times of the year. More than 94 percent of the food of these young magpies was animal matter. This contrasted with 82 percent for the parent birds. Insects made up the greater part of the animal matter fed to nestlings, and the groups best represented were caterpillars (nearly 18 percent), grasshoppers (more than 11 percent), and flies (more than 11 percent). This last group consisted chiefly of larvae and pupae of flesh flies that the parents obtained from carrion. The indications are then that the adults visited the carrion for the "purpose of procuring the insect food for their young, even in preference to the carrion itself." Kalmbach also pointed out that "the magpie's depredations on wild birds and domestic poultry may be attributed mainly to a desire to satisfy the appetites of its young."

About three-fifths of the food of adult magpies examined was of animal origin; the greatest proportion was found in May, during the breeding season. November, December, and January mark the period of smallest consumption of animal food. Insect food constitutes the predominant item for the magpie through the year. The species is more highly insectivorous than any other of the common species of the crow family in this country. The kinds of insects eaten are chiefly ones that live on or close to the surface of the ground. Grasshoppers form a conspicuous part of the diet during the late summer and fall. Insects associated with carrion are important in the magpie's food. Kalmbach thinks that in many local outbreaks "magpies doubtless have an important controlling influence" upon insect abundance. Two other items of animal matter important in the food are carrion and small mammals. Magpies congregate on highways to eat remains of animals killed by automobiles.

The stomach examinations indicated that the magpie is "by preference carnivorous and that the vegetable portion of its diet is taken more or less as a matter of necessity and not from choice. Notwithstanding the fact that wild fruit of one kind or another is as readily available in September as in August or October, the magpie's food preferences lead it to resort extensively to grasshoppers during that month and to reduce its consumption of wild fruit. There is every indication, also, that the grain eaten by magpies during the winter months is consumed largely as a matter of necessity. Grain could be secured in quantity during July and August at many points in the bird's range, but it turns naturally to an animal diet during those months. The rigorous weather of

November, December, and January forces the magpie to adopt a diet that is more than 60 per cent vegetable, while in May the abundance of animal food permits it to reduce the vegetable portion of its diet to 8 per cent of the total."

The notion is widespread that magpies provide a serious threat to all kinds of birds in their vicinity by robbing nests and eating the eggs or young, but the evidence to support this opinion is scanty. The manner in which some smaller birds drive magpies from the vicinity of their nests indicates that they recognize a potential danger to their young. On several occasions I have seen Brewer's and red-winged blackbirds, from nesting colonies, chasing magpies. In a group of blackbird nests a magpie could reap an appreciable harvest of food.

A magpie has been observed (Wheelock, 1904) taking both eggs and young from nests of tree swallows in hollow piles of a deserted pier at Lake Tahoe, Calif. This bird, a male, would search over the colony of swallows, and wherever the size of the opening to the nest cavity permitted it would reach in and take the contents, eggs, or young. These were then carried and given to the brooding female magpie. Young domesticated chickens were also taken by this bird.

Kalmbach's (1927) thorough study of the magpie led him to the conclusion that depredations against smaller birds are primarily in the breeding season and that the "serious cases of bird destruction reported against the magpie are probably localized or due to some peculiar environmental factor, as lack of cover for the birds attacked, an over-abundance of magpies, or scarcity of other food." Only 8 of 313 stomachs contained remains of wild birds. Specific identifications could not be made. Remains of eggs of native birds were found in two stomachs, "those of a robin and what appeared to be those of a shorebird being recognized." Three young from the Bear River marshes in Utah had been fed portions of coots, "probably disabled by alkali poisoning."

In this connection the significant observation was made by Saunders (1914) in an area near Choteau, Mont., that the magpies nested earlier than other kinds of birds. After nesting they left the area so that smaller birds there were not molested by them.

Behavior.—The general manner of a magpie is that of a bird well able to take care of itself. It is extremely suspicious yet is inquisitive to a high degree. It takes alarm quickly and rushes away from threatening danger, but it responds to kindness and is easily tamed.

Much of a magpie's time is spent on the ground in search of food. The walk is somewhat jerky, but it has been characterized as being graceful. The tail is slightly elevated and is constantly twitched. When the bird is in a hurry the ordinary walk is sometimes varied to a series of hops. Small droves of magpies were watched by Fisher (1902) as they caught grasshoppers every morning in a field near Mono Lake, Calif. Their agility in dodging and circling showed how mistaken persons are likely to be in forming an estimate of a bird under ordinary conditions. "Usually nonchalant and absurdly dignified in their demeanor, these birds could at times assume the utmost interest in their occupation, and dart with surprising speed here and there."

Bendire's (1895) comments on flocking in this bird were that: "Although more or less quarrelsome, it is social in disposition and likes to be in the company of its kind. I have frequently seen from twelve to thirty feeding together near a slaughterhouse or some other locality where food was abundant; but such gatherings are oftener met with in late fall and winter than during the season of reproduction."

Kelso (1926) records magpies in British Columbia as occurring in winter singly or in small flocks of up to 8 or 10 birds. When they were unusually numerous as many as 10, 20, or even 30 or 40 individuals made up the flock. Winter flocks in Washington contain any number of birds up to 50, according to Dice (1917). In western Nebraska, Zimmer (1911) observed magpies to occur abundantly, but usually singly or in pairs, never in flocks.

It was the opinion of Goss (1891) that the small flocks so often met resulted from the social natures of the birds holding the family groups together. In Nevada, Taylor (1912) observed late in June and early in July that adults and young were traveling in company. According to Dille's (1888) observations in Colorado, after the young are out of the nest and for the balance of the year the birds roam over the country in large flocks. In the same State, Rockwell and Wetmore (1914) saw usually not more than six together, although in one November evening a straggling flock of at least 50 was seen flying across a valley. In a detailed study of a small area in Montana, Saunders (1914) learned that all the magpies left after nesting was over.

One purpose in coming together in flocks is for roosting. In central Nevada, after the nesting season, groups of magpies sometimes roost together in some suitable place. I discovered one of these just after dark late in June 1930. Toward the end of a slough was a thick border of tall willow clumps through which rose vines were tangled. Ten or twenty magpies had just settled in this thicket for roosting. When found they were still making persistent cries. As the birds were disturbed they could be heard flying ahead out of the bushes and, finally, in small groups crossing openings.

Roosting habits of black-billed magpies in western Oklahoma were reported by Sutton (1934), as follows: "Once the birds had gone to roost they were loath to leave the trees, and upon being frightened flopped about clumsily, making their way to trees nearby, where they became quiet as soon as possible. If disturbed in the early evening at a favorite roosting-place they frequently flew to the mesas, then trailed back, one by one, in a series of swift, headlong plunges, just at nightfall." Skinner (MS.) reports that he has found magpies roosting in the thick foliage of Douglas firs.

It was stated by Kalmbach (1927) that "during the winter magpies sometimes roost much after the fashion of crows, and in one instance these two species were found using the same small island in the Snake River in eastern Oregon as a place of nightly resort." In the winter of 1922, a cattle shed near Treesbank, Manitoba, was regularly used as a sleeping place by a group of six or seven magpies. The birds rested on the backs of the cattle overnight (Criddle, 1923).

Bendire (1895) characterized the flight of the magpie as "slow and wavering, and in windy weather evidently laborious. The long, wedge-shaped tail seems to be decidedly in the way and a positive disadvantage, causing it no little trouble in flying from point to point, and in such weather it will only leave through necessity the sheltered bottom lands it usually frequents." Also the flight is never very protracted.

Taverner (1926) writes of the magpie that it is "more often seen retreating up the coulée, chattering as it glides from bush to bush. * * * At other times, a small flock or family party will be seen passing noisily along the tops of the hills, from brush clump to brush clump. Again, they steal silently into camp or about the farm buildings intent on any mischief that may present itself, but flee away in consternation when disturbed."

On many occasions, however, as indicated by Goss (1891), magpies when pursued do not fly away wildly but will tempt the pursuer by fussing about just out of reach. That observer also pointed out that although the birds sustain themselves by rapid strokes of the wings, the effort is too great for extended flight.

In a strong wind magpies tend to fly low, just over the tops of the bushes, and they raise and lower their flight according to variation in level of the bush tops. They probably avoid much of the force of the wind by doing this.

In his notes supplied for this account, M. P. Skinner writes that the flight of a magpie is level, with wing beats slow and measured, yet the flight is really swifter than it appears. At times they fly with a short period of about five wing strokes alternating with a short sail on spread wings. They fly low to escape a head wind. He has seen them fly down a hill slope with a peculiar dipping, wavering flight, with head held up and long tail thrust up to act as a rudder. In flight the white on the wings is conspicuous, giving rise to the term "side wheelers" as they are sometimes called. Individuals are quite apt to follow one another, separated by several hundred feet, and not in flocks. Even when flushed from food they leave one at a time. Magpies often are seen flying across a broad valley, well up above the ground.

The black-billed magpie is usually so wary as to give little opportunity to watch any of its activities closely. I have never observed one bathing in the wild, but observations on caged young birds revealed that they take to water readily and make constant use of it in caring for their plumage. When a pan of water was first placed in the cage, each of the young birds (which had been taken from a nest and, hence, could never have had experience with water) went through almost exactly the behavior described by Pycraft (1918) for the magpies in Europe. At first, just as described for those birds, there were some misguided attempts to bathe on the dry floor, but the habit soon became regulated and adjusted so as to eliminate these wasted movements. Within half an hour after water was placed in the cage for the first time, each of the birds had discovered it and had made use of it for drinking and for bathing. In succeeding months bathing was a part of the daily routine of each of the three birds. In fact, they appeared to await their daily supply of water with as much concern as they watched for a new food supply.

Man encroaches upon the territory of the magpie in nearly every part of the range of the bird. This has been true especially in the range of the black-billed kind in North America since the comparatively recent occupation of the land by the white race. Through much of that area the requirements of these two kinds of animals overlap so much that they come to occupy common ground. This is especially striking here because in most places the combined habitats of man and magpie involve only a small part of the total area of land. Concentration of these two animals on the same ground results partly from their need for water, but their competition is mainly for food materials that are produced there.

When man settles in magpie country, he immediately begins to "improve" his surroundings. Very often this also means that the environment is improved for the magpies. The birds usually need, and they are quick to take advantage of, increased food stores that human settlement brings. This is not a new trait, for magpies have been reported as normal attendants at Indian camps. Also, it was noted by Baird, Brewer, and Ridgway (1874) that "the party of Lewis and Clark, who were the first to add this bird to our fauna, also describe them as familiar and voracious, penetrating into their tents, snatching the meat even from their dishes, and frequently, when the hunters were engaged in dressing their game, seizing the meat suspended within a foot or two of their heads." They add further that "Mr. Nuttall, in his tour across the continent, found these birds so familiar and greedy as to be easily taken, as they approached the encampment for food, by the Indian boys, who kept them prisoners. They soon became reconciled to their confinement, and were continually hopping around and tugging and struggling for any offal thrown to them."

Improvement of the habitat by the magpies, if it takes place, is usually not noticed at all by people. However, if the magpies remove, or interfere with, any article claimed by people, this is likely to be noticed immediately and to be followed by some kind of retaliation. The result often is the destruction of a certain part of the magpie population. But the magpie is a hardy kind of animal, and unless the destruction is organized and well planned the birds have a good chance to survive, at least in small numbers. It is rare that human concentration on an area within magpie range reaches a point where the continued presence of the bird is hindered, unless direct killing is resorted to by the people.

The hatred that many persons hold for the magpie has found expression in the carrying on of contests in an attempt to "exterminate" the species. An item from a newspaper in British Columbia gives some results of one of these contests as it was conducted in 1931 in the Okanagan Lake region. Two teams, of six persons each, killed a total of 1,033 magpies in one season.

In western States magpies in certain localities have hindered campaigns against predatory animals, by raids on the baited stations, to such an extent that special efforts have been made to remove the birds before spreading poison. Kalmbach (1927) reports that "during campaigns against coyotes in the winter of 1921-22 along Butter Creek, in Umatilla County, Oreg., it was conservatively estimated that 5,000 magpies were killed. In Douglas County, Colo., magpies were practically exterminated in the country covered by poison lines placed for coyotes in the winter of 1922-23. In the winter of 1921-22 a coyote campaign planned on the Pyramid Lake Indian Reservation, Nev., called for preliminary measures against magpies. On the first day after placing the baits three grain sacks full of dead magpies were picked up. An inspection of this reservation during the following winter showed not a dozen magpies, where in the previous year there were probably more than a thousand. At one poison station at Summit, Utah, 143 of these birds were accounted for within a few days."

The same writer concluded, concerning the magpie, that "over much of its range, where it appears in moderate numbers, the bird is not an outstanding agricultural pest or a serious menace to other wild birds, and the present study has revealed the fact that there are times when its influence may even be decidedly beneficial."

One of the ways magpies come into conflict with man is by interference with his domesticated animals. Magpies come about the herds of stock, in the corral or on the range, mainly for the extra food available there. A large part of this is the group of carrion- and dung-inhabiting insects that they search for and eat. But they sometimes examine the large animals for parasites they may be carrying, and when opportunity offers they open sores or cuts and eat the flesh of the animal itself. This habit has resulted in considerable losses on occasion, and the bird has a reputation for damage among stockmen, probably far beyond justification. Instances have been reported many times showing the attacks may persist until the death of the horse, cow, or sheep. A full account of injury to sheep by magpies in Montana has been published by Berry (1922).

It has occurred to many observers that such a habit as the attacking of large domestic animals must have developed first with relation to the larger wild herbivores, and some evidence has been given to verify the supposition. Packard (MS.) sends the information, from Colorado, that magpies are frequently seen picking insects off the heads and backs of Rocky Mountain mule deer and American wapiti, especially in spring, when these animals are infested with ticks. They also have been observed on Rocky Mountain bighorns. These animals appear to make no effort to disturb the birds while they are engaged in this activity, although they occasionally turn their heads to look at them. Another observer (Cameron, 1907) concluded that the deer did not appreciate this attention, after he saw a doe push a magpie from her back with her nose.

A possible indication of the close dependence of magpies on these larger animals was shown in an account of the changes in status of some of the animals in central Alberta, reported from the testimony of old-time buffalo hunters by Farley (1925). He wrote concerning this bird, as follows:

The appearance of the Magpie in large flocks in this section of the province during the last ten years has been the cause of much discussion. Until 1907, they were unknown north of the Red Deer River. In October of that year the writer observed a pair about six miles north of the town of Lacombe. The following year magpies were reported from the vicinity of Bittern Lake, and from then on, they have gradually become more numerous, until at present they are our commonest winter resident bird. Magpies were very numerous during the buffalo days when flocks would follow the hunting parties and live on the refuse of the hunt.

The bird was considered a great pest in those times on account of its habit of alighting on horses, with saddle or harness galls, and persistently pecking at the sores until the death of the animal resulted. The only means of saving the horses when thus attacked was to stable or blanket them. With the extinction of the buffalo, the magpies disappeared and the present incursion is the first which has occurred since that time. [The buffalo was plentiful in that district until 1875.]

Skinner (MS.) reports from the Yellowstone region that magpies frequently linger about horses, elk, and buffalo for the sake of the manure. He has seen them feed on carcasses of those animals, which they attacked first by picking out the eyes, next the eyelids and lips, and then the neck.

Magpies are partly dependent too for food on another group of mammals, the carnivores, but in a different way. These birds seem to know that a carnivore is likely to leave scraps of food, and they are able to take advantage of the circumstance. My attention once was directed to the location of a coyote in an aspen thicket by the commotion of magpies near it. Skinner (MS.) writes that magpies find coyote kills so promptly that he sometimes thinks they follow coyotes purposely.

An account supplied by A. A. Saunders tells how he once watched a pair of magpies scold a cat. The cat was trying to hide in a thick growth of willow and cottonwood, but the magpies followed it about, alighting a few feet above it, and calling. The cat would try to move on to another spot, only to be discovered there also, and its presence announced derisively to all the bird population.

Voice.—The ordinary call note of the black-billed magpie has been written (Bendire, 1895) as a querulous *cäck, cäck,* or *chäeck, chäeck,* uttered in a high key, and disagreeable to the ear. That writer adds that: "It frequently utters also a low, garrulous gabble, intermixed with whistling notes, not at all unpleasing, as if talking to itself, and if annoyed at anything it does not hesitate to show its displeasure by scolding in the most unmistakable manner." The distinct chatter of the usual notes impressed Ridgway (1877) as being unlike the notes of any other bird of his acquaintance. The more musical note, which he heard uttered frequently, sounded like *kay e-ehk-kay.* He could detect no difference between the notes of this bird and those of the yellow-billed kind.

Brooks (1931) writes that during four years in France he "was surprised to note the great difference in voice between the Old and New World Magpies; the latter to his regret have no call that he can imitate sufficiently well to decoy the birds to him; the former on the other hand had two easily imitated calls and decoyed readily."

Saunders (MS.) notes that the common cackling call sounds to him like *ca-ca-ca-ca-ca.* It is in a harsh, cracked voice, higher pitched than a crow's caw. When one is near the nest and the birds are scolding with this call, it has a derisive sound. On March 14, 1909, Saunders heard a magpie producing a faint, twittering sound, much as the blue jay does on some occasions, a sound he now would class as a primitive song.

The general demeanor of the black-billed magpie was characterized by Grinnell and Storer (1924) as being "decidedly quieter than that of most of the other members of the jay-magpie-crow family. Its voice is far softer than that of the jays, and it does not 'bawl out' intruders as do those birds. Many of its notes are low and pleasant chuckling sounds, recalling certain notes of the California Thrasher. On one occasion one of our party was attracted by a noise arising in a mountain mahogany bush and sounding like two of the branches rubbing together. It proved to come from a black-billed magpie. Even in early fall, when bluejays and nutcrackers are at their noisiest, the magpie is noticeably quiet."

Magpies have long been favorites among captive birds as pets. Partly this results from the ease with which the black-billed ones may be obtained from their nests as young nearly ready to leave. But also it comes from their varied mannerisms and especially their trait, so well exhibited, of learning to imitate words and phrases that they hear in the households of their keepers. The young birds can learn and repeat an amazingly long and varied vocabulary, if we can believe the accounts that have been printed. Just when the limit of plausibility in the stories of their accomplishments is reached is hard to determine. Even the most commonplace of these accounts, however, is rather remarkable.

Field marks.—Any native bird seen in the United States or northward whose length is 15 to 20 inches, with more than half of this tail and with conspicuous pattern of black and white, is a magpie. The large white patches on the wings appear and disappear as the wings open or close. Close examination reveals iridescent greenish blue and bronzy green in the feathers of the wings and tail. Also the sharp line separating the white belly from the black breast, along with the white patches on the shoulders, helps to verify the identification. And the black bill distinguishes the present form from the yellow-billed one occurring only in California. Such a strikingly marked bird should require no characterization for recognition, but a surprisingly large number of people inquire as to its identity on their first encounter with it. Once learned, it is not soon forgotten.

Predators and parasites.—Watching the behavior of black-billed magpies gives the impression that they are subject to being captured by predators, but there is little direct evidence to demonstrate it. Once in central Nevada I watched a small group of magpies flying about excitedly among the desert bushes. Then a prairie falcon flew up carrying a dead magpie, apparently freshly killed. These magpies probably were young ones and might have been captured more easily than old ones. In a report on the food habits of hawks in Canada, Munro (1929) mentions the flushing of a goshawk from the still-warm body of a magpie.

A special study of the invertebrate fauna of occupied magpie nests in Montana was made by Jellison and Philip (1933). The extreme infestations of the blood-sucking dipterous larvae of *Protocalliphora avium,* which they observed, indicated that the large, twig-canopied, mud-plastered, fiber-lined nests of magpies served as favorable habitations and the nesting birds as excellent hosts. From five of the magpie nests examined, 108, 187, 190, 343, and 373 larvae were taken, respectively. The last was the greatest number reported to that time from a single nest of any bird. Two hymenopterous parasites, *Marmoniella vitripennis* (Walker) and *Morodora armata* Gahan, both chalcids, were reared from the puparia. Larvae of the beetle *Dermestes signatus* LeConte were observed to be predacious on the puparia of the flies.

Blood-gorged midges, *Culicoides crepuscularis* Malloch, were abundant in nests built close to a stream and seemed to be at home in the debris of the nests. Two kinds of Mallophaga were taken from the nestlings, *Docophorus communis* Nitzsch and *Myrsidea eurysternum* (Nitzsch). Additional kinds of beetles found in the nests were: *Dermestes talipinus* Mannerheim, *Anthrenus occidens* Casey, *Helops convexulus* LeConte, and *Cratraea* sp.

Migration.—The migratory habit is developed to different degrees in the various kinds of magpies, but nowhere is it well marked. In the southern part of the range the birds move scarcely at all. Farther north they migrate, sometimes great distances, but always probably in immediate response to severe winter conditions. In the United States fall and winter movements are noted regularly within the general range of the bird, and in some years well-defined migrations occur outside that range.

In many parts of the range of the black-billed magpie local movements of the birds may be detected in fall, usually in September. On the Taku River, Alaska, in the latter half of September, Swarth (1911) observed numerous flocks of eight or ten individuals flying from the interior out toward the coast, where they spent the winter. The same observer (1926) reported a similar migration, also in September, in northern British Columbia. Fall dispersal of magpies was detected from August 28 to late in September by Taylor and Shaw (1927) on Mount Rainier.

The return to the interior takes place early in spring by way of the major passes through the mountains. In one example, cited by Dawson (1909), D. E. Brown saw, on March 4, several bands of magpies passing eastward at a considerable height, perhaps between 3,000 and 5,000 feet. The birds were unrecognizable until glasses were trained on them, and at least 50 were counted.

At numerous places in the mountains the fall movement is upward to high levels. Saunders (1921) reports that in Montana a fall movement into the mountains takes place in October at the time of the first cold weather and snowstorms. The birds have been seen as high as 8,000- and 9,000-foot altitudes. Skinner (MS.) points out that in Yellowstone National Park magpies appear in August and September and are numerous in winter, especially in stormy weather. Packard sends the information that in the vicinity of Estes Park, Colo., magpies are occasionally found at timberline or above, in September or October, when small flocks visit the alpine meadows and feed on grasshoppers.

Still another type of magpie movement is that mentioned by Bendire (1895), who records that along the eastern border of its range the magpie occasionally wanders eastward late in fall and in winter. He thought that the birds were driven away from their usual haunts by scarcity of food or the severe storms that so frequently occur in those sections of the country. An especially well-marked movement of this sort took place in the Missouri Valley in the fall of 1921. Record of exceptional magpie movements that year were reported for Iowa, Nebraska, Kansas, Minnesota, and, farther north, in Manitoba. The birds sometimes go beyond the ordinary limits of their range on the south too. Great flocks of magpies late in October 1919 came into Death Valley, Calif., from the north. They had never been seen there before, and they gradually drifted away until few were left by the end of December.

A possible indicator of rate of travel in these fall movements was reported by Mrs. Bailey (1928), who observed a flock of 17 magpies at a 10,000-foot altitude in New Mexico. Two days later the same flock was seen 5 miles farther up the valley at 10,700 feet.

A single recovery of a banded black-billed magpie, reported by Lincoln (1927), gives information concerning the direction and extent of movement. The bird, banded at Laramie, Wyo., on May 30, 1925, was recovered on January 14, 1926, at Rosita, Colo. The latter locality is approximately 220 miles from the station of banding and is almost directly south of it.

DISTRIBUTION

Range.—Alaska and the Western United States and Canada; casual in the eastern parts of the North American Continent; nonmigratory, but given to erratic wanderings.

The normal range of the American magpie extends **north** to Alaska (Kings Cove, Nushagak, and Little Savage River); Yukon (Fort Selkirk and Carcross); southern Alberta (Glenevis and Mundare); and southern Saskatchewan (Wiseton and Qu'Appelle). **East** to southeastern Saskatchewan (Qu'Appelle); eastern North Dakota (Devils Lake and Dawson); South Dakota (Faulkton and Rosebud); central Nebraska (Niobrara Refuge, Kenesaw, and Red Cloud); western Kansas (Coolidge); western Oklahoma (Brookhart Ranch and Kenton); and northeastern New Mexico (near Raton and Watrous). **South** to northern New Mexico (Watrous, Santa Fe, and Shiprock); southern Utah (probably Bluff and Panquitch); central Nevada (Toquima Mountains, Peavine Creek, and Carson); and east-central California (Bridgeport). **West** to eastern California (Bridgeport, Markleeville, Beckwith, Susanville, and Tule Lake); Oregon (Klamath Lake, Drews Creek, Prineville, and The Dalles); Washington (Kalama, Yakima Valley, and Seattle); British Columbia (probably Port Moody, Ashcroft, and Atlin Lake); and Alaska (Yakutat, Kodiak, and Kings Cove).

Casual records.—Among the records that are well outside the normal range are the following: One was taken on Hotham Inlet, Alaska, sometime prior to 1900; one was taken at Forty-mile, Yukon Territory, on October 15, 1899; in northern Manitoba a specimen was obtained at Brochet, on Reindeer Lake on October 12, 1934, and one was taken at York Factory sometime prior to 1891; in Ontario, one was taken at Odessa on March 12, 1898, one at Port Sidney in the summer of 1898, and it was reported at Kingsville on March 31, 1916; in Quebec, one was recorded about 1883 from Montreal, another was seen in that vicinity on May 17, 1920, while two were seen near Hatley on October 17, 1915.

There are several records for each of the States of Minnesota, Wisconsin, Iowa, and Missouri. Among the records for Illinois is a report of seven seen at Knoxville on May 16, 1896, one seen at Philo on April 26, 1914, and a specimen taken at Lake Forest on November 10, 1918; one was seen at Bicknell, Ind., on December 24, 1907, and again on February 10, 1908; and a specimen was obtained at Toledo, Ohio, on May 9, 1937. There are a few records for Atlantic coastal localities, all of which must be open to suspicion as escapes from captivity. Among these are one seen at Point Lookout, Md., on June 28, 1931, one seen on Edisto Island, S. C., in May 1934, and one seen near Palm Beach, Fla., on January 17, 1934.

Egg dates.—Alaska: 3 records, May 28 to June 19.

California: 30 records, April 9 to May 13; 16 records, April 14 to May 6, indicating the height of the season.

Colorado: 80 records, March 26 to May 29; 40 records, April 24 to May 8.

Montana: 17 records, March 28 to May 23; 8 records, May 6 to 12.

Washington: 20 records, April 1 to May 15; 10 records, April 7 to 19.

PICA NUTTALLII (Audubon)

YELLOW-BILLED MAGPIE

PLATE 26

CONTRIBUTED BY JEAN MYRON LINSDALE

HABITS

California contains within its borders the whole range of the yellow-billed magpie. Localities occupied are known with exhaustive detail. They are restricted to that part of the State west of the Sierra Nevada from Shasta County, at the north end of the Sacramento Valley, southward to Ventura and Kern Counties, and are chiefly in the Sacramento and San Joaquin Valleys and the coastal valleys south of San Francisco. The area occupied is less than 150 miles wide and extends for about 500 miles from north to south.

The yellow-billed magpie is obviously a close relative of the black-billed magpie. Some persons like to think of this relationship as subspecific; others consider the two kinds as distinct species. Probably it makes little difference which way we think of them so long as we recognize the nature of the characters and ranges of the birds, insofar as they represent the true relationship, for it is scarcely possible to prove the correctness of either opinion. The most nearly obvious distinctions have to do with the possession of the yellow pigment, which shows in the bill, claws, and some places in the skin of the yellow-billed form, and its generally smaller size. Some differences in habits also may be seen on close study of the two birds. The ranges do not overlap; in fact, the gap separating them is about 50 miles wide at its narrowest place.

The situation is not much different on the opposite side of the range of the black-billed bird, where it approaches the nearest representative of the group in Asia. The relationship indicated there seems even more remote than that with the yellow-billed bird, but it is commonly recognized as a subspecific one. It is true that the birds in western Europe appear structurally to be much like the American black-billed ones, although these two kinds are separated by several forms that differ considerably from them. Somewhat similar problems arise in determining the phylogenetic status of the magpies in southwestern Europe and northern Africa. The anatomical, behavioral, and geographical situations there are much like the ones encountered in California. The whole question of relationships and trends of variation in the magpies is an attractive one for the person who may be able to collect the pertinent evidence.

A feature common to situations inhabited by the yellow-billed magpie is the presence of tall trees, usually in linear arrangement bordering streams or in parklike groves, either on valley floors or on hills. Another is open ground either bare, as in well-kept orchards, or comprising cultivated fields or grassy pastures and slopes. This particular kind of magpie appears not to extend its range into lands where there is frequent high wind, long, snowy, and cold winters, or especially dry and hot summers. The nature of the restriction in each case is more or less obscure—sometimes, as with the strong wind, it is evidently some direct influence of the environment upon the birds. Again, the limitation may act indirectly by so reducing the available supply of food that magpies could not exist for the whole year or for a time sufficient to rear their young. Restrictions of water supply may be important in preventing spread of these birds into desert regions. Water seems to be necessary for the birds to drink and also as an aid to nest-building.

Courtship.—Observations pertaining to courtship in the magpie are hard to separate clearly from those concerned with competition and with intolerance exhibited toward other individuals. Until the suitable distinctions between these types of behavior can be made, it may be better to consider all the observations made in the early part of the breeding season, which appear to indicate special attention of one member of a mated pair toward the other member. Also it may be permissible to extend the scope of this topic to include examples of attention directed toward other birds, even of other species, exhibited at this season.

Observations made on the Frances Simes Hastings Natural History Reservation, in Monterey County, Calif., where most of the material contained in this account was obtained by numerous watchers, show that activities connected with nesting begin early in fall. In one instance a magpie in a morning early in October (3d) flew from a sycamore into a locust, carrying a piece of sycamore bark 3 by 2 inches in dimensions. It hopped about, eyeing four other magpies already in the tree. After visiting three twig clusters such as provide nest sites, the bird dropped the bark and paid no further attention to it as it fell to the ground. The other birds ignored it also. One on October 31 was carrying a 6-inch-long stick or root in its bill. This behavior was considered to be a sign of early nest-building.

Another and more easily interpreted example was noted on the morning of November 12, 1937, when one of two magpies in a regularly used blue-oak nesting tree was carrying a dead twig about 10 inches long as it moved from branch to branch. At about the same hour the next morning the two magpies were seen again in this tree and one of them was carrying a 10-inch stick. A few seconds later there was excited calling and then a pursuit flight round and round in the top of the tree. Several magpies flew to the tree and joined in the chase.

Fifteen minutes later two magpies flew into this blue oak and wiped their bills on branches, apparently returning from a foraging expedition. After a few seconds they flew, together, downslope to where two others were foraging, but when these flew up toward them and called, the first two circled back and returned to the tree. Later they left together in another direction. This behavior surely indicates segregation by pairs.

After another return to the tree these two magpies flew down and joined the two they had approached earlier. All four strutted about with tails held high for a few minutes, and then the first two flew back to the oak.

Further evidence of segregation into pairs in fall was recorded on November 18. Two birds were foraging in a stubble field and occasionally flying up to fence posts. One took some food, probably a large insect, to a post where the morsel was picked to pieces. When a person approached the birds, one flew off to willows along the adjacent creek, while the other, engrossed in its foraging, stayed a moment longer and then flew off to an oak in the opposite direction. The two then called to each other with several rattling calls, which were answered. Other calls heard up and down the canyon indicated that magpies were scattered over an area extending for several hundred yards. Several times birds in flight were in pairs.

In the afternoon two pairs were perched in a locust tree, the birds of each pair sitting within a few inches of each other. Low, musical notes, a primitive song, were heard. Both pairs flew off at about the same time. Other magpies, also active and noisy in the vicinity, were flying from one tree top to another, usually in pairs. Even when they started for the roosting place in the evening, magpies on this day seemed still to be segregated by pairs. Two birds started off across the canyon, followed immediately by ten others from various points. These converged until all were strung out in a single file along the same line of flight.

It is desirable to keep in mind, in considering these happenings, that they took place before the start of winter, long before the start of nest-building and several months before time for egglaying. Through much of this interval most of the magpie activities, too, are centered about the flock, in the daytime as well as at night.

Fighting among magpies takes place generally through the spring months, beginning, in the yellow-billed form, usually in January. On one of these mornings, January 20, when rain was threatening, magpies seemed to be more quarrelsome than usual on the Hastings Reservation. Three were flying at one another. One would make a short dash at another, which would fly out of reach and then, perhaps, return the attack. Then the third one would attack one of the others. Later, one of five magpies in a tree seemed to be the object of occasional attacks by two of the others. Three or four times when this one hopped to a lower branch, the two jumped at it, causing it to hop out of the way. Occasionally it picked a leaf and let it fall. Once it tugged at a twig but was rather apathetic about it and was driven off by the others.

Apparently members of a mated pair do not always join together in the pursuits. Often a third bird follows the quarreling two but takes no part in the conflict. Once one of three birds was seen to fly to and enter a nest, not taking any nesting material, but it was routed out almost immediately by one of the other two, and all three flew away together. This casualness seems to be a normal feature of the fighting. Often in the nest-building season a magpie can be seen making a short dash toward another, evidently without serious intent, for no response can be detected, and there is no further indication of enmity. Sometimes excited vocal sounds among a small group are the only indication of quarreling, and there is no apparent reason for conflict.

After a brief fight between two magpies on the ground beneath a nesting-tree, one bird called loudly about five times. Several magpies within 30 feet of this spot then quickly flew there, whereupon one of the first two flew away about 20 feet. This ended the disturbance, and the magpies scattered and resumed their foraging.

Fighting in the nesting season does not always take place at the nest. One morning six magpies were foraging in a small pasture beside a creek. Two birds started fighting, and soon two more out of the group were fighting. When the fighting, which lasted only a short time, stopped, one of each pair of fighters went off with one of the other pair. Apparently the two males were fighting, and at the same time the two females were in combat.

Encounters between pairs from adjacent nests in the incubation period were watched on a morning early in April. Twice, one pair went to a nest tree other than their own. The first time, the pair quarreled on the roof of a chicken pen, with the male from this nest, and immediately the female flew down to join the group, but there was no more fighting. Next time, when the same three birds were on the ground directly under the nest, the brooding female flew toward them with many excited calls.

On another occasion the four birds from two nests in trees at opposite ends of a barn were together for about 5 minutes at one corner of the barn. Their loud calls indicated excitement. One, with raised tail, quivered its wings slightly, possibly indicating an early stage in the begging which the females develop. Then there was fighting in which all four birds took part, but which led to no decisive conclusion. Finally one took a stick to one nest, and its mate tried to carry one that was too heavy, so it went to the nest with no load. Both birds of the other pair then went to their nest. The purpose of the fight was obscure; possibly there was no immediate purpose, but only an indistinct urge to fight.

Study of numerous examples such as have been recounted brings the conclusion that the accounts reported so often as examples of courtship and pairing in the European magpie may have been encounters between groups of birds already paired. The pursuits could have been merely attempts to drive away intruders. And the congregation of small assemblies of excited birds could have been exhibitions of the common magpie trait of hurrying to investigate any disturbance. Also the reported examples have occurred too late in the nesting season to expect them to represent the very earliest stage of nesting. Recent observations indicate that pairs are well established in fall and that spring is the season for noisy squabbles incident to competition for nest sites or indicators of jealousy toward intruders. Until marked individuals can be traced through the whole cycle, it is not justifiable to consider this interpretation as conclusively established, but it now seems more reasonable than the traditional one.

There are other segments in the series of actions that amount almost to preparation for the behavior to come in the incubation period, and these are to be observed before, through, and after the period of nest building. Even though the birds are seen oftenest in small groups or flocks, it is probable that the units in the organization are pairs that remain together throughout the year. During and after the long period of nest building, or reconstruction, a large share of the time is spent at or near the nest. The two birds of each pair spend several hours of each fair day perched side by side on some limb close to the site. At such times one of them often utters a song that I have been able to hear as far away as 100 yards. There are other indications that during this preincubation time a magpie's attention is largely centered about its nest and its mate.

One of these attentions is the preening of one member of the pair by the other, presumably the male. I had opportunity to watch this at close range at the San Diego Zoo. In a cage of mixed kinds of corvids there were two yellow-billed magpies, considered by their keeper to be a mated pair. During most of the time I watched, one bird, apparently the male, was perched close to the other, and was working its opened bill through the feathers about, mostly on top of, the head of its mate. This is just what I have seen mated pairs do many times in the wild. The feathers were preened and worked over just as if the bird were searching for parasites, but the real significance of the behavior must be connected with mating. Most of the wild birds observed behaving in this manner have been perched directly on the nest or on a limb very close to it.

The most conspicuous habit in the series connected with courtship in the magpies is mate-feeding by the male. This begins to be developed at about the time the nest is completed and becomes well established by the time incubation begins. One demonstration of an early stage in the development of this habit was watched on a day early in March. One magpie was walking in a circle about 5 feet in diameter. It was fluttering its wings and walking around another magpie, which it seemed to keep in the circle. The second bird walked just a few inches ahead of the fluttering one, which kept its tail turned toward the center of the circle. When a third magpie lit nearby, the antics of the two birds stopped and they began to feed.

Another pair demonstrated the early stages in the establishment of the mate-feeding behavior. These two birds were foraging in a grainfield where the ground was nearly bare. The male walked about, paying little attention to its mate. The female at first ran after and put herself in front of the male, facing him with bill open, head lowered, and wings quivering. This bird seemed to hold its wings less widely opened and to move them more rapidly than did other individuals noted. The response of the male was merely to turn and walk in another direction. Once the female picked at some object on the ground, and immediately the wing-quivering reaction was aroused, and the bird hurried over to its mate, but again the response was negative. After about ten fruitless beggings the female began to pick up objects, presumably food, and for the next three or four minutes she was picking almost continuously, with only an occasional tendency to flutter the wings slightly. Next, the male flew to the top of a fence post. The female flew to the next post, and immediately upon alighting her wings were opened slightly. When the birds were on the ground, the female picked at objects much oftener than did the male. The supposition was that these actions were preliminary to actual incubation which was to begin shortly.

By late March, usually, food begging by females is conspicuous in yellow-billed magpie behavior. This is near the time of the start of incubation. In one such example the female of a pair was first noted perched just outside the nest, uttering the loud food-begging call. Later when the birds were back at the nest after an absence, they lit side by side, the female begging with widely spread wings, but no feeding was seen. Next it appeared that the male led the way to the nest, and when the female came near to it the male quickly left and the female entered and became quiet. It may be that the male thus coaxes the female back onto the nest to incubate when the urge is not strong, possibly in the early stages.

By the time all females are incubating, the late afternoon seems to be a normal hour for the female to come off and beg for food from the male. Males appear still reluctant to feed their mates, especially away from the nest, and they usually avoid the begging female, which crowds near with waving wings. At the nest they appear more tolerant, and it seems certain that feeding takes place at the nest as an inducement for the female to resume brooding. Often the feeding takes place wholly within the nest.

Late in the incubation period the brooding female appears restless and leaves the nest more often than in early stages. Then the feeding usually takes place in a tree but away from the nest itself. Usually the female flies out to meet the male on some nearby perch. It is possible also that the impulse to feed the female latterly becomes weaker in the male. They do not then, however, try to avoid the begging bird but will feed whenever she comes near. Sometimes, though, the female continues the pursuit and begging after it has received the food.

The forage range of individual male magpies during the incubation period varies from the near neighborhood of the nest to a place more than half a mile distant. Sometimes the bird hunts for food on the limbs and among the foliage of a tree, but oftener the foraging is done on the surface of the ground. A male from one nest tends to fly off in the same direction on all trips each day, but this direction may vary through the whole period. All the birds of a colony may forage over the same ground, or they may go in different directions, but, so far as I have been able to determine, they then ordinarily pay little attention to any magpie other than the brooding mate.

The mate-feeding is quickly terminated upon hatching of the young, and with the cessation of the persistent, loud calls, which are a part of the food-begging, the nesting colony becomes suddenly silent and the behavior is inconspicuous.

Presence of other birds about the nest is discouraged sometimes by magpies by vigorous pursuits. Two magpies watched in February were greatly concerned over a golden eagle that perched near their nest, and they tried repeatedly to drive it away. Special animosity is directed toward sparrow hawks in the vicinity of the nest, as if the magpies recognized the intent of these intruders. In one instance great effort was put forth to drive away two hawks from a nest, but when a western bluebird lit on a limb close to the nest, the magpie paid no attention to it. Once when a red-shafted flicker lit close to a magpie nest, the owner came immediately and drove it away. Similar effort has been watched with respect to California woodpeckers near occupied nests.

Other members of the Corvidae are treated with special enmity whenever one approaches a magpie nest. Magpies are able to drive away California jays ordinarily, but sometimes these smaller birds display an extra degree of persistence in refusing to leave the nest tree. Crows near a magpie nest arouse special activity, and they are driven away if it is possible. Sometimes they refuse to be driven and even turn on their pursuers and drive them from the site of their own nest. Once a nesting magpie attacked an intruding meadowlark with such fierceness that the two fell for 20 feet, or halfway to the ground, before the smaller bird escaped and fled with notes of alarm.

Defense of a nest site more than ordinarily effective against intrusion by a crow was noted on a morning early in February. A pair of magpies was discovered in a large valley oak, about a hundred feet from their nest site, where they had driven a crow to seek shelter in a thick clump of branches. One magpie would make a dash at the crow and retreat, and then the other would move toward it, but each took care to keep out of range of the crow's bill. Several times the crow dashed out after one or the other of the magpies, but always it retreated back to the protection of the limbs. This was kept up for 3 or 4 minutes, until four more magpies came, when the crow gave up, moved to the outer part of the tree, and then flew away. The magpies then dispersed.

Another incident in another year but in the same group of trees concerned a crow carrying a twig for its nest, which it had pulled from a blue oak about 80 feet from a new magpie nest. The pair of magpies kept such close watch of the crow and dashed toward it so frequently that it was unable to leave the tree with its stick. Finally, it placed the twig on a limb and tried to drive the magpies away, but this was not successful and it was forced to leave the tree without its twig.

Nearly all the examples of defense of nest site included in this section occurred in early stages of nest-building, before the start of incubation. When this stage is reached, the magpies seem too much occupied with their own program to pay much attention to other birds except on special occasion. Ordinarily this stage of nesting is reached nearly at the same time by almost all the pairs of magpies in a colony.

Nesting.—Habits connected with nesting in the yellow-billed magpie are, in general, like those of the black-billed species, but they contrast in several ways. Possibly the difference in nesting behavior between the two kinds seems more marked than in other types of behavior because the results of it, being definite objects, are more easily perceived by the human observer.

First, the nesting colonies are more compact and the nests are closer together in the yellow-billed form. This may have some connection with a more favorable foraging habitat that permits the yellow-billed form to live in a more gregarious society. Or it may reflect the result of some different need for group response to disturbance by intruders.

The actual position of the nest provides one major difference between the two kinds. In the yellow-billed one the nest is nearly always in some tall tree and far out on the limbs, or if in a medium-sized tree, it is likely to be in the periphery. Thus it is regularly at a different level and in a different site from the low, bushy one occupied by the American black-billed birds in their nesting.

Trees prominent among the ones nested in by yellow-billed magpies are sycamore, valley oak, live oak, blue oak, poplar, cottonwood, locust, and willow. One colony observed near Oroville by W. B. Davis tried repeatedly to nest in a clump of digger pines but with poor success, for these trees provided poor anchorage for the nests. They were easily dislodged by the wind, and sometimes the weight of the nest itself was enough to change the slope of the limb so that the structure would slide off to the ground. (See Linsdale, 1937.)

A curious item of yellow-billed magpie nesting, commented upon at length by Dawson (1923), is the resemblance of a nest to a clump of mistletoe. It happens that in California the area occupied by this bird and that occupied by two kinds of mistletoe are closely similar in their boundaries. Not only are the areas nearly the same, but the species of trees concerned are the same. Cottonwoods, sycamores, and valley oaks are the kinds of trees mainly involved in this peculiar relationship. The bird not only nests in trees having many clumps of this plant, but also it often builds actually within a mistletoe clump. Whether or not intentional selection is made by the bird for this purpose, it is obvious that the close resemblance of the two objects helps to screen the presence of nesting birds. Even a person experienced in detecting the nests is unable to distinguish one from a mistletoe cluster at a distance, so nearly alike are they in size, shape, and position. It seems possible that such a lot of decoys, even if the relation is the result of accident purely, might save some nests from discovery and destruction by persons not closely observant.

The inaccessibility of the nest because of its position on small limbs far above ground is sufficient to save it from the ordinary prospects for destruction by people climbing to it. Although the nests can be reached, the handicap is too great for most climbers. Forty to sixty feet is the normal height above ground for these nests. Thus the birds can live close to human habitation and nest with greater freedom from the kind of molestation ordinarily encountered by nesting colonies of black-billed magpies. This may account partly for the greater apparent lack of fear generally shown by the yellow-billed birds.

The mild winter climate in the range of the yellow-billed magpies seems to encourage, or rather to permit, an exceptionally early start at nest-building. In Monterey County, even in the mountains at the highest levels inhabited by the species, magpies regularly begin to build around the middle of December, before the shortest days come. Often a nest will reach a late stage of construction during a series of warm days at this season, but the coming of storms interrupts the progress, and the pairs rejoin the flock. With the return of warm, clear spells in February or March the building is quickly resumed. Normally the nests are completed soon enough for the laying to be completed before the end of March. Thus the egg-laying comes four to six weeks before the corresponding stage in the cycle of the black-billed birds living near the same latitude, but subjected to the more rigorous climate of the interior.

Warm, cloudless days late in January seem to arouse an extra amount of nesting activity, even when they follow as much as a month of nearly complete inactivity. Once, nest-building at lining stage on January 29 was carried on through a light rain. In three hours of morning watching, the pair carried 12 loads of material, sticks or mud, to the nest. Through a cloudy period the following morning the magpies were busy foraging, but when the sun broke through the clouds they went immediately to the nest. On the same date of the previous year, soon after a rain stopped and while it was still cloudy, several magpies were perched quietly in the vicinity of nest sites. One working pair left when the rain started again.

In this locality twigs for nests are regularly pulled from valley oaks, sycamores, and black locusts. Sometimes many in succession are tugged at before one can be loosened. The birds have some trouble in picking a route through the trees where the twigs they carry will not catch on the branches. During active nest-building, periods from 10 to 30 minutes elapse when no bird appears at the nest and when the pair is off foraging. In the active periods the whole effort of both the birds is directed to getting sticks to the nest and working them into place.

The urge for nest-building seems to grow stronger with the advance of the season. Also the member-pairs of a colony seem to approach such a synchronized program that they reach the stage of incubation at about the same time even though they do not start building together. However, some examples indicate that nests are sometimes begun long after the normal time. At the Hastings Reservation one season a pair of magpies was watched one morning, on May 11, busily carrying sticks to a nest in its early stages. Several sticks picked up from the ground were carried to it. A magpie was seen to enter this nest on July 24, but no actual use of it was made until the following year. Then a brood was brought off in the normal season.

Another late start at building a nest was noted in June. On the 19th a magpie carried a stick to a site in a fork about 50 feet up in a sycamore, and where 35 or more sticks already had been placed, many of them within the preceding 24 hours. No bird was seen about this nest again until the early morning of June 24, when each member of the pair brought a stick. Each bird then called and perched near the nest for about a minute and then they, separately, flew off to the ground. Again, a considerable quantity of material had been added since the preceding day. No more material was added. Two birds perched close to the site on June 27, but 5 days later all the magpies on the Reservation left for a period of days, thus apparently ending the story. But early in the morning of July 15 a noisy flock of magpies settled in this vicinity. One of the birds went three times to the partly built, late nest and crouching on it with wings aquiver uttered low, throaty, harsh calls, which sounded like *currow,* and turned around several times. Half an hour later the same performance was seen at the nest, but there was no further indication of its use at any later time.

Like the other kinds of magpie, the California one builds a nest that is sought by other birds as a home, but this use seems rather restricted to the sparrow hawk. Nearly every colony of yellow-billed magpies has at least one pair of nesting sparrow hawks. Although it may not be evident all through the season, there is considerable strife between these species when nest sites are being selected. After a given nest has been successfully defended and all the pairs are settled, the two species appear to take little notice of each other.

Pursuits of magpies by sparrow hawks are noted often in fall, beginning in September. Sometimes a magpie turns in a chase and pursues the hawk. These pursuits, however, may have little significance in the nesting activities. A different situation is present early in spring. An example was noted on an early day in March, when, just after 5:30 P.M., a sparrow hawk flew to a magpie nest in a sycamore. The two magpie owners came immediately and drove away the hawk. The possibility of the hawks taking permanent possession of a nest at this time of day, just before dark, may provide an explanation for the repeatedly observed circumstance that pairs of magpies keep an especially close guard in the tops of the trees over their nests for about half an hour each evening just before dark.

During the early part of the nesting season whenever sparrow hawks singly or in pairs approached and attempted to enter an occupied magpie nest, one or both of the rightful owners would come immediately and drive them from the vicinity. When smaller birds, for one example a flock of juncos, came near a magpie nest, the magpies paid no attention. They seemed to recognize the nature of the threat offered by sparrow hawks.

Eggs.—Seventy sets of eggs contained in the Museum of Vertebrate Zoology or collected by W. B. Davis made up a total of 455 eggs, or 6.5 eggs per set. Number in a set ranged from five to eight, and the modal number was seven. This indicates a slight tendency toward smaller sets than are laid by the black-billed kind.

Laying time for this bird is usually the latter part of March. Late nests are rare, and as already indicated they are almost certainly never completed or used in the season they are started. Extreme dates for nests with eggs are March 30 and June 2. All but six of the 70 sets mentioned above were collected in April. This no doubt indicates a shorter, and earlier, season suitable for nesting than that of the black-billed magpie.

Dawson (1923) described coloration of the eggs as yellowish glaucous or pale olive-buff, finely and rather uniformly speckled and spotted with buffy brown, or citrine drab, or grayish olive, or deep grayish olive. A considerable degree of variation in color was observed by Kaeding (1897) in the 30 or more sets of eggs he collected. Some were heavily blotched with lilac and buffy or purplish brown. Bendire (1895) observed that eggs with a greenish tinge in the ground color appeared more frequently in this than in the black-billed magpie.

Measurements of 195 eggs of this magpie were given by Dawson (1923) as follows: Average 30.8 by 22.4 millimeters (1.22 by 0.88 inches); index 72.1. Largest egg, 37 by 23.4 (1.46 by 0.92); smallest 26.7 by 20.3 (1.05 by 0.80). Measurements of 62 eggs in the United States National Museum were as follows (Bendire, 1895): Average 31.54 by 22.54 millimeters; largest 34.29 by 22.86; smallest 28.45 by 21.34. Kaeding (1897) has commented on the diversity in shape shown in his collection of over 30 sets; some eggs were short and rounded, while others were long and elliptical.

A set of eight fresh eggs ranged in weight from 7.6 to 8.8 grams, average 8.3, thus being considerably lighter than eggs of black-billed magpies.

Young.—Length of incubation period for the yellow-billed magpie is not definitely known but is assumed to be close to that of the black-billed one, or around 18 days.

Hatching of the young apparently changes the magpies to silent birds. One pair carried food to a nest at least 10 times in the 40 minutes it was watched on the morning of April 12, the visits thus averaging four minutes apart. Usually it was not possible to distinguish any objects in the bill, but once or twice supposed large insects could be seen projecting from the bill. The birds flew directly toward the site, but they perched on some limb 3 to 10 feet away and toward the main crown of the tree for a few seconds before going into the nest. The birds always entered the nest from the same side and left through the opposite one. Nearly always when one of the parents left the nest it flew directly to the ground and immediately began to search for food. On this date whenever a parent visited the nest, the young birds made calls that could be heard by a person 60 to 75 yards distant. These calls began when the parent entered the nest and they ceased as soon as it left. Once, both adults arrived at, and entered, the nest at about the same time. They flew away together a few seconds later, and one of them dropped a fecal sac from its bill when it had gone 50 yards.

These adults nearly always flew to a nearby orchard to forage, and four-fifths of their trips were to some freshly disked ground. On several trips one of the parents perched in the top of an orchard tree before going to the ground. They usually were silent, but once or twice a short series of notes was heard at the nest. The time spent at the nest on each visit averaged between 10 and 20 seconds.

Apparently typical behavior of a family of six young out of a nest and being fed by parents was watched for an hour near the time of nest-leaving. At first three of the young birds perched in a tree 30 yards from the nest. Later this tree held four young and two were in the nest.

The usual procedure in feeding on this day was for the young to keep a sharp lookout and, whenever an adult magpie came within sight, to start up a series of loud calls, higher in pitch than those ordinarily given by adults. If the approaching adult were not the parent of this brood, it continued on its way, and as soon as it had passed the cries would cease. If the approaching bird happened to be one of the parents, it would go to the group of young birds and the cries would be continued until a young one had been fed and the old one had left.

The cries of the young birds were accompanied by energetic flapping of the wings. The white on the wings helped to make the birds conspicuous while thus flapping, so that chances for the attention of the approaching bird being directed to them were increased. This may be an important function of this set of white markings. Whether developed because of its adaptive value or not, it certainly operates to disclose the locations of the young birds to the human observer and presumably likewise to the parent birds when they are approaching with food.

The brood of young magpies, being separated and in different trees, gave a good opportunity to see additional features of the response of parents to begging young. The destination of the approaching parent seemed to be controlled entirely by the amount of commotion made by the young. The group that began calling first and kept it up with greatest vigor was the one finally approached. Sometimes a parent abruptly changed its course when headed toward one group and went to another, apparently because of a greater persistence in begging there. Once, when an adult started to leave, it was attracted by calls from another group and turned back and went there. It was not determined whether any food was delivered to the second group.

The young magpies showed little ability to distinguish their own parents. Any magpie flying toward them aroused the cries and wing flapping. These ceased, however, as soon as the flying bird passed and took a course away from the young birds. Once the young birds begged when a California woodpecker flew over them. The amount of begging seemed to be a direct expression of the degree of hunger. Apparently the two young that stayed at the nest were not yet able to fly. The others could fly; hence they probably were larger and possibly they required more food than the ones at the nest. At least more trips were made to them by the parents. But the ones at the nest were not neglected. For a few trips after food was taken to the nest, the young ones there would remain almost quiet, giving only one or two notes during each visit.

When a parent landed in some tree other than the one holding the young birds, they would fly to that place, flap their wings, make loud calls, and attempt to get in front of the adult. The latter did not remain long after food was placed in the widely opened mouth of some one of the youngsters. Each parent, in turn, left and went to the nearby orchard to obtain another supply of food. The trips were about five minutes apart. The adults generally were quiet, but occasionally they uttered series of alarm notes, usually when away from the young ones.

Between feedings the young magpies moved about on the limbs of the tree by walking, hopping, and making short flights. Their legs appeared to be long, and their claws were the chief means of keeping a hold on the bark. When alighting they had difficulty in regaining a balance. Their tails were only 3 or 4 inches long. Not once was one seen on the ground. Their time was spent picking at the limbs, preening their feathers, or just drowsing. At frequent intervals a young magpie would raise both wings and stretch them over its back, partly folded, but would not extend them.

These young birds were quiet except when a flying bird approached them or they were being fed. During each feeding all the young kept their mouths opened widely while calling. Once one kept its bill widely opened as it flew from one tree to another. On another occasion a young bird flew out 15 or 20 feet to meet an approaching parent, which, however, paid no attention to it but continued on to the tree and fed another one. When a person tested their responses to disturbance by walking over to the tree, at first all the young uttered warning notes. After a few minutes they became quiet, and the ones at the nest withdrew into it. One of the other young ones flew to another part of the grove. Parents came, uttered alarm notes, and left. They returned in half an hour and there were more alarm notes.

In Monterey County a brood of bobtailed young at nest-leaving age was studied early in June. The parents came down to lower limbs within 6 or 8 feet of the intruding person to protest at his presence. Other adults came too. Notes of the adults and young differed considerably, the latter being weaker, softer, and higher. After being disturbed the young magpies moved into higher parts of the tree.

Another young bird, watched in early morning, was begging from an adult perched on a wire nearly 10 feet above ground. It crouched with wings quivering, held its bill near the adult's bill, and uttered low notes, but the old bird did not feed it. The youngster then flew down to the ground and foraged for itself.

An example of communication between adult and young was observed when a young magpie with tail two-thirds grown was handled in a room. Its cries attracted an adult (parent?), which perched on a limb outside the window and squawked long and loudly. Soon after the adult began to call, the young one stopped. The adult flew away. Again the young one called, the adult returned and squawked, and the young one became silent. When the young bird was released outside, the adult perched in a tree overhead, screaming loudly, but made no move. When a person caught the young bird again, however, the adult swooped down at him.

Plumages.—Plumages and changes of them in the yellow-billed magpie seem to be so nearly like those of the black-billed magpie, already described, as not to require separate treatment. Possibly the calendar of molt differs, but this has not been worked out.

On at least several of the magpies I noted on October 9, 1929, in the Sacramento Valley, bright yellow of the exposed skin could be seen extending back from the bill, below and nearly around the eye. On some, if not all, of the magpies observed on November 11, 1930, the yellow, bare area around the eye could be seen distinctly.

Four freshly killed birds from Santa Clara County were examined by me on October 19, 1929. All were in molt. In one, a female, the molt was nearly completed; the sheaths still showed on the contour feathers on the breast and around the head. The skin was yellowish, especially around the head, the base of the tail, and on the body at the bases of the feathers. The yellow bare space behind the eye was 10 by 10 millimeters in size. A male in the same stage of molt showed more yellow on the skin, especially on the under sides of the wings. Another female was farther along in its molt; it showed scarcely any yellow on the skin except around the head. All but the feathers of the throat and chin were free from sheaths. The fourth bird showed sheaths on the feathers about the head, those on the chin and throat being least developed.

Abnormal plumages in the magpie attract more than ordinary interest because of the possibility, which seems almost probability, that some of the existing geographic forms arose by the preservation of this kind of character. This preservation might have been accomplished by means of the kind of geographic isolation that now characterizes the yellow-billed kind. It is interesting, if not significant, that the yellow bill, which is the conspicuous mark of the Californian kind of magpie, has been discovered as an abnormality in other parts of the range of the genus.

Food.—Kalmbach's (1927) study of the food of this species made him conclude that it is somewhat more insectivorous than the black-billed species. At the same time, he pointed out, it is capable of committing practically all the offenses of which the latter is so frequently accused. He considered that its scarcity precluded the possibility of the yellow-billed magpie's doing serious damage. The stomachs examined indicated that 70 percent of the bird's food is obtained from animal matter and 30 percent from vegetable. Insects made up more than half the food. Conspicuous among these are grasshoppers, which appear to be most of the food after midsummer, until the cold weather of fall. Bees, ants, wasps, ground beetles, flies, carrion beetles, and true bugs ranked high. Carrion is consumed in winter and early in spring.

Observations on the manner of feeding have been recorded at length on the Hastings Reservation. Capture of flying insects on the wing is a habit regularly noted. During a period of warm sunshine on a January afternoon, magpies were making flights out and up from a dead oak on a knoll, presumably after insects. The flights ranged in length from 15 to 50 feet. At the end of each one the bird generally swooped and zigzagged up and down as if in pursuit of an insect. Return was to the same dead oak. Similar behavior was noted in the fall.

Another habit, characteristic of foraging magpies, is to search under objects such as chips of wood or cow dung. These sites are hiding places for a great variety of insects and other invertebrate animals. They are generally inaccessible to most foraging birds, which are too weak to uncover them, but magpies can get them with slight inconvenience. In addition, from the heaps of dung they often get grain.

Magpies keep a close watch for new food sources. They quickly find scraps of waste about houses, such as garbage or bits of food that may be thrown out on the ground. They watch other feeding animals, birds or mammals, and rush to retrieve any bit of food that may be lost or discarded. Other foraging magpies even are watched closely, and many pursuits occur when one attempts to carry some item of food. Any object too large to be swallowed immediately or to be carried away is likely to be the center of a contest so long as any of it remains. These encounters rarely reach the stage of actual combat.

To force others away from food, the magpies use a posture as a sort of bluff. Both parties in such a dispute stand very high, point their bills upward at nearly a 70° angle, throw out the breast and throat, and work the muscles as if producing calls. If any are made, they are inaudible to a person 50 feet away. The successful bluffer then walks toward the other bird as if to bump his chest against the other. This sometimes occurs, but oftener the gesture is sufficient to retire the opponent. This pose seems to leave its maker in extremely vulnerable position with sensitive throat exposed to attack, but no blows have been seen struck there. The retiring bird crouches down and shrinks aside, still holding its bill up.

Sometimes a bird resorts to blows instead of bluff when another becomes too persistent. Then a swift hop and peck at the head of the intruder drives it off. So long as the other birds do not try to feed, they are permitted to stand so close to the feeding bird as to bump it occasionally. When pursuits occur, they may be only for about twelve inches, but in the interval an onlooker usually takes possession, and frequently it then refuses to be driven away.

Some individuals merely wait their turn to feed. Occasionally one watches for a long time and then suddenly forces away the possessor. It may be that this period of watching serves to build up courage. Some individuals, which appear to the observer to be weaker ones, rush in to snatch morsels while the feeder tears loose another or pursues another bird. While feeding, these magpies often produce throaty songs, like pleasant squeals. Others squawk as they watch but do not sing.

Magpies exhibit the same sort of nervousness shown by smaller birds when they forage over open ground, and they commonly rush off at intervals to perch in trees or bushes. One morning 23 of them were foraging in a recently planted grainfield. When something disturbed them all flew nearly simultaneously into willows near a creek. If not badly frightened, some lit on fence posts instead. Usually they began to return to the field within 45 seconds. An occasional bird, however, dropped to forage in a pasture on the opposite side of the creek. Generally when two or more birds flew up, the whole flock rose, but one bird's leaving did not cause them to follow. Fewer and fewer returned to the field after each flight until the whole flock was foraging in the pasture.

Storage of food by magpies is noted regularly. It occurs oftenest in winter but has been observed also at other times of the year. Storage takes place usually in shallow pits dug by the magpie in the top layer of soil, but crevices among limbs of trees may be used too. The objects most often stored, at least in one locality, are acorns, but carcasses of small animals and left-over pieces of food may be stored also. Nearly always the cache is covered over with stems of grass or leaves and is so carefully hidden as to be nearly invisible. It may be found by a person only after marking the spot well. On occasion some object may be carried for a long time, as long as half an hour, and then buried, or it may be placed in the open on top of the ground and left. An item being carried may be laid on the ground while the bird examines or eats some other object. Acorns may be buried entire without the shell being opened or they may be partly eaten first. Whether magpies return to a cache once it has been hidden has not been observed, but they have been seen raiding the stores of other birds, always shortly after they were covered.

In some years acorns provide a large share of the yellow-billed magpie's food for several months beginning in mid-September. Live oaks and valley oaks provide most of the ones eaten on the Hastings Reservation. Sometimes the acorns are picked up from the ground, but oftener they are taken directly from the tree. The acorn is then carried to the top of some fence post or to a limb in another tree, where it is held underfoot and pounded until the shell is broken and the desired portion of the kernel is removed. Normally the acorn is carried with the small **end pointing ahead** and only one is taken, but sometimes it is turned, and the bird carries an extra one. Limbs of blue oak, black locust, and valley oak are used as an anvil for pounding the acorn, but the valley oak seems to be the favorite. Apparently the rougher bark and larger branches make this tree more satisfactory.

In hammering an acorn the bird does not strike with vertical blows; instead the bill comes down toward the feet at an angle of 80° from the horizontal. The bill is not lifted immediately on striking the acorn but is pushed into it. Sometimes hundreds of blows, in series of about 20, are required to open the shell. A magpie exhibits jealousy over an acorn in its possession and normally takes it to some secluded spot away from the other birds. Also it appears reluctant to leave one when disturbed by a person. Effort is likely to be made to retrieve an acorn that is dropped by accident. However, on their own accord, they commonly discard any acorn that proves difficult to open, and many partly eaten ones are left for another occasion or where some other bird can get them. These traits are exhibited with respect to other kinds of food, but they are more easily watched when large objects like acorns are concerned.

Additional mannerisms are shown by the following account of an incident watched on the Hastings Reservation. Four foraging magpies, on November 18, assembled under a live oak and looked up at the periphery of the tree where another one was clinging to an acorn-laden limb, which bent to a 60° slope under the weight of the bird. An acorn was wrenched free and carried to the ground. Another bird flew up and, after searching in three places, found a suitable acorn. This was seized at its base, transverse to the axis of the bird's bill, and wrenched free. The acorn fell to the ground, and the bird followed it swiftly, but too late, for one of two magpies on the ground had reached it and then the retriever refused to give it up. The dispossessed bird returned to the tree and obtained another acorn, which also fell. But this one it followed so swiftly that the other two birds could not reach it, and it retrieved and carried away the acorn with a squawk. The bird that had stolen the first acorn deserted it to try for the next one to fall and then returned to the first acorn and began to hammer it. As many as eight magpies were seen carrying acorns under this tree. Nearly all the acorns were obtained by loosening them and following them to the ground. If no other magpie was close, the bird got its acorn; otherwise a bird already on the ground got it. Each acorn finally retrieved was carried away, placed underfoot, and hammered open.

Other kinds of food obtained regularly from plants in this vicinity were figs and fruits of poisonoak, coffeeberry, and grapes. The fruits of coffeeberry ordinarily are carried to some perch where the pulp is extracted and swallowed and the skin is discarded. The seeds seem to be swallowed sometimes and discarded at other times.

When magpies are feeding broods of young they sometimes discover the nests of other birds and take the contents, but this happens on rare occasions. Once at the end of May, in the Sacramento Valley, I observed a commotion caused by a magpie in a large colony of nesting cliff swallows. At my close approach the magpie flew out from under the bridge that held the nests. It went back again and then out and away. All this time the magpie was being pursued by the large flock of adult swallows. Circumstances indicated clearly that the magpie was there to get young swallows, which at that time filled most of the nests. But no actual raid was seen. Many of the nests had long entrance tunnels, and they appeared too long to permit a magpie to reach into the main cavity of the nest.

Nearly 10 years elapsed before I again found a yellow-billed magpie molesting nests of small birds. In one tree where a pair of magpies and three pairs of Bullock orioles each had nests, several encounters were noticed between the species. One morning a magpie went to one of the oriole nests and poked its head into the cavity, but just what happened was not learned. It left and was pursued by the orioles. On other occasions the orioles were particularly bold in attacking young magpies just out of the nest.

In the same season and close to this spot one magpie acquired the habit of searching out and destroying linnet nests placed in crevices about the farm buildings. Apparently these raids were made to get the young linnets, but actual captures were not seen.

Behavior.—The yellow-billed magpie exhibits the general manner of the black-billed kind, but it appears less timid throughout its range and seems to live closer to human habitations. Possibly the black-billed magpie would respond just as quickly to the near presence of people if permitted to do so, but it regularly encounters a more aggressive disfavor. Whatever the cause, it appears obvious that the birds live closer about houses in California and they encounter less molestation. This means that it is easier to study them, for they willingly permit approach in many places to within 10 or 15 feet. At the same time they retain the capability of cautiously watching for danger, and they quickly slip away if disturbed by shooting. Much of the area occupied by the species is relatively free from this danger.

On the ground a magpie walks, hops, runs, dodges, or makes short leaps with the aid of its wings. The flight is usually short, and in the wind it is wavering, for the long tail then proves to be a hindrance, although ordinarily it gives the bird a graceful appearance. Types of perching places oftenest used when the birds are not on the ground are the larger-sized limbs of big trees. On telephone wires they appear to have no difficulty in balancing. When coming to a stop the bird may jerk its tail upward four or five times and then maintain its balance with the tail held close to 45° below the horizontal. Foraging birds may jerk their tails upward independently of need for balance. A slight jerk of the tail often accompanies a vocal note.

When starting to fly away after being disturbed the birds do not flap evenly. Several spurts may be distinguished. In one example the rhythm was three easy beats followed by two vigorous ones. The contrast was audible as well as visible in a bird flying 25 feet overhead. On another occasion this irregular flight consisted of five to eight rather weak wing beats and then four or five rapid, strong beats. The flight of the several individuals, however, was not synchronized. Another habit of flight observed often is that of gliding downward for long distances, extending the wings, and braking the speed at regular intervals.

Flocks of yellow-billed magpies may be seen all through the nesting period, but these are mainly temporary formations, probably accidental assemblages. When the young birds leave their homes, however, the flocking tendency soon becomes conspicuous again, and the birds form definite aggregations that have the quality of permanency. The unit of organization for this species then changes from the pair to the flock. For the next half year the behavior of the flock is our chief concern with this species.

A striking example of responses of members of a flock to a certain note of one of their species was observed in late November. At 4:30 P.M., after the birds had congregated and just before they started off to roost, they were perching quietly in some oaks. A dead snag broke under one of the magpies in the vicinity, causing it to fly away squawking in alarm. The flock, calling noisily, flew in a compact body to the scene of the disturbance. The birds perched on the remaining limbs of the snag and on nearby trees and then became silent. From there they finally flew off, 15 and 20 minutes later, to roost.

Roosting time is the occasion for congregation of the largest and most compact flocks. The birds assemble in tree tops and then seem to await the move of one to act as leader. Sometimes the group flies out to join one or more individuals flying overhead; sometimes they follow one of their number as it makes a start from the perching tree. If one bird turns back the whole group is apt to follow, whether the bird is ahead of or behind the others. On such occasions they are likely to come swooping back down to trees or thickets, swerving erratically, and wings whistling. In these assemblages there is apparent a great reluctance to make the first move, but once it is made the remaining birds rush to follow.

Daily routine of activity in the yellow-billed magpie is, perhaps, more easily traced than in most other birds, mainly because this bird is so conspicuous. Also at many places the magpies are so continuously and so easily accessible for observation in the vicinity of human living quarters that it is possible to trace the daily and seasonal changes year after year. Thus it becomes obvious that while the daily program is fairly rigid it is also highly variable.

The recorded program of the magpies on a normal day begins with the arrival of the flock, as a unit or in sections, from the roost. After a reassembly in trees, the birds scatter somewhat and begin to forage. Late in the morning they retire to trees for a midday rest, which is broken for another period of feeding before they form another group to fly off to roost. Through the main part of the nesting period this behavior is modified considerably by the necessity of keeping close to the nests.

Magpies regularly congregate to roost in a group through most of the year outside the nesting season. The site oftenest used on the Hastings Reservation is in a small ravine about a hundred feet wide, facing the west, and grown over with live oaks. The magpies roost in these dense trees. Each night, nearly an hour before finally settling at the roost, the birds assemble in sycamores or oaks in the canyon or the low hills a quarter to a half mile to the north of the roost. Half an hour after congregating, they fly to the roost. The assembling flock seems to become more and more unified, the longer the birds stay. Often there are squabbles with other birds, as crows or hawks, in which the whole group participates, at least vocally.

For 10 or 15 minutes preceding the flight across the canyon the magpies are rather silent. They perch mostly in tree tops, several in a tree, and there is little foraging. This period is followed by a series of outbursts of calls or a single one. Large groups make greater outbursts. The flight then begins. After a few outcries the birds become quiet as they fly more slowly and gain altitude steadily. The destination of this flight is a group of trees, usually leafless black oaks, used as gathering places both morning and night. Ten or fifteen minutes are required for all the birds to make the flight. Cold, strong wind, cloudiness, and rain tend to advance the time of flight across the canyon. Encounter with some other species tends to delay it. Change of roosting place from a common gathering place outside the normal daytime range of the colony to the nest site occurs usually in January.

Response to disturbance on the long flight to the roost is indicated sometimes by the birds when they suddenly change the course of their flight and dive back downward to the tops of thickets of trees. Their wings make a great roar, then all is silent. Within a short time, two minutes in one example, the flock rises and proceeds normally on its way.

Departure of the magpies from the roost on a fall morning is somewhat as follows: The birds fly up from the roost in live oaks in a ravine and enter large, leafless black oaks on a ridge. Calls are to be heard often before any birds appear and as early as 20 minutes before they finally leave the hill. The flight to the exposed trees is made singly or in pairs, and the birds perch silently, with heads drawn down close to their shoulders. They finally become vociferous, but the calls are short and quiet compared with ones made later in the day. Calls increase slightly or cease altogether before the birds leave. Gradually the single birds begin to move about and combine to make small groups. Sometimes all these groups unite into one big one, especially in disturbed weather, as rain, fog, strong wind, or low temperature. Finally the magpies leave the hill and fly, swiftly and low, to a wooded knoll on the canyon floor, where the long columns of birds converge in the tops of one or two trees. Calls become louder and more frequent than they have been on the hill or in the flight. If the groups are small, 10 or 15 minutes are required for all the magpies to leave the hill; if large, the time may be as little as 5 minutes. Next, the birds scatter from the trees to the ground.

Change in time of sunrise is followed closely by change in time of roost-leaving by the magpies, but there is considerable variation in the time of the actual flight from the hill. On many mornings, especially in December, the magpies, instead of all going to the lower part of the canyon, split up into groups, and some of them fly directly across the canyon to the top of another sunlit, warm hill. From there they move back later in the morning to the floor of the canyon.

Behavior of magpie flocks at the start of their day on the Hastings Reservation was observed on several occasions in the second half of July in 1938. Once, at 5:55 A.M., an observer suddenly became aware of raucous magpie calls. A flock in compact formation arrived near the center of the normal nesting area and split into three groups of six or seven birds each. Twenty were counted in all. Two groups lit in blue oaks, the third in a sycamore. All were calling loudly, harshly, and continuously. There was a constant interchange of individuals between the groups. The birds moved into many trees but stayed in the top branches. When they first arrived the din was terrible, as all 20 birds squawked loudly at the same time. Twenty-five minutes later the birds had spread out and the calls were more widely spaced.

Usually only two to four birds were calling at once. Two came down to drink at a water trough, but none had gone to the ground. The calling slowed down so that intervals of 10 to 15 seconds elapsed without a sound. By 6:30 the interchange from tree to tree had ceased.

In another 15 minutes small groups of two or three birds began to move off toward the north and the number of calls was still further reduced, so that as many as 45 seconds sometimes passed with no sound. Soon all the magpies had left the area where they had first settled.

Water troughs on the Hastings Reservation, originally set up for cattle, provided water for birds, but their shape proved to be a slight handicap in use. Magpies regularly bathe at these troughs by standing on the rim, tipping forward, and flapping their wings. They then fly to nearby trees to dry their plumage. A different procedure was noted on a cloudy, windy afternoon in January when a magpie drank twice from one of these troughs. The bird then jumped about 6 inches into the air and, with beating wings, gradually lowered itself until belly and feet touched the water. With the tail held up so as not to touch the water, it kept this position for about 15 seconds and then flew to the top of a nearby post to rest. After repeating this three times at one-minute intervals, the magpie flew to a locust tree where it ruffled and shook its plumage, picked at one or two breast feathers, and flew back to the trough. It perched beside another drinking magpie for two minutes and then took two more dips. The other magpie then drove this one off to a fence post where it dried its plumage and the two flew off to forage.

In many parts of California, for example in the Sacramento Valley, the planting of trees and the extension of cultivation have apparently favored the local spread of magpies. Study of present-day conditions in that region indicates that extension of human occupation of this land has, also, over a long period of years, resulted in increased numbers of this bird there. At an earlier time, from 1850 to 1890, there was a period of persistent destruction of magpies in California, which resulted in greater wariness of the birds and led to a disappearance of the species from some localities on the edge of its range. Besides the direct killing by shooting, magpies in this area, according to the testimony of numerous observers, have been killed by placing poisoned bait to prevent their taking of cultivated crops, by poisoned baits placed for coyotes, and by poison used in rodent-control campaigns. Despite the rather widespread notion, however, that the yellow-billed magpie is rare and that it is on the verge of extinction, there seems to be at present no reason for immediate concern over its welfare as a species. Extermination might conceivably be possible, but it would be so expensive and difficult that it would not occur under ordinary circumstances.

The yellow-billed magpie exhibits the tendency shown by magpies elsewhere to be attracted to herds of large mammals. The birds are seen regularly about sheep, cattle, and horses, but they seldom cause any actual injury to these animals. Mostly they are after insects and grain, which they find in greater abundance close to domestic stock. Horses seem, ordinarily, unconcerned at the attentions of magpies. Once I watched a cow that appeared much disturbed by magpies; several times it moved quickly toward one on a fence post and by shaking of its head caused the bird to move on to the next post.

Magpies in the vicinity of one house developed an active feud with a sheep dog, which continued for several months. The birds learned that a certain whistle by a person meant that food was to be given to the dog. They always came too and sometimes arrived even before the animal. The resulting quarrels over bits of food seemed to trouble the dog so much that it would become aroused over the mere presence of magpies or other birds of similar size and would rush after them with many barks whenever they came close to the ground. Late on a summer afternoon a magpie, perched on a clothesline, was watching the dog eat a bone. Three times the dog started to leave and each time the magpie flew down to the spot only to be driven off by the return of the dog. On the fourth departure the dog did not return when the magpie flew down to the ground, picked up the bone in its bill, and carried it away for at least 60 feet.

Yellow-billed magpies may be called resident wherever they occur even though there may be periods of several days each year when not a single individual can be found. Usually the longest period of absence from the Hastings Reservation each year lasts for about 10 days for the species and possibly longer for many individuals, and it comes in the early part of July. Apparently the helpless young hold the parents at the nesting site even after living conditions may become unsuitable in the long, dry days of midsummer. When the young are able to fly and care for themselves, small groups of magpies may be seen for a few days, and then some morning it is realized that not a single magpie is in sight. How far and just where and why they go are questions that have not been answered. Before the birds come back to stay regularly, single individuals may show up for a few hours or a flock may come to roost for a night or so, but obviously these birds are not following the regular schedule which is the routine for the species for most of the year.

This well-marked break in the regularity of seasonal occurrence may result from some local peculiarity in the environment that makes it intolerable for a few weeks. The annual extreme in dryness usually reached at this time when there is a minimum of green vegetation, of animal activity, and of moisture on the ground may drive away these birds, as soon as they are free of nesting duties, along with other species that disappear at about the same time. The exodus may last only until the shortening of the days reduces the evaporation and brings better conditions. Movement toward the coast of only a few miles would bring the birds to cooler and moister places.

The annual departure of the magpies, however, may reflect merely physiological change in the birds independent of the conditions in their habitat at this season. After the young are released from parental care, there may be no attraction in one spot of ground to hold any of the birds—nothing to keep them from wandering freely. But after a rest of a few weeks, faint beginnings of a new reproductive cycle may require a definite home area, and thus the birds come back to begin anew the cycle they have so recently completed.

No doubt a nucleus of the returning birds consists of individuals that left the same place, but the recorded observations indicate that a different number and presumably a slightly different set of individuals return. Some of the recently hatched birds may stay in new spots; they may join with other wandering groups and go to their home sites; they may come back with the parent colony. Thus the returning number may be smaller or larger than the colony at the end of the nesting, but it is rarely of the same size. The stabilization of numbers may require several months, and always it extends over a much longer period than the actual absence of the species from the area.

Thus may be seen, in a species ordinarily considered as strictly resident, behavior that appears exactly like that of migratory kinds which leave for long periods and which travel long distances. Once more it appears that migration is a characteristic of all birds and may be exhibited only in lesser or greater degree. It is not necessarily a basis for sharply limited classifications of species.

Voice.—Special attention to study of the voice of the yellow-billed magpie led Richard Hunt to conclude that in fall the birds had only one type of utterance, which, however, was varied. (See Linsdale, 1937.) The three variations or phases listed here he considered distinct enough to be described separately. His statements have been verified in field observations by me. The three phases are as follows:

1. *Qua-qua, qua-qua-qua,* etc., given in series from two to six *qua's.*

The utterance is usually quite rapid when the *qua's* are more numerous. The note is loud and the expression is rather good natured or well disposed. The timber is raucous. It has more than a slight resemblance to that of the California woodpecker's "cracker" notes. When birds of the two species are heard calling at the same time, the timber

of the two calls is almost indistinguishable. An element in this utterance suggests the rich, harsh, scolding *chaack* note of Bullock's oriole.

2. *Quack?* A single note, rather mild in expression, yet querulous.
This note has the same general timber as No. 1.

3. *Queck* or *kek*. Sometimes uttered alone and sometimes heightened
from phase No. 2. The utterance has an almost absurdly weak tone.
It reminds the observer of the call of the black-necked stilt. It is more
piping than the other types of notes and is a little nuthatchlike. When
first heard it was written down as *pêip*. The sounds in this note are
less distinct and of the three types it is least spellable and least utter-
able by a human being.

Comparison of the voices of the two kinds of magpie in America is
difficult when the birds must be studied separately. Some observers
have been unable to distinguish them on this basis. Wheelock (1904),
however, considered the call note of the yellow-billed form as less harsh
and loud than that of the black-billed, and this is an observation that
might be anticipated after studying other habits and the surroundings
of the birds.

The primitive song similar to that of other corvids is produced often
by yellow-billed magpies in December, January, and February, and apparently it is a normal part of the early segments of the nesting season. Indications are that it has significance in the nesting habits and
possibly in other phases of magpie life.

Field marks.—The yellow bill provides an easy and certain means of
distinguishing this species from the black-billed kind at ordinary distances. Its slightly smaller size is of little help because the two kinds
do not occur together naturally. It may be separated from other birds
by the general characters of the black-billed magpie.

Predators.—The horned owl may sometimes eat magpies, but so far
the evidence is only circumstantial. At the Hasting Reservation, once in
June, 20 minutes after three magpies had gone to the roosting place, a
great horned owl flew up to a ridge near them where it hooted three
times. One of the magpies moved over to investigate and became very
excited, calling loudly for about four minutes before becoming quiet
again. Other disturbances heard at magpie roosts were thought to be
caused by the near presence of a horned owl. Most of these occurred
before the birds settled for the night or after they left their roosting trees.

A long series of observations of accipiters and yellow-billed magpies
brings the conclusion that magpies must sometimes be captured by sharp-
shinned or Cooper's hawks. In summer and fall flocks of magpies carry
on almost continuous squabbles with these hawks. Usually the hawks
appear to take the initiative in the pursuits, but actual captures have not

been seen, and many times the chases seem to be only a form of exercise. Many times when capture appeared certain, the hawk turned away just before reaching the magpie. Once two accipiters flew after the same magpie. Possibly these flights serve to make the magpies less cautious so that capture is easier when the hawk is really hungry.

One flock, in August, was flushed by a Cooper's hawk that flew into the tree. The hawk pursued the birds as they scattered and then re-formed a group, each one flying erratically and yelling in a sort of "confusion chorus." Termination of the chase was not seen, but it was thought that no capture was made.

Teamwork on the part of two magpies to drive away a sharp-shinned hawk was seen early in November. They took turns maneuvering into position to dive at the hawk as it pursued or fled from the other. The hawk soared upward, which it could do as fast as the magpies could fly. Thus it got above them and out of range of easy flight for them, but it was forced finally to leave the vicinity.

When a sharp-shinned hawk struck and carried off a *Zonotrichia,* one magpie fled before it, but four others immediately pursued it to a rose thicket, dived at it three times, and forced it to double back and seek refuge in a more dense thicket. The magpies then stationed themselves around the hawk, one above on a fence post, one in the bushes, and two on the ground, and they remained there watching silently for nearly five minutes.

In another example magpies in and close to a blue oak were excited over pursuits by a sharp-shinned hawk and a sparrow hawk, both with quarters in the same tree. The former was much more persistent in its drives, pursuing the magpies more swiftly and going closer to them. Each pursuit, however, was abandoned after about 50 feet, and the birds would return to the tree, the hawk in the lead. Behavior when the magpies were driven from the ground was much the same. On such occasions a harsh, growling note is uttered by each magpie just before the hawk reaches it, and this may have something to do with the latter's turning aside just before reaching the magpie. No magpie was touched, so far as could be seen.

Once three magpies, all making the growling note, joined in pursuit of a sharpshin, flying about 10 feet behind the hawk, and following it into a sycamore. Another time this hawk pursued a single magpie, which zigzagged to evade three attempts at capture and growled continuously. The mere presence of the hawk as well as its pursuits seemed to bother the magpies. After these disturbances the magpies moved to denser parts of the foliage of a tree and especially to places where there was a protective barrier of branches close overhead. Flocks pursued by hawks in the evening seemed to be harried more persistently than in chases at other times of the day.

DISTRIBUTION

Range.—Confined to California; nonmigratory.

The range of the yellow-billed magpie extends **north** in the Sacramento Valley to Redding and Anderson. To the **east** it is found to Smartsville, Placerville, Hornitos, casually Dunlap, and Three Rivers. The **southern** limits of its range are in the vicinity of Santa Paula, Santa Barbara, and the Santa Ynez River. **West** to San Luis Obispo, Paso Robles, and Monterey.

Egg dates.—California: 112 records, March 9 to June 2; 56 records, April 9 to 22, indicating the height of the season.

CORVUS CORAX PRINCIPALIS Ridgway

NORTHERN RAVEN

PLATES 27-34

HABITS

The raven is a cosmopolitan species, widely distributed over all the continents of the Northern Hemisphere; it has been separated into several subspecies, only two of which are recognized as North American. The range of this subspecies extends, according to the 1931 Check-list, from the Arctic regions in "northwestern Alaska, Melville Island, northern Ellesmere Island, and northern Greenland south to Washington, central Minnesota, Michigan, coast region of New Jersey (formerly), and Virginia, and in the higher Alleghanies to Georgia." This seems like a very extended and rather unusual distribution and suggests that Dr. H. C. Oberholser (1918) might be justified in giving the name *C. c. europhilus* to the bird he described from the Eastern United States.

The haunts of ravens and their behavior vary greatly in different portions of their range, depending on where they can most easily find their food and where they are least likely to be disturbed. In the far north they range widely over the open treeless tundra, along the seacoast and the banks of rivers, hunting for the carcasses of animals slain by hunters and the remains of sea-animal life washed up by the storms, or stealing the bait from fox traps; here they are also common about the Hudson's Bay Co. stations and the camps and villages of the natives, where they can usually find scraps and are not molested.

When we stopped for supplies at Ketchikan in southern Alaska, we found ravens very common and familiar. They came flocking down from the heavily forested mountains back of the town to compete with the gulls and crows for the garbage thrown out on the shore. They seemed much at home in the village also, perching unafraid on the roofs of houses or on the totem poles. They are useful as scavengers here and are not disturbed.

We found ravens common all through the treeless Aleutian Islands, frequenting the steep grassy hillsides and the rocky cliffs. In Iliuliuk Village on Unalaska Island they were especially abundant and absurdly tame. Along the beach and about the houses they were as tame as hens, sitting on the fences or on the roofs of houses like tame crows. They knew that they were safe here and made no attempt to fly away, unless we approached too near, when they merely hopped off to one side or flew a short distance to some low perch.

Farther south, along the Pacific coast and islands of Alaska, and on the Atlantic coast from Maine northward, ravens frequent the rocky cliffs along the shores and are especially apt to establish themselves in the vicinity of sea-bird colonies, where they can prey on the eggs and young of these birds. Here they are also found on the islands that are heavily wooded with spruces and other coniferous trees, sometimes placing their nests in the midst of heron colonies, which suffer from their depredations.

From Pennsylvania southward, ravens are mountain birds, living in the Carolinas usually above 3,000 feet, far above the range of the crows; from these heights they sometimes descend to the valleys, or even the islands along the coast, to forage among the colonies of sea birds. Dr. Samuel S. Dickey (MS.) tells me that in the mountains of Pennsylvania and the Virginias "most of them prefer to dwell among rocks, such as serpentine, quartzite, sandstone, and shale. They resort to perpendicular cliffs, to escarpments thrust above forests on the flanks of mountains, and to sloping talus beds in the valleys of streams. When such sites are molested by too frequent visits of mankind, or when blasting takes place for construction of railroads and highways, then ravens will move away. They will, if the case requires them to do so, take shelter in various species of evergreen growth." The Rev. J. J. Murray tells me that the raven is fairly common in Rockbridge County, in the center of the valley of Virginia. "It seems to me to be commoner now than it was 10 years ago. This is particularly true in the Blue Ridge Mountains."

Courtship.—Richard C. Harlow (1922), who has had considerable experience with ravens in Pennsylvania, believes that they remain mated for life. He bases this assumption on the fact that certain pairs that he has watched year after year show certain individual characteristics by which he can recognize them. The males show striking peculiarities in behavior and voice. Certain pairs always nest on cliffs, though suitable trees are readily available; other pairs always nest in trees, close to

available cliff sites; and the eggs of each female run true to form each
year. These are not, of course, positive proofs of his theory, but they
are at least suggestive. He says of the courtship:

> The pair return to the cliff together usually the first week in February, at
> first only for a short visit each day, and later several visits. A heavy storm at
> this time usually delays these visits for several days. At this time I have seen
> them go to the nesting ledge, the female usually alighting on the ledge and the
> male on a dead stub nearby and spend ten or fifteen minutes there. At this time
> they often soar together high up in the air with wing tips touching, the male
> always slightly above the female. At times he will give a wonderful display of
> his prowess on the wing, either dropping like a meteor for several hundred
> feet and fairly hissing through the air in the manner of the male Duck Hawk, or
> tumbling like a pigeon over and over. During this period also, I have found
> them perched together high up in an old dead tree caressing each other with
> bills touching.

Nesting.—In the far north, beyond the tree limit, ravens have to nest
on the cliffs, usually near the coast, and often on the same cliffs with
gyrfalcons. But where suitable trees are to be found, they often nest in
them. MacFarlane (1891) found this species abundant at Fort Anderson and on the lower Lockhart and Anderson Rivers. "All but one of
the eight recorded nests were situated on tall pines, and composed of
dry willow sticks and twigs and thickly lined with either deer hair or
dry mosses, grasses, and more or less hair from various animals."
Major Bendire (1895) says: "While nesting sites on cliffs are generally
resorted to along the seashore, in the interior of Alaska on the Yukon
River, as well as on the numerous streams in British North America
flowing into the Arctic Ocean, they resort to some extent to trees, probably on account of the absence of the cliffs. Mr. James Lockhart found
a nest in a cleft of a poplar tree, 20 feet from the ground, at Fort Yukon,
Alaska, on May 29, 1862. * * * Their nests resemble those of the American Raven in construction. Near the seashore they are usually lined
with dry grasses, mosses, and seaweed, while hair of the musk ox and
moose is often used when procurable in the interior."

In the Magdalen Islands I saw three nests, quite inaccessible with any
means at our disposal, on high rocky promontories facing the Gulf of
St. Lawrence. In northern Ungava, Lucien M. Turner (MS.) found
the ravens nesting on cliffs near the seashore and about the mouths
of rivers.

The northern raven breeds regularly on the wooded islands on the
coast of Maine, where I have seen several nests in the vicinity of Penobscot and Jerico Bays. On June 10, 1899, I visited Bradbury Island in
Penobscot Bay for the purpose of investigating a breeding colony of
great blue herons. This is a high island, with steep rocky sides and open

pastures in the center, and is heavily wooded at both ends with firs and spruces and a few white birches. There was a rather large colony of the herons here, and in the midst of the colony was a raven's nest. A pair of ravens were flying about overhead, croaking and cawing angrily, and on the ground nearby were three of the herons' eggs, with big holes in the ends and the contents still fresh, as if recently taken from a nest; evidently we had disturbed the ravens at their stolen feast.

During the next two years I came earlier and found several old and new nests on Dumpling and Fog Islands in Penobscot Bay, and on some of the islands in Jerico Bay. The nests were all in spruce trees in thick woods, at heights varying from 25 to 32 feet above ground. Most of them were conspicuous from the ground below, but one was well hidden in a thick top. They were mostly huge structures, 2 to 3 feet in diameter and nearly as much in height; evidently they are sometimes added to from year to year, as we know that the Dumpling Island nest was used for three years in succession. They were made of crooked sticks as large as a man's thumb, mixed with smaller sticks and twigs. The nests were deeply hollowed and were warmly lined with sheep's wool and sometimes a little usnea; in one nest there was a patchwork lining of black-and-white wool. These ravens evidently lay at irregular intervals, for on April 23, 1900, I examined a nest containing two fresh eggs and another with two lusty young.

But Maine ravens do not all nest on the coastal islands. Paul F. Eckstorm writes to me: "On March 28, 1940, I took a set of five eggs from a nest situated in a crevice of a cliff 27 feet above the highest shelf accessible on foot. The nest was about 4 feet in diameter from front to rear, with the cavity at the rear 6 inches from the back wall. The nest was made roughly of course sticks, largely hemlock, and lined entirely with deer hair taken from some old carcass. The top of the cliff bulges into a great overhang extending like a roof about 6 feet above and, in places, 10 feet beyond the nest site. The nest was located near a large pond and about 15 miles back from the general coastal trend. The cliff has a southern exposure and warms up in advance of the adjacent flatter country."

Mr. Harlow (1922) has given us a most comprehensive account of the nesting of the raven in Pennsylvania, from which I quote the following extracts:

There are two distinct types of nesting site chosen here in Pennsylvania—the cliff site and the tree site (the cliff nests outnumbering the tree nests in the proportion of about eight to one). * * *

One feature is almost invariably demanded by the cliff nesting Ravens and that is that the location be dark and well shaded. Usually the darkest available section of the cliff is selected where the ledges are shaded by hemlocks which often grow on the smallest ledge on the face of the cliff. Very frequently the nest will be placed under an overhanging tongue of rock so that it will be protected from above and I have yet to see a nest in use that is not sheltered either by trees or by an overhang. * * * The height of the cliff seems to be a secondary consideration to the shade, though rarely is a cliff with a straight drop of less than fifty feet chosen and they run from there up to two hundred feet.

In the case of the tree nesting Ravens, the first requisite they seem to demand is the highest available tree, and the second is good cover in the very top of the tree. The tree nests are giant structures over four feet across and yet the birds conceal them so well in the very top of the tree that they are frequently very hard to see from the ground. * * * The tree nests are usually placed in a double or triple vertical crotch from seventy to over one hundred feet up, nearly always the highest available strong crotch but in one instance a horizontal crotch four feet out on a large limb was used.

The base of the nest varies from little more than three feet to five feet in the largest nests with an average of almost four feet. The cavity averages a foot in diameter and six inches in depth, the depth varying considerably. * * * The base is composed almost entirely of dead branches and sticks, freshly broken by the birds themselves. When built upon last year's nest, the freshly broken sticks make a sharp line of contrast where they are built upon the old excrement bespattered rim of the previous year. Some of these dead branches are over three quarters of an inch in diameter and over three feet long. * * *

The two most constant features of the cup lining are bark shreds and deer hair, the latter predominating when available. * * * The bark strips, shreds and fibres are obtained from dead trees, underneath the rough outer bark and they frequently use grapevine shreds as well. Some nests are lined almost entirely with white hair from the belly of the deer and some with red from the back, the birds using just what is available from the carcass. Outside of these main features the lining varies according to material available in the various localities. Tufts of hair from domestic cattle or from dogs as well as horse hair are frequently found. Bits of fur from the skunk, opossum and wildcat, sheep wool, bits of green moss scraped from the sides of rocks are all used by various pairs. I have found one nest heavily felted with material which the birds had been picking from an old felt hat and in another lining were bits of rope. Perhaps the most striking nest was one containing a heavy lining of deer hair and flourishing on one side of the cavity was the entire tail of a deer. * * *

The Raven is essentially a solitary bird and the nests of different pairs are usually a considerable distance apart. The only pairs I know of which nest at all near to one another are six miles apart. I know of no bird which comes into direct contact with the Raven during the breeding season but the Duck Hawk. * * * There seems to be a mutual respect between the two species and though they have occasional disagreements I have known them to nest on ledges only forty feet apart, the Raven having young while the Duck Hawk had eggs.

Dr. Samuel S. Dickey has sent me some extensive and interesting notes on ravens in various parts of the country, but space will allow only a few extracts. His notes on Pennsylvania ravens agree very closely with the foregoing quotations from Mr. Harlow's published paper. Out of 17 nests recorded in his notes, 13 were on cliffs or ledges, 3 were in hemlocks at heights varying from 45 to 80 feet, and one was in a white pine at 85 feet above ground. He says that when the season is not too backward and cold ravens may begin carrying sticks for the nest during the middle of February, and he has seen nests finished as early as February 25, but that most nests are not ready for eggs until March. "Ravens usually take what they want rather near at hand, although they may move off some miles for substances suitable for the lining. I have known them to enter the forest, remain either in undergrowth or low branches, and shortly arise with a sizable stick in the bill. After the bird had arisen to a height of several hundred feet, it would begin to circle, the stick in its bill visible through a field glass. Then it would toss the stick loose from its hold, would snap at it, thrust forth the body and take it again, and even drop the stick and plunge admirably downward, taking the stick from the air before it struck the ground."

Walter B. Barrows (1912) mentions a nest, found by Dr. Max M. Peet on Isle Royale, Lake Superior, that was in a very unusual location. He quotes Dr. Peet as follows: "While exploring the ruins of the deserted town near the head of Siskowit Bay, on September 10, a nest of the Northern Raven was found in the old stamp mill. It was placed in the small hollow formerly occupied by the metal plate upon which the head of the stamp fell. The side walls of the stamp mill are broken down in places so that the entrance to the interior was simple."

Eggs.—The northern raven is said to lay two to eight eggs to a full set. Four and five are the commonest numbers. The largest sets seem to be found in the far north; MacFarlane (1891) says six to eight, but Harlow (1922) reports that in Pennsylvania sets of three are rather common and that certain pairs never lay more than three or four; he says that six is very rare and that he has only one record each of seven and two. Dr. Dickey records only one set of seven. The eggs are indistinguishable from those of the American raven, which are more fully described hereinafter.

Some eggs of eastern ravens are so heavily marked that the ground color is nearly obscured, and others are so faintly and sparingly marked that they resemble some types of eggs of the white-necked raven. Often dark and light types occur in the same set, suggesting that the pigment may have become nearly exhausted before the last egg was laid. The measurements of 50 eggs average 50.2 by 34.3 millimeters; the eggs showing the four extremes measure **56.0** by 33.3, 50.8 by **36.1**, **41.7** by 33.0, and 44.5 by **30.2** millimeters.

Young.—Several observers agree that the period of incubation is about three weeks and that the young remain in the nest about four weeks. Harlow (1922) says that during incubation "the male feeds the female upon the nest but does not as a rule sit upon the eggs except in cold stormy weather when the female leaves the nest for food."

Dr. Dickey says in his notes: "When the eggshells curl and burst, the infants squirm in the cup of the nest. They are weak organisms, streaked with orange, yellow, and dusky and having areas of dusky gray down upon them. They are gorged with food periodically, about every half hour during daylight hours, by both male and female parents. Thus they grow fast and within five days disclose bands of slate-blue pinfeather shafts upon their wings and tails, as well as in stripes on their breast and sides. The pinfeather shafts then disintegrate and scatter the deciduous scales; these fall into the nest and spot its rim. Thus the dull, lusterless first feathers appear; they almost conceal the bare skin coloration. Gradually the entire pinfeather scabbards disintegrate and the first plumage dominates."

W. Bryant Tyrrell has sent me some notes on two nests, found on ledges in Shenandoah National Park, Va. In one of these the young were just hatched on March 26, 1939, and were well feathered on April 23. He says that the young "stay in the nest four or five weeks, though the adults have to look after and feed them for some time after their leaving the nest."

Young ravens, during their first summer at least, are often absurdly tame. Langdon Gibson (1922) says that young birds that he observed in Greenland "were trusting and inquisitive. At our boat camp in August, 1891, on Hakluyt Island, some young birds alighting on the flat shelving rocks on which we were cooking our evening meal, literally walked into camp, and at distances of no more than fifteen feet, ate the entrails of Guillemots that we tossed to them. We found them playful and at the expense of 'Jack,' a Newfoundland dog, amused themselves by leading him a chase. The birds would allow 'Jack' to approach within a few feet and then with a flop or a hop, would keep just out of his reach."

Theed Pearse tells me that on Vancouver Island young ravens are very unsuspicious, settling on nearby low trees and gurgling, and allowing approach to within 25 or 30 feet, or flying over within easy gunshot range.

Young birds, taken from the nest shortly before they reach the flight stage and reared in captivity, make interesting and amusing pets, much like young crows in behavior.

Plumages.—Two young ravens that I found in a nest on the coast of Maine were about as large as pigeons; they had evidently been hatched blind and naked, for their eyes were not quite open, and they had developed only a scanty growth of grayish-brown down on the dorsal tract. They were not attractive objects; their abdomens were fat and distended, as if they had been well fed; and their great, gaping, red mouths were wide open, as they stretched up their heavy heads on their weak and shaky necks.

The development of the plumage is referred to above. The juvenal plumage is practically fully acquired, with most of the natal down rubbed off, before the young bird leaves the nest. In the full juvenal plumage, the wings and the tail are much like those of the adult, clear lustrous black with greenish and purplish reflections, but the contour plumage of the head and body is dull brownish black, without any metallic luster. A partial postjuvenal molt, involving the contour plumage and the lesser wing coverts, but not the rest of the wings and tail, occurs in summer, beginning in July or earlier; this molt is sometimes completed in July and sometimes not until August or early in September. This produces a first winter plumage that is practically adult, full lustrous black, with the peculiar shaggy and attenuated feathers on the throat. Adults have a complete postnuptial molt in summer and early in fall, apparently at about the same time as the young birds; I have two adults in my collection, from Alaska, that were in full molt, body, wings, and tail, on June 11; and in some cases the molt is not completed until October. The sexes are alike in all plumages. Spring birds show some signs of wear and fading, but apparently no molt. Theed Pearse tells me that molting is very irregular and that he has seen adults molting their primaries as early as May 15 and others still molting as late as October 21.

Food.—The northern raven is one of our most omnivorous birds and a filthy feeder. Almost any kind of animal food that it can catch, kill, or find is grist to its mill. In the far north, especially in winter, it must live largely on carrion, the carcasses of various animals that it finds cast up on the shores. Dr. Dickey was told that in the dead of winter, when hard pressed for food, ravens will follow the dog teams and fight for the steaming dung as soon as dropped by the dogs.

Dr. George M. Sutton (1932) writes of their winter feeding habits on Southampton Island: "Rarely, if ever, did they prey upon ptarmigans or Arctic Hares, though they were known to pursue and even occasionally to wait for lemmings; but their principal food appeared to be the carcasses of walruses, seals, or whales, which were located and regularly fed upon before the winter set in. A dead whale thus sometimes furnishes a flock of ravens sustenance for the winter, after the gulls have departed and the Polar Bears gone to sleep. In patrolling their range they keep an eye open for all seals killed at the edge of the floe, or for caribou, freshly dragged down by the Arctic Wolves. And there are always, of course, the fox-traps, where they can steal bait, pull the foxes to pieces, or tear up the Snowy Owls, which have been caught."

Lucien M. Turner says in his unpublished notes on Ungava: "In the fall of the year they eat great quantities of berries and, after having satiated their hunger, repair to the rocks on a point of land and digest them. Their stains are everywhere visible on the rocks." In October he found scores of ravens along the Koksoak River, "where they had collected to feed upon the refuse of the hundreds of carcasses of reindeer, which had been speared by the Indians and Eskimos, and decomposing along the banks, whither the winds and currents had drifted them."

In the summer time along the coast and islands of southern Alaska, where the ravens live in the vicinity of sea-bird colonies, they make an easy living by robbing the nests of gulls, murres, and cormorants. As soon as a nest is left unprotected, the ravens dash in, seize an egg or young bird, and fly off with it. When a man invades the colonies all the sea birds leave their nests, and the ravens make repeated raids, returning again and again to carry off egg after egg, concealing for future use what they cannot eat at once.

Theed Pearse mentions (MS.) some feeding habits of ravens on Vancouver Island. He has seen them while feeding on the tidal flats "fly up and down with a bump on wet sand and search the surrounding area, presumably for sandworms disturbed." One was seen following a grazing heifer, keeping close behind it and picking up the insects disturbed; one appeared to follow right at the heels of the beast, "kept looking up, then periodically it would fly up to the flank, either picking up an insect or, as the action suggested, impatient at the slowness of progress." He has also seen ravens following a plow, as the gulls do; and once he saw one "feeding on Saskatoon berries, from which it drove away a flock of crows." He says, in its favor: "During the years of great abundance here, there were broods of ducks raised close to where there would be 20 or more ravens each day. I never saw any sign of ravens attacking young birds or chickens, and the congested area was all farm land with chickens running about the fields."

J. A. Munro reports to me that the stomach of a raven, taken on July 25 in British Columbia, contained a mass of blackberry pulp and seeds, 90 percent, and the fragments of a shore crab; another, taken August 14, held 10 fly maggots, 70 percent, fragments of an amphibian, two winged ants, and 3 seeds.

Dr. Dickey (MS.) writes of the feeding habits of ravens in Pennsylvania: "Along the major rivers of the Appalachians I have noticed that they frequent the banks of streams to procure dead animal matter cast up by freshets. They take crayfish, mussels, minnows, fish, tadpoles, and frogs. Where mountain folk haul carcasses of horses and cows into lonely recesses of the uplands, I have known ravens to appear and cleanse the bones. They contend with crows, starlings, blue jays, and turkey buzzards for morsels of food. I have found that, when they have gorged themselves on organic matter, they will dig circular holes in sod, about 3 inches wide and 4 inches deep, in which they bury pieces of meat that they desire to have properly seasoned. They return and utilize it at an opportune time."

Reid McManus (1935) tells of a raven that entered a henhouse in New Brunswick, when food was scarce in the winter, and killed a sickly hen; it escaped when surprised but returned to feed and was killed; its stomach contained only a piece of skin from the hen and a few feathers. Mr. Harlow (1922) has known ravens "to eat the buds of various trees when hard pressed for food." There are several other items, not referred to above, that have been mentioned as included in the raven's varied diet, viz: Mice, rats, lizards, snakes, various insects such as beetles, grasshoppers, and crickets, several forms of marine invertebrates picked up along the seashore, and mollusks. The raven seems to have learned from the gulls, or perhaps the gulls have learned from the raven, the trick of breaking the shells of mollusks by dropping them on the rocks.

A study of the food of the raven would seem to indicate that it is not a serious menace to man's interests. The harm that it does to young lambs, poultry, or wild birds' eggs is probably overestimated and more than offset by the good it does in the destruction of injurious rodents and insects. Most ravens live far away from human habitations, and where they do come in contact with villages, trading posts, and camps in the north they are useful as scavengers.

Charles Macnamara tells me that in the lumber camps of Ontario in winter "the shanty men, working too far from their camp to return for dinner, were always careful to bury in the snow the flour bag containing their frugal meal of bread and pork, so as to hide it; for the raven, if he found it, would promptly tear it open with his powerful beak and devour the contents. The French Canadians interpreted the birds' hoarse cry as 'Poch! Poche!' ('Bag! Bag!'), and said he was calling for the lunch bag."

Francis Zirrer says in his notes that ravens "often frequent those parts of heavy timber where the waters of the spring thaw and later rains remain longest. Very little vegetation develops in such places; the ground remains mostly bare. In the rich, black humus, however, an enormous number of larvae of various species of Diptera live.

And the ravens, besides many other birds, take full advantage of the abundant and nutritious food. Sedately they walk, swinging their bodies from side to side, or jump awkwardly back and forth, turning the leaves and pieces of bark and decayed wood or boring after the small but juicy morsels. During this period, and only then, one hears their metallic click, sounding like the stroke of a light hammer on a piece of heavy tin—one of the most remarkable sounds in the north Wisconsin woodlands. No one lucky enough to hear it will pass it without marvel, comment and inquiry as to the origin of it."

Behavior.—The flight of the raven is so fully described under the following subspecies that it is hardly necessary to say anything further about it here. It shows great mastery of the air in its majestic flight; it can stand almost motionless in the teeth of a gale, hover in the air like a sparrow hawk, or take advantage of the upward current on a steep hillside to rise and circle like a large hawk. Mr. Pearse tells me that when these birds were so abundant there, there was a regular flight line night and morning to and from their feeding grounds toward the mountains in the interior of Vancouver Island; they always passed over sometime before dark and would return in the morning at a corresponding period after sunrise. They never went by in a flock, but in small parties of eight or more, once as many as 40. They probably had some roost in the interior. Baird, Brewer, and Ridgway (1874) mention a roost discovered by Captain Blakiston near Fort Carlton; his "attention was first drawn to it by noticing that about sunset all the Ravens, from all quarters, were flying towards this point. Returning to the fort in the evening by that quarter, he found a clump of aspen-trees, none of them more than twenty-five feet high, filled with Ravens, who, at his approach, took wing and flew round and round. He also noted the wonderful regularity with which they repaired to their roosting-place in the evening and left it again in the morning, by pairs, on their day's hunt. They always left in the morning, within a minute or two of the same time, earlier and earlier as the days grew longer, on cold or cloudy mornings a little later, usually just half an hour before sunrise."

The raven is one of our most sagacious birds, crafty, resourceful, adaptable, and quick to learn and profit by experience. Throughout most of its range and under ordinary circumstances it is exceedingly shy and wary; it is almost impossible to get within gunshot of one in the open; one is seldom seen flying from its nest, as it hears the intruder coming and departs; I have never seen one return to even the vicinity of its nest while I was near it. Yet it knows full well where and when it is safe; about the northern villages and stations, where it is appreciated as a scavenger and not molested, it is as tame as any dooryard bird; but even here it is always on the alert, and, if one picks up a stone or makes any other suspicious move, it is off in an instant. Kumlien (1879) relates the following, to illustrate its resourcefulness:

I have, on different occasions, witnessed them capture a young seal that lay basking in the sun near its hole. The first manoeuvre of the ravens was to sail leisurely over the seal, gradually lowering with each circle, till at last one of them dropped directly *into* the seal's hole, thus cutting off its retreat from the water. Its mate would then attack the seal, and endeavor to drag or drive it as far away from the hole as possible. The attacking raven seemed to *strike* the seal on the top of the head with its powerful bill, and thus break the tender skull. * * *

I witnessed a very amusing chase after a *Lepus glacialis*. There were two ravens, and they gave alternate chase to the hare. Sometimes the raven would catch the hare by the ears, and hare and raven would roll down the mountain side together thirty or forty feet, till the raven lost his hold, and then its companion would be on hand and renew the attack. They killed the hare in a short time, and immediately began devouring it. * * *

Young reindeer fall an easy prey to them. When they attack a young deer, there are generally six or seven in company, and about one-half the number act as relays, so that the deer is given no rest. The eyes are the first parts attacked, and are generally speedily plucked out, when the poor animal will thrash and flounder about till it kills itself.

C. J. Maynard (1896) writes: "Dr. E. L. Sturtevant informed me that he was at one time standing on a beach at Grand Menan, when he saw a Gannet soaring very high in the air with, what appeared to be, a black spot above and below it. The bird seemed distressed and continued to mount upwards until both dark spots were seen to be above it, when suddenly it fell from that immense height, struck the ground, and was actually dashed to pieces by the force of the shock. Dr. Sturtevant approached it, when a Raven sprang from the body and flew away."

The behavior of ravens with other species of birds, notably crows, hawks, and vultures, has been commented on by many observers, but it is not always apparent which is the aggressor. Emerson Tuttle writes to me that the raven "rarely, if ever, leaves a sentinel on watch, relying on the crow or the herring gull to give the alarm. Once on the ground among crows and herring gulls, the raven dominates. I have seen a gull utter his screaming challenge in the face of a raven, but once the raven moved forward, the gull gave way. I have seen the raven and the goshawk together on several occasions. I watched a young goshawk chase and strike at a raven. The raven did not seem disturbed, though each time the goshawk rolled to one side and struck at him, the raven let out an oath and avoided the touch by rolling and dropping. It would be reading too much into the episode to suggest that the raven enjoyed the chase, but such was the impression he gave. The goshawk tired first and gave it up."

Crows often mob ravens, as they do owls or hawks, but seldom seriously attack one. Dr. Dickey (MS.) writes: "Two ravens emerged from a gigantic cliff. All at once a turkey buzzard flew down near the cliff and acted as if it were searching for something. One raven pursued this buzzard and actually struck it; the raven continued to pursue the slow-moving buzzard until four crows drew near. The crows harassed the raven, but it was too nimble on the wing to be actually hit by them. The raven would move speedily to the right or left every time the crows struck. Then the mate of the first raven appeared from trees, and two of them were attacked by the four crows. The buzzard in the meantime joined the throng; all the birds ended up in an apparent playful manner on the wing near the crags; they continued, while I watched, to make dives and sallies at one another."

He tells, also, of a "vicious combat" that took place between a red-tailed hawk and a raven. "The raven, ired as it was about its molested nest, whipped and drove off the predator."

Rev. J. J. Murray writes to me: "I have reported in *The Auk,* on the word of a very trustworthy mountaineer, the amazing habit in the raven of worrying the turkey vulture until the vulture disgorges the food and then eating the vulture's vomit. I have commonly seen crows chase ravens, but have only once noted the reverse."

Ravens sometimes display decidedly playful tendencies (some of which are mentioned under the American raven), aerial acrobatic feats, and spectacular dives. Theed Pearse tells me that he has seen similar behavior. One bird was seen carrying a fir cone in its beak. The tall Douglas firs "seemed alive with ravens," and it was interesting to see them picking the cones; "the bird would fly up to the branch and hang onto the cone with its beak, with the wings partially extended, and get the cone off by tugging at it. There was one particular branch that seemed to attract them, at the top of a tall ragged tree open at the top. Birds would come to this same branch and clip off a small twig with the beak, sometimes holding it in the beak for a minute or so, even flying away with it, but usually the twig would be dropped when detached." He saw another playing in the air with what looked like a piece of dried skin, dropping it and catching it in its claws.

Dr. Nelson (1887) says: "They have a common habit of rising high overhead with a sea-urchin (*Echinus*) in their beaks, and after reaching an elevation of several hundred feet of allowing the shell-fish to fall. As a consequence, it is common to find the shells of these radiates scattered all over the hill-sides in the vicinity of the sea; apparently the ravens do not do this with the intention of gaining readier access to the contents of the shell, and I do not recall a single instance where a raven followed the shell to the ground, although on several instances I have seen the birds dive hastily after the falling shell and capture it in their beaks before it reached the ground, apparently in sport."

Team play often enters into the raven's activities. B. J. Bretherton wrote to Major Bendire (1895): "I saw a native dog one day with a bone which he vainly endeavored to eat. While so engaged he was espied by a Raven, who flew down and tried to scare the dog by loud cawing, in which he was shortly afterwards assisted by another, both birds sidling up to the dog's head until they were barely out of his reach. Just at this time a third Raven appeared on the scene and surveyed the situation from an adjacent fence, but soon flew down behind the dog and advanced until within reach of his tail, which he seized so roughly that the dog turned for an instant to snap at him, and at the same moment the bone was snatched away by one of the Ravens at his head."

Lucien M. Turner (MS.) relates the following performance that he witnessed on the banks of the Koksoak River: "A few miles below the falls on the river I saw at one time over a hundred of these birds. The banks of the river at this locality were very high and crumbling with the process of freezing during the night and thawing during the day. Here the birds resorted to have the fun of coasting down this hillside. A dozen at a time would stand, either sidewise or with their heads upward, and start down with the rolling pebbles and clay, each bird constantly uttering its harsh croak, which reverberated among the hills until the air was filled with their coarse notes. This noise was heard over a mile before we paddled up to the birds, where we stopped to witness their amusement. The trees in the vicinity contained numbers of ravens aiding the sport with their cries of approval, or taking their turns as the others became tired."

Referring to its character, he says: "The raven is bold and fearless when able to cope with an adversary and rarely fails to drive any intruder but man from the locality. I have seen a single bird successfully attack a white gyrfalcon and cause it to forsake the hillside adopted by the raven for its home. On the other hand, the raven is one of the most cowardly birds, rarely attacking without certainty of superiority in itself, or trusting to its harsh notes to call assistance from its comrades."

Mr. Zirrer (MS.) adds the following notes on the behavior of ravens: "Although they brave storms when no other bird ventures in the open, they are, especially the young, much afraid of the heavy summer thunderstorms. Again and again I have noticed several of them, young birds I presume, sitting during the thunder, lightning, and heavy downpour on a strong, horizontal, lower branch of a big tree, under the protective canopy of densely leaved branches above, expressing all their fear and anxiety by stretching and craning their necks in all directions, and emitting many peculiar, plaintive sounds. At such times it was possible to approach them very closely without taking much precaution; the birds were plainly too frightened to be watchful.

"In localities where ravens are not persecuted and feel secure, they come very near the buildings and become bold. They will attack a cat within sight of a dwelling and take away whatever little game the cat might be carrying at the time. Early one morning, when our big white tomcat was on the way home with something, apparently a meadow mouse, and no more than 100 feet away, he was suddenly attacked by a pair of ravens with a design on that mouse. Without warning the two big birds, which must have been sitting on a tree nearby, dived at the big cat, which, surprised and not knowing what was happening, gave an enormous leap, dropped the mouse and ran. This, of course, was what the birds wanted. Picking up the mouse and disappearing among the tree tops, they went faster than I was able to tell."

Voice.—The raven has a variety of notes. As I recorded it many years ago, on the coast of Maine, its commonest note seemed to be a loud croak, deep-toned, and audible at a great distance, *croake-croake*; we also heard occasionally a hoarse *croo-croo,* not so loud or so penetrating; on one occasion we recorded a richer, more musical note, *croang-croang,* with the resonance of a deep-toned bell, on a lower key than the other notes, less harsh and rather pleasing, and sometimes ending in a loud cluck. Then there was the short, guttural *cur-ruk* or *cruk,* with the rolling r's, given mostly on the wing, singly or repeated several times.

Mr. Harlow (1922) has heard "a very distinct hollow, sepulchral laugh 'haw-haw-haw-haw.'" And he says: "During the period of courtship and incubation there are two distinct notes that I have not heard at any other time. One is a soft 'crawk,' which the male gives to the female when he is sitting near her while she is on the nest ledge or incubating. The other is a series of 'crawks' given while on the wing and with rarely a note best expressed by the syllables 'ge-lick-ge-lee' given either between the 'crawks' or still more rarely as a single note."

J. Dewey Soper (1928) gives the raven credit for considerable musical versatility. He writes: "The northern raven possesses a musical, guttural note with a slightly bell-like quality. This note is employed at times throughout the year. The raven at any time may, also, utter a strange call like *thung-thung-thung,* which bears a remarkable resemblance to the mellow twang of a tuning-fork, being, like it, rich, full, vibrant, and musical. Another expression has a metallic, liquid-like quality after the style of the red-winged blackbird, though greatly magnified in volume.

The ravens possess a great range of notes, from their customary melancholy croaks, through numerous performances in striking imitation of other birds such as geese and gulls, up to the melodious accomplishment first mentioned."

Mr. Tuttle took his flight pictures of ravens by imitating their rallying cry, which, he says "is rather like the second note of the peacock's raucous call—'harraowh'. More than any bird I know, the raven will converse with himself for hours at a time, a curious gargling, strongly inflected talk. It is not very hard to steal up on him when he is so engaged." He adds the following, as the raven's conversation: *Cáhonk-cáhonk; cwaanh; cwahonk; onk-onk; craaounk;* and *koeh, koeh.*

Dr. Dickey says in his notes that "they rarely give evidence of what may also be called a song, so ardently do they vent a long, drawn-out strain, such as *spor-spree-spruck-spur-per-rick-rur-ruck.* Lisps, croaks, buzzing sounds, and gulps may be heard at odd intervals from ravens in the breeding season."

Mr. Zirrer writes in his notes: "From the middle of August to about the end of September, and as a rule in the afternoons only, they congregate in a secluded spot of heavy timber and hold their daily concerts. For this purpose they select one or two of the tallest trees, sit facing one another and sing, mostly solo, but sometimes more at once. The song is a musical warble, not very loud and, considering their size and otherwise rough, croaking call, extremely attractive. The birds, however, are very alert throughout the performance and when frightened once will not return to the same spot again, but otherwise they will return daily."

Field marks.—To the casual observer a raven may look like just a large crow and so not be recognized. But to the trained eye of an ornithologist there are several points of difference. The raven is decidedly larger, with a wing expanse of over 4 feet, against less than 3 feet in the crow; its tail is also proportionately longer and more rounded. But size alone is not a safe guide unless there is direct comparison at the same distance.

Its voice is quite distinctive, as explained above, though young ravens sometimes "caw" like crows. And its flight is very different from that of the crow, swifter and less steady, with frequent turnings from side to side, accompanied by two or three rapid wing beats and with occasional attempts at tumbling; its sailing or soaring flight is majestic and often used.

Mr. Tuttle says (MS.): "The four field marks by which one can most easily distinguish the raven from the crow, lacking the presence of both birds for size comparison, are the heavy, triangular head, with apparent bulges at the base of the jaws as seen from below (probably the part where the brow joins the beak), the sharp break of the wings at the shoulders, the openings between the primaries, and the large fan-shaped tail. All these features can be clearly seen in the flight pictures submitted." See plate 33.

Enemies.—Ravens have few natural enemies. They have been known to have occasional squabbles with gyrfalcons, duck hawks, red-tailed and red-shouldered hawks, and crows, but such encounters generally result in favor of the ravens, with little damage inflicted on either party. J. Southgate Y. Hoyt writes to me of such an incident that he witnessed near Lexington, Va., on April 7, 1939:

> Just as we located this year's nest, I heard the cry of a duck hawk. From around the end of the range came the raven with the duck hawk flying high above it, calling loudly. The raven croaked a few notes of protest, but continued its slow and deliberate flight along the range. As I watched this unusual sight, I saw something at which I still marvel.
>
> The duck hawk stooped at the raven, calling faster. Just at the point when I expected to see the raven get a hard blow, it flipped over on its back with its feet up in the air and warded off the blow. I could not see whether it used its feet or just assumed an attitude of guard. The raven did not seem to use its wings in turning over but was upside down in a small fraction of a minute. At this the falcon swooped up in the air again, still screaming loudly. The raven turned over again just as quickly as it had turned onto its back and resumed its course slowly and steadily along the face of the mountain.
>
> The duck hawk, having again reached its position over the raven, stooped as it had before. Again the raven turned over onto its back to ward off the blow. This performance was repeated eight times as the raven crossed before me and finally settled in a pine tree at the end of the cliff. The duck hawk swooped up to a tall dead tree nearby and sat there motionless. The next I saw of the raven was the pair of them flying back along the top of the mountain, and the duck hawk was nowhere to be seen.
>
> Visiting this same mountain again this spring (1940), I witnessed a similar performance between the raven and the duck hawk. This time the fight continued for several minutes high in the air over the edge of the mountain.

The raven's worst and most effective enemy is man, because of the damage it does, or is supposed to do, to domestic animals, some wild animals, poultry, and nesting wildfowl and other game. Fortunately for the ravens, they are so sagacious and wary that very few can be shot, but many have been killed in crow traps and in various animal traps. Theed Pearse (1938) tells of large numbers that were trapped near Comox on Vancouver Island; 76 were trapped in 1933, 120 in 1934, 62 in 1935; "in 1936 the number taken was sixty-three, and in January alone of 1937, seventy were killed. Thus, during these years of abundance, four hundred Ravens were destroyed in the Crow traps alone, and it would be safe to add another hundred as having been shot or otherwise destroyed (I came across one caught in a trap set for Mink). The local Game Warden gives the huge total of 535 accounted for up-to-date."

He says that he "never saw a Raven doing anything that could be described as harmful to the farmer, the sportsman, or other bird life." Ducks, mallard and teal, bred in the sloughs between the two slaughter houses where the ravens fed, and no diminution in the broods of these ducks was noted during the periods of greatest abundance of the ravens. One of their chief feeding grounds "appeared to be recently ploughed land and grass-fields where the birds could be seen picking up food, probably noxious insects such as cutworms, etc."

Fall.—Most ravens are apparently resident throughout the year over the greater part of their range, but there is some evidence of at least a partial migration from extreme northern habitats. Hagerup (1891) referred to what seemed to be migrations at Ivigtut, Greenland, as follows: "I frequently noticed that when a strong wind blew from the north they migrated in great numbers toward the south. The largest of these migrations took place August 30, 1887, when one hundred to two hundred crossed the valley. They were seen through the entire day coming from the north side of the fjord, flying low over it, stopping a little at the south shore, then crossing the valley until they reached the mountains. At the base of the hills they first began to rise in the air, working upwards in spiral curves without any flapping of wings, until abreast of the summit, when they sailed away to the south."

Mr. Pearse's notes state that "there appears to be a regular line of migration along the east coast of Vancouver Island." Near Courtenay, on August 16, 1923, 30 were seen going south, following one another in a scattered formation and flying parallel to the shore line. Eleven were seen on October 12, 1936, and a flock of 25 or 30 on December 8, 1935, all flying along the shore in the same direction. He says: "Where the cliff makes an abrupt turn west, the birds seemed undecided and stopped, wheeling around and some even playing. After a short time the greater part of the flock moved seawards, going in an easterly direction away from Vancouver Island and in the direction of another island between there and the mainland, about 15 miles away. The other birds remained wheeling around above the cliff, evidently not liking to face the sea, though the day was fine and the sea calm. It was rather amusing to follow the actions of these birds; first a party of ten started off; others followed, so that more than half of the flock was on its way; there were some faint hearts among these, which straggled back to join the birds that were still wheeling over the land. Twelve at least continued the journey, and, shortly afterward, the faint hearts were out of sight around the bend of the cliff, following the shore line."

Winter.—At least a few ravens remain all winter, even at the northern limits of their breeding range. Donald B. MacMillan (1918) records it as a winter resident at Etah, northern Greenland, but says that the "majority migrate south about September 15th." And Langdon Gibson (1922), referring to McCormick Bay, in latitude 77° 40′ N. in northern Greenland, says: "I am fully satisfied that these birds do not all migrate in the fall because, after the sun had disappeared for the winter, we heard their hoarse croaking and five days before the sun reappeared, February 7, 1892, I saw in the dim twilight on the beach near our house a Raven lazily flopping along."

Other explorers have recorded ravens in winter on Baffin Island, Southampton Island, in Ungava and northern Labrador, and along the Arctic coast of Canada, where the few that remain must eke out a meagre living, with deep snows covering the ground and hiding all the familiar feeding places; then, driven desperate with the pangs of hunger, they risk their lives in attempts to steal the baits from fox traps, which often results fatally, as they are either killed outright or left to freeze under a pall of drifted snow.

CORVUS CORAX SINUATUS Wagler

AMERICAN RAVEN

PLATES 35, 36

HABITS

The ravens of the Western United States have long been called by the above scientific name and the rather inappropriate common name for a bird that is so decidedly western. George Willett (1941) has recently shown that we might well recognize two western races within the United States. The measurements that he has accumulated "appear to indicate a large race *(principalis)*, with heavy bill and tarsus, in Alaska and British Columbia; another large race *(sinuatus)*, with slender bill and tarsus, in the Rocky Mountains and Great Basin region; and a small race *(clarionensis)* ranging from interior valleys of California to Clarion Island, Mexico."

The subject of this sketch might well have been called the western raven, as it occupies the western half of the United States and much of Central America. It is smaller than the northern raven, with a relatively smaller and narrower bill and a longer and slenderer tarsus. It is a wide-ranging species, with a scattered distribution, and seems to have no especially favored haunts. It is at home alike in the mountains and on the plains or deserts, in the forests or on the open ranges; it may be seen flying from its nest on some high cliff in a deep rocky canyon, or perched on some tall pine high up in the mountains.

M. P. Skinner tells me that in Yellowstone National Park ravens are seen almost anywhere and at all seasons, perched on the ground or on some prominent rock, or about the geyser basins, and they are common in the lodgepole and fir forests from the lowest altitudes to the highest peaks. "In spring ravens are on the edge of the lake ice about to break up; they are rather frequent about the buffalo herds and often visit garbage dumps and old camp sites; they even visit occupied camps."

Mrs. Nice (1931) states that the raven was formerly an abundant resident in Oklahoma in the days of the buffalo, but that with the disappearance of the bison the ravens have gone. Many ravens were killed by eating poisoned baits and the viscera of wolves that had been poisoned. "Here seems to lie the explanation of the practically complete disappearance of this once abundant bird from Kansas and Oklahoma—the extermination of the buffalo on whose carcasses it fed, and the unintentional, yet wholesale, poisoning by cattlemen."

According to Dickey and van Rossem (1938) this raven is a "fairly common resident of the interior mountains and foothills" of El Salvador "from Los Esesmiles eastward. * * * The raven occurs principally in the pine regions of the Arid Upper Tropical Zone, but in late fall and winter descends to the foothills. Extremes of altitude are 800 to 8,500 feet. * * * In the pines on Los Esesmiles ravens were decidedly more numerous than anywhere else in El Salvador and were seen almost daily. There were at least a dozen pairs within a radius of five miles from camp at 6,400 feet, and these were scattered at elevations of from 6,000 to 8,500 feet. Below 6,000 feet ravens were less numerous, but nevertheless were distributed generally all over the pine country down to about 3,000 feet."

Bendire (1895) says of the haunts of ravens: "It seems to make little difference to these birds how desolate the country which they inhabit may be, as long as it furnishes sufficient food to sustain life, and they are not hard to please in such matters. One is liable to meet with them singly or in pairs, and occasionally in considerable numbers, along the cliffs of the seashore, and on the adjacent islands of the Pacific coast, from Washington south to Lower California, as well as in the mountains and arid plains of the interior, even in the hottest and most barren wastes of the Colorado Desert, as the Death Valley region, and through all the States and Territories west of the Rocky Mountains. * * * I have met with them at every Post at which I have been stationed in the West."

Courtship.—With the springtime urge of love-making, the otherwise sedate and dignified ravens let themselves go and indulge in most interesting and thrilling flight maneuvers and vocal performances. Chasing each other about in rapid flight, they dive, tumble, twist, turn somersaults, roll over sidewise, or mount high in the air and soar in great circles on their broad, black wings. Their powers of flight shown in these playful antics are no less surprising than the variety of their melodious love notes, soft modulations of their well-known croaks, varied with many clucking and gurgling sounds. Their exuberant spirits seem to be overflowing at this season.

Other forms of playful springtime antics are described by Dawson (1923). One he called a "game of tag," in which several birds took part, chasing each other about and playing with a "yellow something," passing it from bill to claws, or from one bird to another. "After this I witnessed an aerial minuet by two gifted performers,—a tumbling contest, wherein touching hands (wing-tips), with one bird upside down, was varied with simultaneous somersaults and graceful upright, or stalling, presentations."

Nesting.—I have seen a few nests of the American raven in Arizona and in California. At the northern end of the Huachuca Mountains, Ariz., on April 14, 1922, we saw a pair of ravens building their nest on a steep rocky declivity; they were flying about, carrying nesting material and croaking, but the nest was not finished. On April 20, my companion, Frank Willard, climbed to an almost inaccessible nest on a high perpendicular cliff in Apache Canyon in the Catalina Mountains; it was located on a ledge under an overhanging rock, but by the skillful manipulation of a long rope he managed to reach the nest and collect a set of five eggs. In a neighboring canyon, on the same day, we found a big nest in a large cottonwood tree that a pair of ravens were repairing; this was the only tree nest that we saw in Arizona. We saw some other old ravens' nests on high, precipitous, rocky eminences, some of which were occupied by western red-tailed hawks.

In California, J. R. Pemberton gave me two very interesting days with the ravens, March 19 and 20, 1929, in Kern County, driving for many miles among the abandoned oil wells in the valley between the Kettleman Hills and Wheeler Ridge. We collected five sets of eggs, two of six, two of five, and one of four eggs. The ravens were nesting in the abandoned oil derricks, usually near the tops, at heights ranging from 58 to 104 feet above the ground. The nests were securely built on the framework, either in a corner or against the ladder, which made it a simple matter to climb to them. They were made mainly of the stems and branches of sagebrush, mixed with other sticks and rubbish, deeply hollowed and warmly lined with a profusion of wool of various colors, which, judging from the smell, must have been taken from dead sheep; this was mixed with such matter as cows' hair, bits of hemp rope, and pieces of cloth. They varied in height from 18 to 24 inches; a typical nest measured 24 inches in outside diameter, 14 inches across the lining, and the inner cavity was 8 inches in diameter and 5 or 6 inches deep. The birds usually left the nests as we approached, but some remained on until we were part way up the ladder. One bird did not fly until my head was nearly on a level with the nest. Some birds departed at once, but others flew around close by, croaking.

A few other nests were noted in various parts of California, mostly inaccessible, on rocky cliffs or in potholes in sandstone cliffs. One that I saw when I was out with the Peyton brothers in Ventura County, on April 7, 1929, was in a pothole in a perpendicular sandstone cliff, about 50 feet high; the nest was about 30 feet from the bottom of the cliff and was reached with the aid of a rope ladder. The nest was made of sagebrush and other sticks and was lined with cows' hair of various colors, bits of rag, and strips of yucca fiber. It contained five eggs.

I saw no tree nests in California, except one shown to me by Wright M. Pierce; this was in a Joshua tree on the Mohave Desert (pl. 36). And Major Bendire (1895) says that about Camp Harney, Oreg., where ravens were very common, "out of some twenty nests examined only one was placed in a tree. It was in a good-sized dead willow, 20 feet from the ground, on an island in Sylvies River, Oregon, and easily reached; it contained five fresh eggs on April 13, 1875." Dawson (1923) mentions a California nest in the top of a white oak, and remarks: "In an experience covering some scores of nests, this was the only example of a tree-nesting Raven. I am told, however, that they do nest in trees in Mendocino and Del Norte Counties, where they are also exceptionally common."

In central Lower California, according to Griffing Bancroft (1930), "they build in a normal manner on cliffs or more often in tree yucca or multifingered cardón." And Dickey and van Rossem (1938) say, referring to El Salvador: "On February 8, 1927, a pair of ravens was found working on a nest in the topmost branches of a forty-foot pine at an elevetion of about 7,000 feet on Los Esesmiles. The tree was one of a group of half a dozen growing on a bare ridge and was directly above a trail over which a dozen or more people traveled daily. This nest could be seen half a mile away and would have been conspicuous even without the presence of the builders, both of which were constantly arriving and departing."

James B. Dixon (MS.) tells me that in San Diego County the ravens nest in trees nearly as much as on cliffs; out of the ten records of nests that he sent me, five of the nests were in trees. Ravens often build their nests on cliffs overhanging the seacoast. A. D. DuBois sends me the data on a nest in San Diego County that was 20 feet below the top of a bluff overlooking the Pacific Ocean; it was in a pothole, about 18 inches back and well protected from the weather; it was composed of sticks and lined with cow's and skunk's hair. W. E. Griffee (MS.) says that "occasional pairs of ravens nest in the western Oregon valleys and they occur more frequently along the coast, but the heavy timber west of the Cascade Mountains makes these occasional pairs decidedly inconspicuous." Most of his experience with ravens has been east of the Cascades, where, he says, a large majority of them "nest in rimrocks, usually low rims not over 50 feet high." But he has also found their nests in boxelder, locust, juniper, poplar, and willow trees.

Old ravens' nests are often used by hawks and owls. I took my first and only set of prairie-falcon eggs from the remains of an old raven's nest, and I have found red-tailed hawks and horned owls appropriating ravens' nests that were still in good condition. It is a common occurrence to find the ravens and falcons nesting in the same canyon, or on the same cliff, and not far apart; it seems to be a sort of tradition that where one is found the other will be found in the vicinity, but Mr. Griffee, who has had considerable experience with both, thinks that they nest together only where suitable sites are scarce; and he mentions two cases where ravens formerly nested close to falcons and are now nesting in trees at some distance. This community of interest is not due to any affection between the species, as is shown by the spirited encounters that sometimes occur between them.

Bowles and Decker (1930) give an interesting account of the nesting of this raven on, or in, man-made structures in a deserted agricultural community between the Yakima and Columbia Rivers in Washington:

In travelling over many miles of this country we have seen the following varieties of nesting sites: Several different parts of windmills; rafters in small one-room shacks; in barns; in various places in houses; one a few feet up in a small tree; and one on top of a bookcase in a school house. * * * Only one nest was built on the outside of a house, this being placed on a porch directly above a small bay window. * * * In the low, river country, where natural sites are scarce, we have found the nests on high tension poles, oil derricks, telegraph poles, and on the beam of a railroad bridge. One of the last mentioned was only twelve feet from the ground and two feet below the rails. [A freight train rumbling over this bridge did not cause the bird to leave its nest.]

Another interesting proof that these birds do not mind disturbance in and around the nest was where a windmill had been used as a site. For some strange reason the nest had been built around the plunging rod, which, the mill being in working order, went up and down through the outer wall of the nest whenever the wind happened to be blowing. * * *

The material used is almost literally anything that strikes the fancy of the birds, although the common types are composed outwardly of coarse sticks and twigs for the most part. However, we have several times found them built almost altogether of different kinds of wire, while at other times the ribs of sheep and the smaller bones of cattle form a large percentage. One nest contained a large jawbone, with most of the teeth intact. * * *

"A curious feature of their nest building," they say, "is that they never pick up a piece of material that has fallen from the nest, even though they may have to fly for miles to get more." They cite a case where a pair of ravens had made a number of unsuccessful attempts to build a nest on an insecure board inside of a small building, but finally succeeded. "As a result the floor beneath the nest was one great mass of almost every imaginable sort of material that could be found for miles around, there being included dozens upon dozens of bones of many kinds. In all we estimated that there must have been between twelve and fifteen bushels of material, showing how pertinacious these birds are when they have decided upon a site for their nest."

The raven's nest is often filthy and unsanitary; the wool and hair used for the lining are often taken from dead animals and so are highly offensive to the human nostrils; and Dawson (1923) says that "as if this were not enough, the sitting bird drenches the whole recklessly with its own excrement, making it a veritable abode of harpies." And Bendire (1895) found that "when the nest was occupied the lining was always alive with fleas."

He says further: "The American Raven becomes attached to a site when once chosen, and although its eggs or young may be taken for successive seasons, it will return and use the same nest from year to year. I have taken three sets of eggs (evidently laid by the same bird) from the same nest for successive years; they were readily recognizable by their large size and style of markings." Bowles and Decker (1930) say: "Should their first set of eggs be taken another is laid, usually in the same nest; and in some cases three sets have been laid in the same nest, with intervals of from seventeen to twenty-two days between sets. Sometimes the same number of eggs is produced in each set, but often the second and third sets will contain one egg less than the first. We have found that one egg is deposited daily until the set is complete." Bendire (1895), on the contrary, says that the eggs are laid on alternate days, or even at longer intervals.

Eggs.—The American raven lays from four to seven eggs to a set, but five and six are the commonest numbers, and as many as eight have been recorded. Mr. Griffee (MS.) says that larger sets are laid by northern birds than by those breeding farther south; he estimates that of all complete sets in northern Oregon 30 percent would have five eggs or less, 35 percent six eggs, 30 percent seven eggs, and 5 percent eight eggs.

The eggs vary in shape from ovate to elongate-ovate, or rarely cylindrical-ovate. They are merely large editions of crows' eggs and not so much larger as one might expect; some of the smallest ravens' eggs are not much larger than large crows' eggs. The colors and markings of ravens' eggs have nearly all the variation shown in crows' eggs, though I have never seen the darkest types of crows' eggs quite matched. The ground color varies from "glaucous," through various shades of "greenish glaucous," to "pea green"; Bendire (1895) adds greenish olive and drab to the list of variations. The markings, in shades of dull, dark browns, drab and olive, show considerable variation in pattern; some eggs are sparingly marked with small spots, and some are profusely covered with small spots and fine dots; others are unevenly marked with irregular blotches and scrawls.

The measurements of 54 eggs in the United States National Museum average 49.53 by 32.76 millimeters; the eggs showing the four extremes measure **60.5** by 37.6, 51.8 by **48.3, 40.9** by 31.6, and 48.3 by **30.5** millimeters.

Incubation.—Major Bendire (1895) writes: "Only one brood is raised in a season. Incubation lasts about three weeks, commencing when the set is completed, and I believe both sexes assist in this labor. When the female is sitting on the nest the male may frequently be seen perched on some small bush or a dead branch of a tree on the opposite side of the canyon from where the nest is situated, uttering an occasional 'klunk-klunk' and keeping a sharp lookout. Should anyone approach in that direction, though some distance off, he will warn his mate, uttering a low alarm note while flying past the nest, when she will usually slip off and try to keep out of sight, while he endeavors to draw attention to himself, acting at the same time as utterly unconcerned as if he had no interest whatever in that particular locality."

Young.—The young are well cared for, fed, and guarded by both parents. When the birds are four weeks or a month old their wings are sufficiently developed for flight and they are ready to leave the nest. Attended by their parents for some time after that, they are taught to forage for themselves. Soon after they have learned how to hunt for their food they all disappear from the vicinity of their nesting site and resort to the valleys where food is more easily obtained. After a few weeks the family party breaks up, and the young, now able to shift for themselves, are deserted by their parents.

Plumages.—The plumages and molts are the same as in the northern raven, to the account of which the reader is referred.

Food.—Ravens are not at all particular about their choice of food; almost anything edible will do, from carrion to freshly killed small mammals and birds or birds' eggs, other small vertebrates, insects, and other small forms of animal life; garbage and various forms of vegetable material are also welcome.

No thorough analysis of the year-round food of the raven seems to have been made, but A. L. Nelson (1934) has published a thorough study of the early summer food of this raven in southeastern Oregon, "based on examination of the stomach contents of 18 adult and 66 nestling birds, the latter representing 18 broods." Bird remains occurred in 21 stomachs, the bulk percentage amounting to 6.37 for nestlings and 7.72 for adults. "Shell fragments of birds' eggs were noted in 14 stomachs, forming by volume 2.03 percent of the bulk." But this probably does not come anywhere near representing the number of eggs destroyed, for bits of shell are seldom eaten and egg contents are not easily detected. Small mammals formed the largest percentage of the food, 34.26 percent for adults and young combined. "Examination showed that thirty-five of the sixty-six nestlings, or 53 percent, were fed on rabbits, while eight of the eighteen adults, or 44 percent, had fed on these animals." These were mostly young rabbits, and probably some of them were carrion.

Amphibians formed 7.40 percent of the food of the young and 3.62 percent of the food of the adults. "The total percentage of reptile food for nestlings amounted to 6.43, for adults 0.84, and for all birds 5.23. * * * Insects, as a group, stand next in importance to the rabbit as a food item, amounting to about 33 percent of the total. The adults had a greater percentage of insects in their diet than did the nestlings, the percentage for the former being 48.56, and for the latter 29.74. * * * In the order of their importance in the diet, from the percentage standpoint, representatives of the following seven orders of insects were identified: Homoptera, Diptera, Hymenoptera, Coleoptera, Lepidoptera, Orthoptera, and Heteroptera. The orders Orthoptera and Heteroptera were so sparsely represented as to be insignificant, together amounting to less than ¼ of 1 percent of the total diet.

"* * * The only vegetable item taken by adults was corn. It was present in two stomachs, being recorded to the extent of 35 percent in one and 2 percent in the other. Of the nestlings, eight stomachs contained vegetable material, two stomachs containing corn to the extent of 42 and 33 percent, respectively, and three, containing oats in percentages of 62, 15, and 8, respectively." Thus it appears that, although some of these stomachs contained rather high percentages of these grains, the number of birds involved was so small that "the determined vegetable material, corn and oats, amounted to" "only "2.35 percent of the total diet" of all the birds involved. And probably, at other seasons of the year, vegetable matter forms a larger proportion of the raven's diet.

Mr. Skinner says in his notes from Yellowstone Park: "Ravens habitually feed on such carrion as dead elk, deer, and small animals; and I believe they follow bears and coyotes at times to benefit by anything they may find or kill. They frequent the garbage piles for scraps and they show little fear of the bears. I have seen a raven on marshy ground eating a frog; and I was once greatly surprised to see a raven on a tree limb reach up three inches and grab a fly that attempted to fly over."

Bendire (1895) writes: "Among various misdeeds it is charged with killing young lambs, chickens, and turkeys, as well as with destroying the eggs and young of different species of wild fowl; and while this is true to some extent, yet where these birds can get a reasonable amount of food from other sources they rarely disturb domestic animals of any sort. I have more than once seen a Raven feeding among my poultry, apparently on friendly terms with both young and old; they never molested any to my knowledge; nor have I ever heard complaints of shepherds that their lambs were troubled, much less killed, by them. Their food consists principally of carrion, dead fish, and frogs, varied with insects of different kinds, including grasshoppers and the large black crickets so abundant at some seasons in the West; they also eat worms, mussels, snails, small rodents, including some young rabbits, as well as refuse from the kitchen and slaughterhouse."

Charles A. Allen wrote to him, however, that "in the interior of California the Raven destroys many young chickens and turkeys around the ranches. In the spring months I have frequently seen one of these birds flying overhead with a young fowl or an egg in its bill." The chances are that most of the damage complained of is done by comparatively few individuals and that the species as a whole probably does more good in the destruction of injurious rodents and insects than it does harm. Ravens must also be credited with their usefulness as scavengers.

Behavior.—The flight of the raven is sometimes slow and measured, like that of the crow, with which it is often confused by casual observers, but it is more majestic, grander, stronger and swifter, varied with sailing or soaring in a manner that would rival a *Buteo,* or with spectacular dives and plunges.

Mr. Skinner says in his notes: "I have seen them high above a snowy ridge, apparently 'riding the gale' seemingly for the mere pleasure of it.

They are given to circling in spirals above carrion quite after the manner of vultures. I have seen ravens fly by, croaking, and at occasional intervals turn back to make a circle before going on. One day I noted four ravens performing various evolutions in the wind, one had some prey that he would carry a distance in his claws and then transfer it to his bill for a short distance before changing back."

W. W. Rubey (1933) witnessed some remarkable flight behavior of ravens at the summit of Wyoming Peak (elevation 11,363 feet), Wyo., of which he writes:

Shortly after noon [October 5] we reached the summit. Immediately we were set upon by a flock of Ravens that dropped down upon us most unexpectedly. The birds, about thirty of them, rushed at us in long, nearly vertical dives, croaking, snarling, and almost barking out their harsh notes. So real did their "attack" appear that we threw rocks in an effort to drive them off. On the first dive, each bird veered off from us at distances of 25 to 100 feet, fell past the peak, then swerved back up and dived again. For a moment, retreat seemed not a bad idea; but soon the Ravens tired of their sport with us and took to another game in which they exhibited a type of bird-flight entirely new to me.

To the west, Wyoming Peak falls off rather abruptly 3500 feet to the valley of Greys River. The Ravens rose perhaps 500 feet above us, then plunged suddenly into a remarkable series of dives, spins, and coasts which eventually carried them almost out of sight to the forests far below. Their maneuver was carried out somewhat as follows: At the top of the preliminary climb each bird turned sharply straight down and fell a short distance with closed (or at least closely cupped) wings. Then, as the speed of fall increased, the wings seemed to open part way and the dive was deflected somewhat from the vertical. Promptly, the Raven began to spin or 'barrel-roll' about its longitudinal or bill-to-tail axis, slowly at first, then more and more rapidly. This rotating fall continued at an accelerating velocity through a vertical distance of several hundred feet. At length, perhaps because the speed could no longer be endured, the wings were opened wider, the angle of dive began to level off, and the axial spinning gradually slowed down until, when the coasting flight became horizontal, rotation ceased. Each bird immediately swerved back up as far as its momentum would carry it and, from an elevation about 500 feet below that of the start, dived again. Thus, the entire performance was repeated over and over again, each successive dive leveling off farther and farther down the steep mountainside. * * *

In the two hours that we remained on the peak, the Ravens were there no less than eight times. Each time, if I remember correctly, they displayed their trick of spinning dives, and on four of their visits they made their mock attacks on us.

Three times, however, they found better game than men for their bullying. Once they put up a Golden Eagle from some ledge on the cirque wall north of the peak, and the majestic bird fled shamelessly and with all speed for a peak two miles to the east, with the whole pack in noisy pursuit. Soon they returned and quickly routed another Eagle from near the same ledge. This bird fared worse than the first one because he failed to get started far enough in advance of the Ravens. The entire flock surrounded and badgered him relentlessly for some time as he literally fought his way toward the Salt River Range, miles to the west.

Yet it was on the last one of their visits—while we were there—that the Ravens found their greatest sport. In the intervals between Raven raids, I had noticed that we were in the midst of a large but (at first) widely scattered flock of Leucostictes. These small birds were industriously feeding on the snow and among the rocks of the peak, and they seemed not at all disturbed by our presence. * * * Finally, the Ravens on one of their swooping raids somehow managed to frighten the Leucostictes into flight; and the entire flock of approximately 200 individuals took to the air almost simultaneously. Immediately, the Ravens were at them, dashing swiftly and noisily through the thickest of the compact flock, scattering it, then charging again each time that it reformed. Not content with merely this disruption of the flock, the Ravens began following up the separated groups of apparently panic-stricken Leucostictes, diving into them viciously. We saw no actual casualties but it seems probable that some of the Leucostictes, despite their expert dodging, must have been struck down during the repeated dives of the larger birds.

Mr. Skinner writes to me: "Frequently I find an eagle on the ground or feeding on carrion with a circle of ravens about him; they are there, I think, more for the sport of mobbing the eagle than anything else. When so tormented the larger bird seeks refuge in a tree top; we often flush an eagle and his attendant ravens from the thick top of a cedar. But, if the ravens mob the eagles, they have their own tormentors in the little Brewer's blackbirds. I have seen a big raven fly past closely pursued by eight blackbirds, and he seemed unable to defend himself in the air or to escape from his more agile pursuers by flight, so he alighted in the top of a small pine, where by constant snapping and several fierce lunges at his tormentors, he managed to keep them at a distance. Soon he tried to escape by flight, but was forced back to his tree again. I have often noticed that, if a raven happens to pass within sight of a Brewer's blackbird nest, all the blackbirds within sight and hearing take after him, and do it every time a raven passes. By late August and September the blackbirds give up this sport of mobbing ravens."

On the ground the raven is sedate and dignified, walking easily with a stately tread, when not hurried, or hopping less gracefully forward or a little sidewise. As a rule it is a very shy and wary bird, difficult to approach, but it is sagacious enough to know when and where it is safe and is often quite tame under such circumstances. Mr. Skinner tells me that he once rode his horse to within 15 feet of one on the ground, and then it merely hopped away. About ranches and farmyards, where it knows that it will not be molested, it is often quite tame, but in the wilderness it seems to know how far a gun will shoot.

Voice.—The various notes of the western ravens do not seem to differ much from those of the eastern or northern birds, which are more fully treated under the northern raven. Major Bendire (1895) says:

"Their ordinary call note is a loud 'craack-craak,' varied sometimes by a deep, grunting 'koerr-koerr,' and again by a clucking, a sort of self-satisfied sound, difficult to reproduce on paper; in fact, they utter a variety of notes when at ease and undisturbed, among others a metallic-sounding 'klunk,' which seems to cost them considerable effort." Bowles and Decker (1930) mention a pair that "gave an endless variety of creaks and croaks, quacked very much like a Mallard duck, bawled like a cat, and, in short, made it exceedingly easy to believe that there would be little difficulty in teaching them to talk." I have never heard western birds give the deep-toned, bell-like note that I have heard from birds on the coast of Maine, nor have I seen it mentioned in print, unless Bendire's "metallic-sounding 'klunk'" or Dawson's (1923) "curious, mellow, *hunger-ó ope*" may refer to it.

Winter.—Mrs. Bailey (1928) says that, in New Mexico, "in the fall the Ravens with their grown young ascend high into the mountains, even to the tops of the highest peaks," 11,000 to 13,000 feet, but that "the snows of early fall drive the birds from these extreme altitudes. The winter is spent in the valley and foothills for the most part below 7,500 feet. * * * In the winter, Mr. Ligon has found the Ravens going about in pairs and he thinks that they remain mated. At this season they come into towns and are far less shy than during the early summer. At Albuquerque one was seen by Mr. Loring perched on a cow's back, and at Deming they were found feeding in the streets acting as important scavengers, while a dozen seen in a hogyard, feeding with the hogs, allowed a person to pass within twenty feet of them without their flying away."

Fred Mallery Packard writes to me from Estes Park, Colo. "Small flocks of ravens may be seen almost daily in winter near Estes Park between 7,500 and 8,500 elevations, occasionally flying higher. After February fewer are to be seen, and these usually in pairs flying near the tops of the mountains above 10,000 feet. In September and October they are to be seen in small numbers flying over the alpine meadows and southward down the canyons at 12,000 feet or higher, descending to the lower valleys when the snows fall on the heights."

John E. Cushing, Jr. (1941), summarizes his report on the winter behavior of ravens by saying: "The ravens in the vicinity of Tomales Bay, Marin County, California, roost together in a brushy canyon on a small hill near Valley Ford, Sonoma County, during the fall and winter months. During the day the birds disperse over the surrounding country, some of them travelling at least forty miles a day. The colony numbered about 200 birds on the two times that counts were made. It has probably been in existence for at least nine years, quite possibly much longer."

DISTRIBUTION

Range.—Circumpolar; North America, northern Central America, Europe and northern and central Asia; nonmigratory.

The American races of the raven are found **north** to northern Alaska (Cape Lisburne, Cape Beaufort, Meade River, and probably Demarcation Point); northwestern Mackenzie (Fort Anderson and Fort Pierce); northern Franklin (Winter Harbor, King Oscar Land, Cape Sabine, and Cape Lupton); and northern Greenland (Polaris Bay and Navy Cliff). **East** to eastern Greenland (Navy Cliff, Renet, Cape Wynn, and Ivigtut); Labrador (Port Manners and Gready Island); Newfoundland (Lewis Hills and Base Camp); Cape Breton Island (Englishtown); Nova Scotia (Wolfville, Halifax, and Grand Manan); formerly western New York (Canandaigua Lake and Ithaca); central Pennsylvania (State College and Chesteroak); West Virginia (Coppers Rock); southwestern Virginia (White Top Mountain); western North Carolina (Grandfather Mountain and formerly Craggy Mountain); formerly northwestern South Carolina (Caesars Head and Mount Pinnacle); northeastern Georgia (Brasstown Dome and formerly Toccoa); formerly central Texas (San Angelo); Veracruz (Jalapa); central Guatemala (Chanquejelve and Barrillos); northern Honduras (between Opotelma and Siguatepeque); and northwestern Nicaragua (San Rafael del Norte). **South** to northwestern Nicaragua (San Rafael del Norte); El Salvador (Volcán de San Miguel and La Reina); southern Guatemala (Volcán de Fuego and Quezaltenango); southern Oaxaca (Tapana); the Revillagigedo Islands; and Clarion Island. **West** to Clarion Island; Baja California (Natividad Island, Cerros Island, Guadalupe Island, and Todos Santos Island); California (San Clemente Island, Anacapa Island, Farallon Islands, and Tuscan Buttes); western Oregon (Prospect and Cape Foulweather); western Washington (Grays Harbor and Bellingham); western British Columbia (Friendly Cove, Nootka Sound, and the Queen Charlotte Islands); and Alaska (Forrester Island, Near Islands, St. Matthew Island, St. Lawrence Island, and Cape Lisburne). The raven is now uncommon or rare over most of its range in the United States.

The range as outlined is for the two races that are currently recognized as North American. The northern raven *(Corvus corax principalis)* is found across the northern part of the continent from Alaska to Greenland south to the northern United States and, in the Allegheny Mountains, to northern Georgia; the American raven *(C. c. sinuatus)* is found chiefly in the West, from southern British Columbia and North Dakota south to Nicaragua, formerly east to Missouri and Indiana.

Casual records.—One was reported as seen at St. Georges, Bermuda, on December 23, 1918. There are also several records, chiefly for the Northeastern States, that appear to be outside the normal range. Among these are: New Hampshire, one was recorded from Sutton on December 20, 1878, and one was taken at Warner on February 18, 1879; Vermont, one was obtained at Bennington on November 7, 1909, and another at Hartland on November 19, 1912; Massachusetts, one was taken at Tyngsborough prior to 1859, one was taken in the fall of that year at Springfield, two were taken about the same time at Dedham, and one was taken at Northampton prior to 1901; Connecticut, one was taken on September 18, 1890 at South Manchester, and one was seen at Norwalk on May 25, 1919; eastern New York, one was taken in 1848 at what is now Brooklyn; New Jersey, one was reported from Morristown during the winter of 1881-82, and individuals were recorded as seen at Barnegat Inlet on April 13, 1924, and January 17, 1932, with several other observations between these dates; and Maryland, a specimen was collected at Sunnybrook on November 8, 1929.

Egg dates.—Alaska: 3 records, April 26 to May 29.

Arctic Canada: 9 records, May 1 to June 16.

California: 96 records, March 2 to May 19; 48 records, April 1 to 16, indicating the height of the season.

Labrador: 8 records, April 15 to May 12.

Maine: 9 records, March 24 to April 29.

Nova Scotia: 27 records, March 23 to May 11; 13 records, April 3 to 13.

Pennsylvania: 24 records, March 3 to April 10; 12 records, March 13 to 20.

Washington: 65 records, March 6 to May 26; 33 records, April 1 to 23.

CORVUS CORAX CLARIONENSIS Rothschild and Hartert

SOUTHWESTERN RAVEN

As suggested by George Willett (1941), the A. O. U. (1945) committee has decided to admit to our Check-list the "small race *(clarionensis)* ranging from interior valleys of California to Clarion Island, Mexico."

Mr. Willett's study of this species indicates that there are three subspecies recognizable within the limits of the United States, as mentioned under the preceding form *(sinuatus)*.

What information we have about the habits of the southwestern raven will be found under the preceding form, as that account was written before this subspecies was recognized.

Plates

PLATE 1

Alberta.   S. S. S. Stansell.

CANADA JAY.

PLATE 2

March 28, 1940.

A. D. Henderson.

Belvedere, Alberta, March 22, 1939.

TWO NESTS OF THE CANADA JAY.

PLATE 3

Isle Royale, Mich., April 1935.   J. V. Coevering.

Ben East.

Adult.

CANADA JAYS.

PLATE 4

Bear Lodge, Wyo., March 24, 1905.   P. B. Peabody.

Nesting site.

Colorado, May 30, 1931.   A. M. Bailey and R. J. Niedrach.

Adult on nest.

ROCKY MOUNTAIN JAY

PLATE 5

Crater Lake Park, Oreg., August 10, 1926.   J. E. Patterson.

ADULT GRAY JAY

PLATE 6

Near Toronto, Ontario.   W. V. Critch.

NORTHERN BLUE JAY.

PLATE 7

W. V. Critch.

YOUNG NORTHERN BLUE JAYS.

Toronto, Ontario, June 15, 1939.

PLATE 8

H. M. Halliday.

NORTHERN BLUE JAYS IN WINTER.

Near Toronto, Ontario.

PLATE 9

Eliot Porter

NORTHERN BLUE JAYS

Illinois, June 8, 1942.

PLATE 10

Near Toronto, Ontario.

NORTHERN BLUE JAYS: MALE FEEDING FEMALE.

PLATE 11

Duval County, Fla., June 24, 1931.   S. A. Grimes.

St. Cloud, Fla., April 9, 1924.   A. A. Allen.

SOUTHERN BLUE JAYS ON NESTS.

PLATE 12

Sequoia National Park, Calif.   Gayle Pickwell.

San Bernardino Mountains, Calif., April 21, 1940.   J. G. Suthard.

BLUE-FRONTED JAY.

PLATE 13

Huachuca Mountains . Ariz., May 30, 1922.   A. C. Bent.

NEST OF LONG-CRESTED JAY.

San Bernardino County, Calif., June 23, 1935.   J. S. Rowley.

NEST OF BLUE-FRONTED JAY.

PLATE 14

S. A. Grimes.

FLORIDA JAYS.

St. Johns County, Fla., April 1932.

PLATE 15

St. Johns County, Fla. May 1931.   S. A. Grimes.

Fledgling.

Duval County, Fla., April 1932.   S. A. Grimes.

FLORIDA JAY.

PLATE 16

Englewood, Fla.   W. F. Smith.

Feeding tame adults.

St. Johns County, Fla. April 1931.   S. A. Grimes,

FLORIDA JAYS

PLATE 17

California.   H. D. and Ruth Wheeler.

LONG-TAILED JAYS

PLATE 18

Jackson County, Oreg., May 6, 1924.   J. E. Patterson.

NEST OF LONG-TAILED JAY.

PLATE 19

W. L. Finley and H. T. Bohlman.

Near Los Angeles, Calif.

CALIFORNIA JAY

PLATE 20

San Bernardino County, Calif., May 16, 1916.   W. M. Pierce.

Azusa, Calif., November 15 1939.   R. S. Woods.

CALIFORNIA JAYS

PLATE 21

Cochise County, Ariz. F. C. Willard.

WOODHOUSE'S JAY.

Oracle, Ariz., December 1903. E. R. Forrest.

ARIZONA JAYS.

PLATE 22

Huachuca Mountains, Ariz., May 1, 1922.   A. C. Bent.

Two nests in one tree.

Huachuca Mountains, Ariz.   F. C. Willard.

ARIZONA JAY.

PLATE 23

Russell Reid.

Bismarck, N. Dak., May 22, 1923.

W. L. and Irene Finley.

Eastern Oregon.

AMERICAN MAGPIE.

PLATE 24

J. E. Patterson.

Klamath Lake, Oreg., April 25, 1925.

J. E. Patterson.

Swan Lake, Oreg., April 1925.

NESTS OF THE AMERICAN MAGPIE

PLATE 25

Burley, Idaho, June 1935.　　　　　　　　　　　　　E. C. Aldrich.

W. L. and Irene Finley.

YOUNG AMERICAN MAGPIES.

PLATE 26

J. E. Patterson.

Merced County, Calif., March 25, 1934.

NEST OF YELLOW-BILLED MAGPIE.

PLATE 27

S. S. Dickey.

Centre County, Pa., March 16, 1919.

S. S. Dickey.

Centre County

NESTING SITES OF THE NORTHERN RAVEN.

PLATE 28

TYPICAL SET OF EGGS OF THE NORTHERN RAVEN.
(Natural size.)

PLATE 29

May 27, 1940.

Nesting site.

Near Bar Harbor, Maine, May 14, 1940.

Maurice Sullivan.
Courtesy National Park Service

NESTING OF THE NORTHERN RAVEN.

PLATE 30

W. B. Tyrrell.

Shenandoah National Park, Va., March 31, 1940.

NORTHERN RAVEN LESS THAN A WEEK OLD.

PLATE 31

W. B. Tyrrell.

Shenandoah National Park, Va., April 14, 1940.

NORTHERN RAVEN ABOUT THREE WEEKS OLD.

PLATE 32

Shenandoah National Park, Va., 1937.   W. B. Tyrrell.

NESTING SITE OF THE NORTHERN RAVEN.

PLATE 33

Emerson Tuttle.

A. D. Cruickshank.

Emerson Tuttle.

Marquette County, Mich.

NORTHERN RAVENS.

PLATE 34

Marquette County, Mich.   Emerson Tuttle.

NORTHERN RAVEN.

PLATE 35

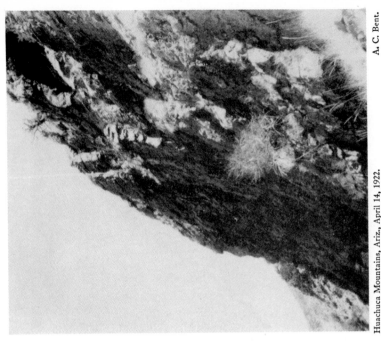

Kern County, Calif., March 19, 1929.   A. C. Bent.

Huachuca Mountains, Ariz., April 14, 1922.   A. C. Bent.

NESTING SITES OF THE AMERICAN RAVEN.

PLATE 36

Nest in A. M. Ingersoll collection.

Mohave Desert, Calif.   W. M. Pierce.

Nest in a Joshua tree.